AN INTRODUCTION
TO MATHEMATICAL
LEARNING THEORY

AN INTRODUCTION TO MATHEMATICAL LEARNING THEORY

Richard C. Atkinson
Gordon H. Bower
Edward J. Crothers

Stanford University

JOHN WILEY & SONS, INC.
New York · London · Sydney

To William Estes and Patrick Suppes

PREFACE

Among recent developments in the social sciences, the application of mathematical methods has become an important and rapidly expanding sphere of activity. No longer confined to the statistical treatment of data, mathematical methods are increasingly used in theory construction and evaluation. Because of its own unique methods, experimental psychology has offered a useful source of systematically collected observations to guide an empirically oriented theory. Application to one area of experimental psychology, the psychology of learning, is the major focus of this book.

But how does our treatment differ from other books on mathematical psychology? The answer is that we have tried to write a "primer" for students and research workers who possess only a modest degree of mathematical training. In our view, such a primer should teach some of the basic mathematical methods and their relation to experimental data, and illustrate these methods by specific case studies of selected theories. Our experience from teaching courses in mathematical psychology convinces us that other available books do not fulfill this need for beginning students. Similarly, many research workers indicate an interest in learning about mathematical psychology but confess to not knowing how or where to get an entering wedge into the often lengthy technical literature on the topic. Our intent was to write a book that meets such students more than halfway; a book that begins by making contact with the likely mathematical abilities of the student and proceeds to build from that level. The mathematical prerequisites for this text are a knowledge of college algebra and an elementary course in statistics (each of which covers some probability theory). Basic notions of probability are developed as needed here, with the main review being presented in Chapter 2. Occasionally, we require an elementary understanding of matrix algebra but at a level that would usually be covered in a course in college algebra. A few sections of the book employ the calculus. These are among the starred sections and may be skipped without loss of continuity. Throughout the book some familiarity with the psychology of learning is assumed.

One goal of the book, therefore, is to prepare the reader to assimilate the more advanced developments in mathematical psychology. Equally important, many readers will want to construct models of their own areas of specialization after they have mastered some of the techniques. Here we encourage them to go beyond the topics presented in this book so as to gain a broader perspective concerning the available formal tools.

To help maintain the interest of the psychology student, we have elected to organize the chapters around individual psychological topics. For each topic, one or more mathematical models are selected for intensive case study, using those mathematical techniques that are necessary. On occasion, derivations of similar mathematical results are repeated in different contexts, since the same formal properties often recur in models for different phenomena. In our experience, the beginning student benefits from the repetition. An alternative plan would have been a book organized as a graded progression of mathematical topics, with the psychological topics introduced as they related to a particular mathematical technique. Our approach is in some respects a compromise since we have tried to introduce the simpler models earlier in the book. Our concern with psychological relevance is indicated not merely by the chapter organization, but also by the detailed investigation of questions regarding empirical adequacy: there is a major emphasis on specifying experimental procedures for testing models, methods of parameter estimation, goodness-of-fit criteria, and model revision. Thus, this is a psychology book, not a mathematics book, as any mathematician will readily see.

Chapter headings reflect both our pedagogical orientation and our personal biases about what are interesting research topics. The dominant criterion for selecting material was that the model have some demonstrable empirical adequacy and also that it lend itself to a simplified exposition, but not at the cost of misrepresenting the basic theoretical or empirical developments. Although this book manages to cover a relatively broad range of topics and models, it is not intended to be a survey in either of two senses: first, we do not claim to survey all of the learning models that have been proposed in the literature; second, we do not attempt an exhaustive survey of the empirical evidence related to the particular models discussed. Nor is there the implication that the models selected for discussion are necessarily the best from an empirical viewpoint.

Rather, the intention is to give a fairly complete picture of how a model works in action—from its formulation to its detailed testing in one or more specific experimental applications. In many instances the vehicle for illustrating mathematical techniques consists of models and data for which the authors and their colleagues at Stanford University are responsible. This state of affairs is attributable partly to our research interests and partly to the availability of these data for the extensive analyses that we feel are demanded for comprehensive model evaluation. Throughout, the formal development is rigorous. The simplification accrues both from our restriction to more elementary techniques and our detailed exposition of mathematical derivations. Readers with more mathematical sophistication will, we hope, skip the tedious details and glean the major results.

After Chapters 2 and 3 have been read, the remaining chapters can be pursued somewhat independently, according to the reader's interests. Chapters 2 and 3 review notions of elementary probability theory and also introduce Markov chains and linear difference equations. Because of the wide latitude in topics, various sections of the book can serve as collateral reading for a survey course on quantitative methods in psychology.

Certain parts of this book were previously distributed in mimeographed form, and the authors are indebted to many students and colleagues who found errors or proposed improvements during this period. We are particularly indebted to William K. Estes, R. Duncan Luce, and Patrick Suppes for their careful reading of the manuscript and for making a number of valuable suggestions. We also wish to express our appreciation to Thelma Weeks for coordinating preparation of the final manuscript and for assistance in reading proof.

Richard C. Atkinson
May 1965   Gordon H. Bower
Stanford, California   Edward J. Crothers

CONTENTS

CHAPTER 1

INTRODUCTION

What is mathematical learning theory? Simply defined, it is the conduct of theorizing and research on learning by explicit mathematical means. If mathematics is viewed broadly as rigorous, logical thinking, then any scientist who states his theory with precision and derives its implications by logical arguments is engaged in applying mathematics to his own science. In psychology, mathematical theories have developed primarily in the field of experimental psychology, especially in learning, perception, and psychophysics. The data in these areas display the kind of consistent regularities that are necessary for formulating empirical laws. The existence of such a set of empirical laws makes possible the formulation of a theory from which these separate laws can be derived. A good theory will imply the known empirical laws; additionally, it will often imply other regularities that have not yet been discovered. These latter implications are called predictions, and scientists collect data to see whether the predictions will be verified. If so, the theory is confirmed; if not, it is discredited for giving either an incorrect or an incomplete analysis of the situation to which it was applied.

In a sense the label "mathematical learning theory" is a misnomer. One should not imagine that mathematical learning theory represents a position that is opposed to other theories of learning. The label refers to the method of theorizing, not to the substantive ideas expressed in particular theories. What is being expressed is an increased use of mathematics in theoretical formulations irrespective of whether the theory is oriented toward stimulus-response notions, cognitive constructs, expectancies, or some other approach. As we shall see, issues that in the past have supposedly differentiated opposing theoretical systems can, when formulated in precise mathematical fashion, be comfortably accommodated within a single system. The use of mathematics has allowed the

1

psychologist to analyze theoretical assumptions more precisely and to determine whether a particular set of data are consistent with these assumptions.

In this book we shall be concerned with the description and analysis of several mathematical theories of learning. Consequently, it will be useful to begin by briefly discussing the nature of such theories. Then we shall examine the role of mathematics in theory construction, and finally pass on to the central topic, mathematical theories in learning. For our immediate purposes, there is no need to offer a precise characterization of the term "theory." It suffices to say that theories are advanced to explain facts already collected, to predict future events, and to guide experimentation. A theory is formulated by inference from the factual observations at hand. The theorist states a set of axioms (assumptions and postulates are equivalent words) that he believes adequate to account for the salient features of the data. Then, by using the tools of logic and mathematics, the theorist attempts to deduce consequences from his axioms. One of the important features of this deductive step in theoretical work is that frequently a number of consequences of the axioms are discovered that were not immediately obvious or that may even appear at first glance to be inconsistent with the original axioms. The critical question is whether the consequences derived from the axioms agree with the data. If not, the strategy is to revise the theory or to set forth a new theory. If, however, the theory does appear to be supported by the data, an explanation of the facts has been attained. Next the theory is invoked to predict the outcome of phenomena that have not yet been observed. The appropriate experiments are then performed, and the cycle of theory formulation, deduction, and verification is repeated. Our confidence in a theory increases as more and more of its predictions are verified. On the other hand, further testing may persuade us to reject a previously held theory. Very often the rejection of one theory stimulates the development of a better theory; one that is better in the sense that it explains both those old facts on which the discarded theory was based and those new facts that discredited the old theory.

1.1 THE ROLE OF MATHEMATICS IN THEORY CONSTRUCTION

It is a familiar historical fact that as science progresses, its theories become more and more mathematical in form. Verbally stated propositions are replaced by exact quantitative language. Obviously, formalism is not an end in itself, but it is a powerful tool for theory building. Philosophers of science have written at length regarding the advantage of casting a theory in mathematical form. We shall not attempt to review their arguments here, but we do want to make some remarks regarding the advantages (and disadvantages) of mathematical work in psychology.

In our view the advantage of a mathematical theory depends upon the complexity of the theory and upon the amount of detail required in examining a specific implication of the theory. If a theory involves a number of processes that can interact so as to facilitate or inhibit one another, then in many cases it is difficult to tell at a glance whether a given statement does or does not follow from the theory. If a theory is relatively simple, involving only a few concepts and assumptions, then some general implications of the theory are easily obtained by verbal arguments. However, if the theorist wants to derive predictions of a more precise nature, then mathematics must be used even with the simpler theories. For example, the one-element model presented in Chapter 3 is a very simple theory about associative learning. But if we wish to know the predicted functional relationship between the total number of errors and the trial number of last error, then some extensive mathematical calculations are necessary. Even granted that one understands the axioms they still have a tremendous range of implications that are not obvious or, for that matter, even possible to deduce with an intuitive approach. Mathematics provides us with the tools that are essential to our reasoning; it leads to deductions that can be checked and shown to follow logically from the axioms.

In addition, the construction of a theory in mathematical form has the therapeutic effect of requiring the theorist to think in a precise way about his assertions. Frequently the mathematical analysis is enlightening because it uncovers assumptions hidden in the former verbal theory. Such clarification is achieved any time a theorist devises an explicit model to simulate his theory, whether the model be mechanical, mathematical, or a program inside a high-speed computer. For the model to run, all parts and their rules of operation must be specified. Construction of a model in science is much like giving an existence proof in mathematics: the existence of a well-functioning model, one which "behaves," is evidence that the theorist has at least specified enough operations. Whether the "behavioral" output of the model is interesting in a scientific sense is determined by its correspondence to the behavior of real organisms.

Also, in some cases it may be impossible to evaluate a theoretical concept unless it generates quantitative predictions. For example, suppose that a qualitative theory predicts that a particular phenomenon will be observed under a specified set of experimental conditions. Failure to observe the phenomenon can be excused by claiming that it did in fact occur but was too small to be detected by the measurement technique employed. On the other hand, a quantitative theory will often stipulate the magnitude of the predicted effect; then experimental procedures can be devised to make tests at appropriate levels of sensitivity, so that predictions can be unequivocally evaluated. Succinctly stated, a bad quantitative theory is much easier to reject than a bad qualitative theory.

A related advantage involves knowing how to decide between two opposing theories. Analytical work aids in finding which predictions from one theory conflict with those of the other. Then an experiment is done to see which, if either, prediction is upheld. We shall see that certain predictions from quite different sets of axioms may be surprisingly similar or even identical. This counterintuitive fact can be discovered by deduction from the theories. In this way, the use of mathematics can reduce the danger of running experiments that yield no relevant information.

Finally, mathematical representation aids the theorist even when his predictions go awry. When a qualitative theory fails, the theorist is sometimes tempted to resist its demise by asserting that the theory is essentially correct and that only minor corrections are needed to accommodate the data. If the theory is put into mathematical form, he can more easily establish whether the new wrinkle really does rectify the trouble. Or instead of being forced to doubt the entire theory, he can often localize the trouble in one or two axioms and suitably modify these.

Despite these advantages, we should state at the outset that good mathematics does not make a good psychological theory. There are some good verbal theories in psychology and some bad mathematical ones. The worth of a theory to the scientific community is judged by such features as its ability to explain or predict several phenomena and its usefulness for subsuming several apparently diverse phenomena under the same theoretical system. Other criteria are how diverse and interesting the implications of the theory may be; the generality of the circumstances in which the theory will deliver correct predictions; how much research it tends to stimulate; and so forth. The history of psychology includes many theories that have been formulated in mathematical terms and yet have been found wanting when measured against this list of desiderata. The feeling is often expressed that quantification of any particular set of ideas in an area of research is premature until we have been assured through qualitative experimentation that our ideas are worth pursuing (see Deutsch, 1962; Broadbent, 1958; and Skinner, 1950). A theory based on fundamentally incorrect notions is still a bad theory, no matter what its degree of mathematical formalism.

When a new empirical area is just beginning to be explored, the arguments abjuring premature quantification seem sound. It is obviously a waste of time to attempt to construct a mathematically exact theory when there is little empirical information to hint at the form the theory should take. But quantification is not premature when we consider alternative theories regarding phenomena about which a great deal is known and where a large accumulation of empirical research has already weeded out the obviously inadequate theories. It is at this point that mathematically expressed theories serve a strategic role in the scientific enterprise. The precision with which they can be expressed enables us to decide among alternative theories that offer different ways of accounting for the already established empirical generalizations. Exactly when a sufficient empirical backlog has been accumulated to make the statement of a mathematical theory an appropriate next step is a matter of individual judgement, subject to disagreement. The authors of this book feel that the substantive topics covered here represent situational phenomena about which we now know enough to attempt mathematical theorizing. The ultimate success of this approach must be judged by the previously mentioned criteria for evaluating theories.

In the near future it is doubtful whether mathematical theorizing will appear throughout a substantial portion of psychology, any more than it does currently in, say, biology. Many of the interesting phenomena in psychology appear beyond the reach of exact mathematical theories. This general disclaimer is acceptable so long as one does not attempt to list exhaustively those areas where mathematical theorizing will and will not bear fruitful results. The list will change with each generation and with advancing knowledge. At the moment, the record of positive instances of mathematical theorizing includes only those areas known roughly as experimental psychology and mental testing and excludes most of developmental, personality-clinical, social, and physiological psychology.

1.2 MATHEMATICAL THEORIES IN PSYCHOLOGY

This book is intended as an introduction to one of the more prominent applications of mathematics in the behavioral sciences; namely, stochastic models for learning.* Each of Chapters 2 through 7 focuses on a particular class of experiments where stochastic learning theories have been applied. Chapter 2 deals with concept identification, Chapter 3 with paired-associate learning, Chapter 4 with response-strength theories regarded as descriptions of choice behavior, Chapter 5 with sequential decision processes applied to psychophysical detection tasks and probability learning, Chapter 6 with avoidance conditioning, and Chapter 7

---

* For a more comprehensive historical account of mathematical developments in psychology, we recommend an introductory book by G. A. Miller (1964) entitled *Mathematics and Psychology*.

with learning models for multiperson interaction experiments. Chapter 8 is a general theoretical exposition of stimulus sampling theory, with special emphasis on the N-element pattern model. Finally, in Chapter 9 we survey techniques and problems of parameter estimation, especially as they are relevant to stochastic learning models.

For Chapters 2 through 7, the organization is roughly as follows. A model, or several alternative models, are formulated for the behavioral phenomena that command our attention. Following the statement of the model, a number of predictions are derived; a major aim of this book is the attempt to give a detailed explanation of each step in the mathematical arguments. Once deductions have been obtained, the next step is to examine various problems involved in testing the predictions against real data. Thus each chapter is meant to illustrate the various steps involved in theoretical psychology: formulating the theory, deriving predictions from the theory, testing the predictions against experimental results, and finally, evaluating and possibly revising the theory. Our selection of models for presentation in this book does not imply that we consider these to be the only, or even the best possible, theoretical interpretations of the experimental data under analysis. Rather, we have selected for presentation models that are especially amenable to simplified exposition and that illustrate a range of problems and techniques arising in mathematical work.

The reader may realize that we have been using the terms "mathematical theory" and "mathematical model" almost interchangeably. Mathematical logicians have endowed the terms "model" and "theory" with a variety of special meanings. For a comparison of these meanings, the interested reader should consult Suppes (1957, 1961) and Nagel (1961). In this book, we do not make a sharp distinction between models and theories. A model is viewed as a special case of a theory. Theories are general formulations that are applicable to more than one class of phenomena. Restrictions on the general theory lead to specific models for particular experimental situations. Thus, the theory of gravitation is applicable to celestial bodies, to objects on inclined planes, and to bodies falling near the earth; these applications are specific models that flow from the general theory. Similarly, we shall speak of stimulus sampling theory, which is a phrase now widely used in the literature to refer to the general theory of behavior that derives from W. K. Estes' basic paper of 1950. In applying this theory to specific experimental problems, many different models are obtained. For example, we shall refer to the one-element model for paired-associate learning, the linear model for shock-avoidance learning, the multi-element pattern model for discrimination learning and so forth. It should be evident that the distinction between model and theory is a matter of degree rather than kind. Bush and

Mosteller (1955) use the terms "general model" and "specific model" to correspond to our "theory" and "model," respectively. If the reader understands a particular conceptualization, then for our purposes it is of little importance whether he calls it a model or a theory.

The reader is probably aware that the construction and testing of mathematical models is different from other applications of mathematics in psychology. For example, statistical methods are widely used by psychologists to summarize data and to test statistical hypotheses. Although these methods are extremely important, they serve only to describe the data. If properly used, the statistical techniques yield a fairly faithful reflection of the raw data. By contrast, a model reverts to a more abstract level of analysis, proposing hypothetical constructs and relations between them in the hope of thereby explaining the results. A model goes beyond a descriptive system in that it can be an instrument for pre-dicting outcomes of hitherto unobserved events. Another descriptive approach using mathematical techniques involves finding equations that describe relations among experimental variables. This approach generally involves plotting the observed data in Cartesian coordinates and then searching for a mathematical function that comes close to passing through all the points. Here again the curve substitutes for the observations but in no sense offers a theoretical account of the data.

So far, our discussion of mathematical models has been quite general. Now we want to make some remarks about the type of models considered in this book. First of all, almost all of the models we examine treat behavior as a probabilistic rather than as a deterministic process. More precisely, the underlying notion is that of a *stochastic process*; that is, a temporal sequence of events that can be analyzed by using probability theory. The distinction between probabilistic and deterministic theories can be illustrated in terms of classical physics. For example, Newtonian physics is a completely deterministic theory; if sufficient information is available about the past history of a system, then in principle we can predict its entire future. In contrast, statistical mechanics is probabilistic in nature; no matter how nearly complete our information is about the current state of the system, we can still predict only the likelihood of certain events, and usually the amount of information initially available loses its predictive value as time progresses. From the psychological viewpoint the probabilistic, as opposed to deterministic, framework means that variability in behavior is built into the model. Even under identical conditions different subjects will give different sequences of responses, according to the stochastic system. It is an empirical question as to whether or not the amount of variability imposed by the probabilistic structure accords with the amount actually observed.

Either of two rationales can be offered for regarding behavior as a stochastic process. One possibility, of course, is that behavior is intrinsically probabilistic. The other possibility is that behavior is completely determined by antecedent conditions, but that minute fluctuations in the organism and the stimulus conditions from one time period to the next produce the observed variability in behavior. Rather than quibbling over such issues, it seems wiser to judge any stochastic or deterministic theory of behavior according to the more pragmatic criteria already mentioned in Sec. 1.1. In a later section of this chapter, we shall have more to say regarding the rationale for formulating psychological theories as probabilistic processes.

Granted that this book deals primarily with stochastic models for behavior, what do such models look like? Let us examine the formal structure of a model, without worrying for the moment about how the model was developed or how well it agrees with the data. A model has two components: its axiom system and its rules of correspondence. The axioms constitute a set of abstract or uninterpreted postulates, whose constituent nonlogical terms are meaningless in the real world. The axioms state only the relations into which these terms enter and thereby stipulate the formal conditions to be satisfied by anything for which these terms can become labels. To reiterate, the axioms assert nothing about the real world, and they can be explored only with the view to deriving consequences (theorems) from them by methods that do not violate the assumed logical framework. The validity of a theorem is determined solely by whether it follows from the mathematical structure; empirical evidence is totally irrelevant. Nevertheless, models are proposed to account for observations, so in actual practice the form of the theory is suggested in part by the data. This affinity is reflected by the fact that words such as stimulus, response, and reinforcement are used in two senses, both as names for abstract concepts and as descriptions of reality.

The second component of a model is its rules of correspondence (also called coordinating definitions, operational definitions, semantical rules, correspondence rules, epistemic correlations, and rules of interpretation). The rules of correspondence specify relations between the nonlogical terms in the axioms and observable events. For example, the term *response* in a set of axioms may be identified with a certain class of actions by the experimental subject, and the term *reinforcing event* with a class of operations by the experimenter. Thus, the rules of correspondence permit a physical interpretation of the formal system. As definitions, these correspondence rules cannot be "correct" or "incorrect." Rather, they are appropriate or inappropriate according to whether or not they render the theory capable of accounting for the data. For example, in Guthrie's theory (1952) a complex response can be learned gradually even though its individual response components are learned on a one-trial basis. He argues that the gradual incremental effect often observed in learning experiments occurs because on successive trials more and more of the subresponses are being conditioned in an all-or-none fashion. If such were the case, then a model that postulated learning as a gradual process would be more successful with a molar coordinating definition of response than with a molecular definition.

Clearly, an experimental test of the model may fail for either of two reasons: the model might be wrong, or the wrong experimental identification of the basic concepts might have been made. Some philosophers of science have emphasized, particularly in discussions of the general theory of relativity, that by sufficiently distorting the "natural" rules of correspondence, they may save any theory from failure. This viewpoint is usually referred to as the doctrine of conventionalism. It is not appropriate here to examine how scientists apply this doctrine in practice, but in our view the issues of conventionalism are not highly relevant to a newly developing science. However beautiful the structure of a theory may be, if it does not yield stable, nonartificial experimental interpretations leading to new empirical predictions, it does not have empirical significance. We believe that most of the interpretations presented in this book do have such a stable character.

Given the axiom set and correspondence rules, we are in a position to derive from the model predictions that can be tested against data. Some of these predictions specify ordinal relations ("greater than," "equal to") between variables. However, the majority of the predictions are numerical; that is, they are in the form of specific proportions (for example, the theoretical proportion of correct responses on trial 3 is 0.60), or frequencies (for example, the predicted number of errors before acquisition of a shock-avoidance response is 12), or response times (for example, the predicted median response time for a correct detection response is 298 milliseconds), or yet other quantities. Such numerical predictions are only the end-product of the theoretical labor. The entire chain of operations in the order performed is as follows: (1) setting up the model, (2) deriving theoretical expressions, (3) estimating the parameters of the model, and finally, (4) making numerical predictions.

By now the reader undoubtedly has some idea of what is entailed in the first step. However, the remaining steps involve the generally unfamiliar topic of parameter estimation. The theoretical expressions obtained from step (2) are usually functions of one or more parameters whose values are not known prior to inspecting the data. Estimates of these parameters must be made from the data before predictions such as those quoted above are possible. As a concrete example, let us consider the concept identification model to be presented in Chapter 2. It predicts that under certain conditions the average total number of errors involved in mastering a single concept will be $1/c$. Here c is an initially unknown parameter; the model assumes only that c lies between zero and one. A high value of c implies that the total number of errors will be small, whereas a low value of c implies that many errors will occur. Hence c is an index both of the ability of the subject and of the difficulty of the concept. For a given subject, we can estimate c in terms of his observed number of total errors (as will be done in Chapter 2). First, we equate his observed number of errors with the expression $1/c$ and then compute c by solving the resulting equation. For example, suppose a subject generates ten errors in the course of mastering a given concept; then

$$10 = \frac{1}{c}.$$

Solving this equation for c, our estimate is 0.10. Now we are in a position to make a genuine prediction from the model. The concept model also predicts that the average trial number of the last error will be $2/c$. So we substitute 0.10 for c in this expression and find that the predicted trial number of the last error is 20. In this procedure we have used information about the total error data to predict the trial number of the last error. This is indeed a genuine prediction, for without a model there would be no way in which, knowing the total errors, we could predict the trial number of the last error.

In the remainder of this chapter, we want to examine more closely the role of probabilistic theories of learning and also to discuss the nature of theoretical predictions based on parameters estimated from the data. It has been our experience that these topics, more than any others, cause the novice to feel uneasy; hence we shall try to anticipate and answer some of his questions. But before doing this, we want to make a few remarks to place our view of the theoretical enterprise in proper focus. By and large, we have talked about a single model and the evaluation of its predictions against data. The formulation and testing of individual models is frequently done, especially in the early investigations of a given experimental area. However, as a rule the theorist prefers to examine several alternative models simultaneously. Experiments are run not to test a particular model but rather to select from a set of alternative models the one that best fits the data. One reason for this strategy of comparing "competing" models is that by its very nature no model can be expected to agree perfectly with the data in all respects. Therefore, a yardstick of the adequacy of any given model is its relative accuracy when judged against alternative formulations.

Furthermore, we should emphasize that the results obtained by testing alternative models against any single set of data are unlikely to cause the theorist to select one model for future investigation and discard all others. Only as evidence accumulates from many such analyses, will it become clear which theory best meets the criteria of accuracy, generality, parsimony, and so forth. Certainly since the time of Poincaré it has been evident that no theory is correct in any absolute sense. Rather, some theories tend to be more useful than others in accomplishing the goals of the scientific enterprise. The success of relativity theory was not due to the fact that the new concepts of space and time were in any sense more "true" than the old ones, for any of the phenomena that could be explained by the new theory also could be explained on the basis of absolute dimensions of space and time. But such explanations became extremely cumbersome and artificial when contrasted to the explanations offered by relativity theory.

If we accept the notion that tests of alternative models against a single set of data cannot be regarded as crucial in selecting among models, then what is the next step? As indicated earlier, one obvious requirement is to extend the applications of the models to other types of experimental problems. As we make more experimental comparisons, we shall obtain a better understanding of the properties of the models, and gain an opportunity to reappraise their relative power. Moreover, in addition to extending the range of application, we should also inspect the discrepancies between prediction and observation in each experiment to obtain some clues for modifications that will improve the model. This part of the scientific enterprise is extremely challenging. In effect the theorist, by scrutinizing unexpected deviations in the data, attempts to come up with either a modification of the axioms or a new insight as to how the axioms are to be interpreted. We doubt whether such revisions follow any clear or systematic pattern; more often that not the theorist tries many new schemes and then reports the one that seems most promising. From the viewpoint of understanding the scientific process, it is unfortunate that the trial and error stage between successive revisions of a model is not occasionally recorded. Looking at the end product gives the misleading impression that theory develops in a neat and orderly fashion.

1.3   BEHAVIOR AS A PROBABILISTIC PROCESS

Every branch of science seems to go through an initial exploratory period in which, roughly speaking, it tries to discover what its major dependent variables are going to be. A number of psychologists, including Guthrie, Skinner, and Estes have argued that the basic dependent variable in psychology is, or should be, response probability. Skinner, for example, argues for the use of rate of occurrence of a particular response, when it occurs "freely," that is, with no limitations imposed on when it can occur. But, Skinner believes that the rate measure can be transformed into statements about the probability of a response occurring in some fixed time interval.*

If we examine the ordinary discourse that the layman uses in describing behavior, it is easily seen that most of his descriptive statements can be translated into statements about response probability. To say, for example that "Edith has a strong compulsion to gamble" is to say that certain responses (seeking bets, accepting bets, etc.) are highly probable. Most of the layman's statements about character traits or descriptive terms about predispositions of mental life can be so translated. The reader is referred to Skinner (1953) and Ryle (1949) for illustrations of how these transformations may be effected in certain puzzling cases. Our point here is simply to illustrate that when psychologists take response probability as their principal dependent variable, they are not departing in any great degree from the analysis implicit in common-language descriptions of behavior.

In the typical psychological experiment, we set up a classification scheme (often implicit) for assigning small episodes of behavior to one or another category, termed a response class. Illustrative categories might be as follows: turning left at the choice-point of a T-maze, uttering "JEB" as a response to a paired-associate stimulus item, placing a checkmark beside a particular answer on a multiple-choice test, assigning a rating of 5 to the loudness of a tone, and so forth. The response categories utilized vary with the experimental problem, and, in particular, vary with the experimenter's interest. For example, in a verbal conditioning experiment (see Verplanck, 1956), a subject might be asked to emit nouns in a free-association manner. Such verbal responses could be classified in a variety of ways, but the experimenter may be interested in only one particular classification, such as whether or not the word uttered is a plural noun. Most frequently the response classes are dictated by our conditions of reinforcement—that is, we group together all those behavioral episodes that receive the same reinforcement and talk indiscriminately about the entire class.

---

* To effect this translation requires an explicit stochastic model for the free responding situation. The common assumption is that of random responding according to a Poisson process (cf. Mueller, 1950), wherein momentary response probability is related to the reciprocal of the mean rate (e.g., responses per minute). However, a fair amount of evidence contradicts the Poisson model (Anger, 1956; Millenson and Hurwitz, 1961). See papers by McGill (1963) and Norman (1964 c) for a discussion of stochastic models for the free responding situation.

Thus, if the experimenter delivers a reinforcement (saying "Good," or "Uhm hm") when the subject produces a plural noun, then we lump all plural nouns into one class and all other productions into a complementary category. The behaviors thus lumped may differ radically according to some other classification scheme. At most, however, the principle of reinforcement permits one to talk about the entire class of behaviors, for example, by predicting that the probability of plural-noun production will increase. To make more refined predictions about which members of this broad class will predominate requires more information than is implicit in the condition of reinforcement. In particular, the principle of reinforcement does not permit us to make any detailed statements about exactly what it is that the subject has learned. The subject may have learned to give plural names of automobiles, as in "Buicks, Fords, etc.," and yet be unaware that, say, plural animal names would also produce a "Good" from the experimenter. Thus, the question "What is learned?" is an empirical one, where the answer varies as we define progressively more restricted response classes. See Logan (1960) for a discussion of these issues.

In practice, any proposed scheme for classifying behavioral episodes into response classes should meet three requirements. First, the classes should be *mutually exclusive*—that is, any given episode should be assignable to one and only one class. For example, the "plural nouns" scheme must have additional rules for assigning words like "sheep" which can be singular or plural. Second, the classes should be *exhaustive* of the universe to which they are to be applied. This means that every behavioral episode must be assignable to at least one of the classes defined. In practice, this requirement is often glossed over by defining a "residual class" that contains all behavioral episodes not falling into the classes defined previously (for example, the subject's sneezes or coughs or yawns, etc., would be so assigned). Such residual classes are invariably assumed when Skinner talks about time-rate of occurrence of a particular well-defined response: rate is seen as the probability that in some small time unit the subject emits an instance of the class (for example, bar-pressing) as opposed to "doing something else" other than bar-pressing during that time. However, for many purposes, members of the residual class are simply ignored because they are irrelevant to the experimenter's purpose. If the experimenter is concerned with whether the subject depresses the right or left key in a prediction experiment, then the subject's coughs, sneezes, utterances, etc., are of no particular interest in the data collection process, and generally are not recorded.

The third major requirement of response-classification schemes is that they be objective and well-specified in operational terms. With automatic recording of key presses and the like, this is not a problem. However, the problem can arise if a human judge (that is, the experimenter) is the data-recording system. What is required is that the criteria for classification be reliable over experimenters and communicable, so that any two judges would agree in the classification assigned to a particular behavioral episode. This requirement is easily met in the situations we consider in this book; it is however, a problem for many areas of psychological study.

Give such a classification scheme for assigning behavioral episodes to categories, the remaining operation performed by the scientist as a data-collector is the simple task of tabulating the frequency of occurrence of the various responses in a specified sample of behavioral episodes. For example, on trials 1 to 100, this subject pressed the left key 64 times and the right key 36 times. The frequency of occurrence of a response category has all the desirable properties of what mathematicians call the "measure of a set." Dividing the number of observations in a particular response category by the total number of observations yields a proportion that may be treated as a probability. Once obtained, these proportions may be manipulated in analytic ways dictated by the calculus of probabilities. The implementation of this general approach will become clearer as the reader proceeds through this book.

There is one major advantage gained by theories whose domain of reference is to probabilities, involving as they do only the primitive notions of classification and counting. This advantage is that the theorist is not involved at the outset in complex problems regarding measurement of his dependent variables, or inferentially, of his independent variables. Historically, learning theorists have been inclined to develop their theories with reference to "theoretical" dependent variables such as reaction potential, excitation-inhibition, cognitive maps, and so forth. Although such theoretical variables appeared at first to facilitate communication among psychologists, it became clear that the theories were testable only to the extent that the variables were measurable. Thus, most of these theories required an implicit or explicit "measurement theory" to permit tests of the principal predictions. Our purpose here is not to explicate such measurement theories (they reduce to constraints that are expected to hold regarding interrelated sets of response probabilities), but rather to point out that stochastic models of the type illustrated in this book avoid these problems.

In light of our argument for response probability as the basic dependent variable, the reader might be surprised in examining the experimental literature to find many studies in which other measures are taken as the basic dependent variable. These other measures may be conveniently divided into two classes. First, there are those dependent measures which are obviously derived from response probabilities but in which this probabilistic background has been temporarily suppressed. Examples would be trials to criterion in a learning experiment or a plot of threshold values versus tone frequency in a psychophysical experiment. Threshold in the classical detection literature is defined as that stimulus intensity where the probability of a detection response is $\frac{1}{2}$; similarly, criterion is defined as that trial number on which response probability reaches some specified value, such as one or zero. Second, there are those measures such as response amplitude, latency, or speed, which are not derived in any obvious way from simple probabilistic schemes. Examples of amplitude measures would be skin conductance in a GSR conditioning experiment, drops of saliva in salivary conditioning, electrocapillary potentials in a psychoacoustic study, etc. By taking a slightly broader view of probabilities and by redefining response classes, such measures as these can be brought within the probabilistic fold. Instead of defining the response in the simple qualitative way (salivating or not salivating to the conditioned stimulus), we distinguish response classes by their amplitude, employing what Logan (1959) has called the micromolar approach. Thus, we are led to talk about the probability of a response amplitude of x units. In some cases the recording system quantizes the response amplitude into discrete units (for example, drops of saliva, category counts of inter-response time distributions). In other cases, the response is measured on an essentially continuous scale (reaction time, electrotonic potentials), and we talk of probability density functions defined over this continuum. A fair amount of work has been done by mathematical psychologists to describe such continuous probability densities (for instance, Bush and Mosteller, 1955; McGill, 1963; and Suppes, 1959). Thus, in principle none of these other cases provide any counterexamples to the thesis that response probability is the major dependent variable in studies of behavior.

1.4 PARAMETER ESTIMATION

For the models considered in the book, nearly all the prediction equations derived have one or more unknown parameters in them.. For example, if it is claimed that the probability of an error response on the nth trial of a learning experiment is describable by the function

$$(1.1) \qquad\qquad q_n = q_1 \alpha^{n-1},$$

then q_1 and α are parameters in this equation. Some readers undoubtedly will be disturbed by the existence of such parameter in models, so let us try to anticipate and answer some questions that are frequently raised about them.

First of all, a model usually suggests a clear interpretation of its parameters; accordingly, we know what aspects of the behavioral process they are summarizing. Thus, in the equation above, the parameter q_1 refers to the initial error probability on the first trial of the experiment; the parameter α (assumed to be between zero and one) refers to the "rate of learning." The parameter α is the fraction by which the error probability is reduced on each practice trial. Eventually this parameter takes q_n to zero as n becomes large. If α is small (say, 0.05), then the error probability is quickly reduced to near zero, and we would say the task is learned rapidly. If α is large (say, 0.95), then the error probability decreases very slowly over trials. Thus, α summarizes in a number the intuitive sense of saying that something is learned rapidly or slowly.

Because of the way the parameters are identified in the theory, we can usually be fairly confident of what kinds of experimental variables will influence them. For example, the parameter q_1 in Eq. 1.1 would be affected by all those manipulations that influence the initial error probability in the task under consideration. The number of available response alternatives would affect q_1 and so would the amount and kind of preliminary training in the situation. Such experimental identifications of the parameters are an important conceptual part of a theory.

Upon first contact with mathematical psychology, some readers undoubtedly will make the following criticism: given enough unknown parameters in the theoretical equation, parameter values can be so chosen as to fit any empirical curve; the model has *post hoc* validity, but no true predictive validity. There is a grain of useful suspicion about *post hoc* explanations in this argument, but the force of the argument usually dissolves in examination of specific cases. If we look at Eq. 1.1, for example, q_n is predicted to be an exponential decay function of trials, and no values of q_1 or α will make it otherwise. If the mean learning curve were not a simple exponential decay, but were, say, a decreasing straight line, then no choice of values for q_1 and α would make the model fit the observed results. Another answer is that, in principle, the model is supposed to predict everything (every statistic) in the data and much of the data (for example, the number of times a correct response is followed by an error on the next trial) is independent of the mean learning curve. Thus, although the parameters may be chosen to fit the mean error curve, the validity of the model may be tested by how well the model (using these same parameter values) predicts other statistics of the data.

Allied to the type of misgivings cited above is the criticism that since the theorist has to examine the data before estimating his parameter(s) and making his predictions, in some sense he is cheating, since one should not know the outcome of an experiment if he wants truly to predict it.

Again, there is an element of merit to this argument. The reply depends on an analysis of the number of parameters in the theory relative to the degrees of freedom in the data to be predicted. Whenever the number of independent measures in the data exceeds the number of parameters to be estimated, then a test of the model is possible. To take a particularly vacuous illustration of what happens when the number of parameters equals the degrees of freedom in the data, consider the following hypothetical "model": if the parameter β is less than 1, then response A occurs; if the parameter β is greater than 1, then response $\bar{A}$ occurs. The only information we can gather that is relevant to the value of β is simply whether response A or $\bar{A}$ occurs. When put in this schematic form, the vacuity of the theory is obvious. However, a fair number of everyday predictions from the layman's superficial theories about events often reduce to something like that. Consider, for example, the prediction "If he really tries hard, then he will succeed." If he fails to succeed, then, of course, he didn't really try hard enough.

It has been our experience that many of the individuals who object to parameters in prediction equations are not generally familiar with the way mathematics is applied in most of science. Most scientific laws about observable quantities have constants or parameters in them. And in all but a few cases (the so-called universal constants), the values of these constants are unknown until relevant observations have been taken from the system to which the equation is to be applied.

It might be helpful to consider a concrete example. Suppose that I kick a football and wish to know its flight path and how far away it will land. Under certain ideal conditions, the horizontal displacement x and vertical displacement y at time t are given by

$$(1.2) \qquad x = (v_0 \cos \theta)t, \qquad y = v_0 \sin \theta - \tfrac{1}{2}gt^2.$$

And the horizontal distance traveled before the ball returns to the ground is

$$d = \frac{v_0^2 \sin 2\theta}{g}.$$

There are three parameters in these equations. The gravitational constant is g; it is known in advance of the experiment. The parameter v_0 represents the initial velocity imparted to the ball by the kick and θ the angle of inclination of the ascent. Thus v_0 and θ represent the initial conditions of the system under observation, and they must be estimated whenever the equations are applied in actual cases. Equations 1.2 apply, of course, only to the ideal case where the ball travels through a vacuum that provides no resistance to its motion. Under actual conditions of observation, the ideal representation of the problem may be in large error due to neglect of factors such as the direction of the wind, the size of the ball, whether the ball is kicked with a spiral or end-to-end, and so forth. Incorporation of these factors into the model would increase the number of parameters to be estimated and increase the complexity of the model. Such added complexity is the price to be paid for a more accurate description of the behavior of the system under observation. Depending on the nature of the problem, the increased accuracy may or may not be worth the cost of the additional complexities.

The estimation problems encountered in applying mathematical models to psychological data are no different in kind from those encountered in the physical example above. Parameters or unknown constants are involved in behavioral models, and these have to be estimated from the system under observation. In psychology as in the physical example, we often make use of idealizing assumptions to simplify the form of the model; the hope is that in actual applications when the idealized model makes inaccurate predictions, the fundamental theory has sufficient power to suggest what kinds of factors are responsible for the inaccuracies.

Levels of Prediction

As we have said, most of the predictions generated by a model presuppose parameter estimates. Typically, part of the data are used to perform the estimation, and then the model is used to predict the remainder of the data. Several levels of prediction can be distinguished according to how far the model predicts beyond the data used for estimation. For simplicity, let us assume that learning is described by Eq. 1.1 and that q_1, the probability of an error on trial 1, equals 1. After a numerical estimate of α has been made, we can substitute it and values of n into Eq. 1.1 and generate the successive points on the theoretical learning curve. For example, if α were estimated to be 0.5, we would have q_n equal to 1.00, 0.50, 0.25, and 0.125 for $n = 1$, 2, 3, and 4, respectively.

If α were estimated from the very learning curve data we seek to predict, then we would have accomplished a very modest type of prediction; namely, curve-fitting. This operation does, however, qualify as a prediction, because a model will not necessarily provide a satisfactory fit to empirical curves. As noted earlier, describing the data with the given functions by any choice of parameter values may well turn out to be impossible. Thus if a reasonable description of the data is achieved, one must concede that the results provide some support for the model.

The next higher level of prediction involves an element of overdeterminism. A parameter is said to be overdetermined if its value can be estimated for a given set of data in two or more independent ways. For example, for the concept identification model mentioned earlier, we predict that the expected total number of errors in mastering a concept will be $1/c$ and that the expected trial number of the last error will be $2/c$. Thus, c can be estimated from the total error data and also from the trial number of the last error. Related to this notion of overdeterminism is the use of a parameter estimate obtained from part of the data to predict some other independent aspect of the data. As an illustration, if α were estimated from the total error data, the value obtained could then be substituted in Eq. 1.1 to predict the learning curve. This would be genuine prediction, for the total error data do not determine the learning curve. If the predictions are accurate we have indeed gone a step beyond curve fitting.

A still more venturesome and satisfactory level of prediction involves invariance in the parameters over experimental situations. That is, we would like to evaluate the parameters of the model in one experimental situation and then use these estimates to generate completely a priori predictions of behavior in a new situation. As yet, successful examples of prediction at this level are not numerous in psychology but, as we shall see, there are some. This type of prediction is always a difficult feat: in order to achieve it, one requires not only an adequate model but also a detailed understanding of the variables involved in a number of different situations. In this regard, it seems reasonable to assume that ultimately values of some of these behavioral parameters will be determined by physiological or biophysical experiments, but there is little hope of arriving at this stage in the forseeable future.

The levels of prediction discussed above form a hierarchical scale against which the significance of a model can be measured. The goal of the theorist is to develop models that have the property of parameter invariance. At a less ambitious level, we can talk about carrying over a model, but not its particular estimates, from one experimental condition to the next. If the general model fits under these liberalized conditions, a further task would be to account for the lack of parameter invariance. Specific experimental variables whose values differ under the two experimental conditions might be suggested as responsible for the fluctuation in parameter estimates, but a mere *post hoc* rationale without corroborating evidence would not be satisfactory.

*1.5   BRIEF HISTORICAL REVIEW

Since the early work of Ebbinghaus (1885) and Thorndike (1898), experimental studies on learning have been recorded and reported in

---

* This section may be omitted at first reading.

quantitative form. The first applications of mathematics were for the purpose of describing empirical functions. For example, Ebbinghaus proposed that the proportion of material forgotten over time increases as the logarithm of the time since initial learning. The most common method of reporting results of a learning experiment was in the form of a learning curve, a graph depicting how the performance of a subject or group of subjects changed over successive practice trials for particular experimental conditions. In the early days several different analytic functions were proposed as "the learning function," including the hyperbola, exponential growth, Gompertz, and arc cotangent functions. There was some debate about which function was the most appropriate (see Gulliksen, 1934, and Lewis, 1960 for a review). However, none of the functions were derived from fundamental considerations about the nature of learning; as descriptions they were all about equally good, with the closest fit to the data usually obtained by the function that had more free parameters.

Thurstone (1919) was the first to set up a system of axioms, based on psychological considerations, that led to the derivation of a "rational" learning function. The parameters of the function were given fairly specific psychological identifications. Additionally, Thurstone innovated the probabilistic approach, taking as his aim the derivation of the probability of a correct response as a function of the trial number. The theory was later extended by Gulliksen (1934) and applied to the analysis of discrimination learning and transposition by Gulliksen and Wolfle (1938). However, only mean response curves were considered, and no attention was given to the prediction of response distributions and sequential statistics. In addition, no procedures were devised for parameter estimation, and no experimentation was undertaken to determine the validity of the identifications proposed for the parameters of the model. The same remarks apply to the related work by Rashevsky (1951), Pitts (1943), and Householder and Landahl (1945). These individuals attempted to derive learning curves from simplified conceptual models of the nervous system. On the whole, their efforts did not have a significant impact on experimental investigations of learning.

Perhaps the most influential pioneer in the area of formal theorizing in learning was Clark Hull. In his major work, *Principles of Behavior* (1943), he stated a set of postulates dealing with a number of variables that had been identified in earlier experiments. The postulates were stated both verbally and in the form of mathematical equations. In many cases, the postulate was simply a generalization of an empirical result. However, the hope was that the aggregation of postulates would jointly imply much more than the specific experimental facts from which they were separately inferred; this was indeed the case (for example, see Hull, 1952). The basic associative variable in Hull's theory was called habit strength, denoted $_sH_r$ and given by the equation

$$_sH_r = M(1 - e^{-iN}).$$

In this equation N is the number of reinforced practice trials, i is the learning rate parameter, M is the asymptote, and e is the base of the natural logarithm. Hull assumed that the asymptote of habit, M, was determined by a number of variables such as drive level, amount and delay of reward, intensity of the conditioned stimulus, stimulus-response interval, and so forth. For each such variable a postulate was stated (on the basis of available experimental evidence) relating that variable to the asymptote of habit. Finally, habit strength was related to several indices of learning such as latency, amplitude, response probability, and resistance of a response to experimental extinction. Additional postulates were added concerning stimulus generalization and extinction, and theorems were stated regarding discrimination learning, stimulus patterning, spontaneous recovery, and so forth. The theory was deterministic at the level of habit strength and introduced probabilistic factors only as random oscillations about a mean response strength. Hull's theory is discussed in more detail in Chapter 3.

Hull aimed for comprehensiveness in his theory. Perhaps, owing to its relative clarity and generality, the theory has stimulated considerable experimental research. The theory has gone through a variety of restatements and modifications (see Logan, 1959 for a review) and still guides the research of many contemporary experimenters. Despite the mathematical appearance of Hull's writings, the current consensus would seem to be that his important contribution was the statement of a rich collection of qualitative concepts and propositions, some of which have had a lasting influence on the thinking of psychologists. Considered as a quantitative theory, the system has a number of shortcomings (for example, see Koch, 1954; Cotton, 1955). Except for a few notable examples by Spence (1956), the theory has not been tested in terms of its quantitative features but rather by predicting ordinal relations among performance of subjects trained under different experimental conditions. Even the most serious attempt at formal theory construction, *Mathematico-Deductive Theory of Rote Learning* by Hull et al. (1940), predicted qualitative differences, and upon careful analysis the number of theorems hardly exceeds the number of postulates.

From about 1945 to 1950, a movement was initiated to characterize behavior, and learning in particular, as a stochastic process. The intellectual background in which this view originated included the earlier analyses of behavior by psychologists (for example, Guthrie, 1952; Skinner, 1938;

Thurstone, 1919). A second source was information theory. Although the latter discipline was founded to meet problems in communication engineering, the concepts and methods of analysis had general applicability. Application of information theory to psychological problems has produced a long list of accomplishments (for a review see, Luce, 1960c, and Garner, 1962). Of relevance to the learning theorist was its emphasis on event probabilities, sequential effects, and Markov chain representations of the data. A paper by Miller and Frick (1949) entitled "Statistical Behavioristics and Sequences of Responses" developed these notions in some detail.

At about the same time, Estes (1950) and Bush and Mosteller (1951a, b) began formulating their stochastic models for learning. Over the next few years a group consisting mainly of Robert Bush and Frederick Mosteller at Harvard University, Cletus Burke and William Estes at Indiana University, and George Miller and William McGill at Massachusetts Institute of Technology worked in parallel directions developing and testing what have come to be known as *linear models* for learning. Many of the theoretical developments during this period were published in the *Psychological Review*, *Psychometrika*, and in conference volumes (for example, Thrall, Coombs, and Davis, 1954), while a variety of experimental applications of the models appeared in the *Journal of Experimental Psychology*. Much of this early work is reviewed in an article by Estes (1959b).

Linear models will be dealt with only briefly here; they are discussed in more detail in Chapters 3, 5, and 6 of this book. The basic ideas are extremely simple. Consider a two-choice learning experiment where the probability that the subject will make response 1 (rather than response 2) on trial n is p_n. On each trial the subject responds, and some reinforcing event (reward, punishment, knowledge of results, etc.) is provided. If reinforcing event j occurs on trial n, then the new value of response probability on trial $n + 1$ is

(1.3) $p_{n+1} = a_j p_n + b_j$.

This equation expresses the new value of response probability as a linear function of its old value. The parameters a_j and b_j specify whether event j effects an increase or decrease in p_n. Depending on whether event j reinforces response 1, response 2, or neither, appropriate a_j and b_j values are chosen to reflect this fact. Bush and Mosteller provide various rationales for the linear assumption in their book *Stochastic Models for Learning* published in 1955; the book describes much of the early theoretical and experimental work on linear models. Estes and Burke (1953) derived the linear model from Guthrian theory, using the notion that the subject's response is determined by a sampling process defined on a hypothetical population of stimulus elements. This and related developments have come to be known as Stimulus Sampling Theory and will be discussed in Chapter 8.

Since 1955 the number of contributors to mathematical psychology has been increasing at an accelerating rate. A tremendous variety of learning models have been proposed and investigated. Part of the proliferation constitutes alternative models for fairly traditional experimental situations, but many developments signify the advance of mathematical psychology into new areas. Among the contributions are Restle's multiprocess models (1955a, 1958, 1964a), Luce's choice theory (1959a, reviewed here in Chapter 4), and Markov chain models with a small number of states. The prevalence of Markov chain models in this book indicates the authors' belief that they represent an especially promising line of theoretical development. The origins of this particular development were a paper by Estes (1959a) and work by Suppes and Atkinson (1960). Basic to these formulations is the idea that a subject's response probability can take on only a fixed set of values and that reinforcing events produce transitions from one value of response probability to another.

Part of the more recent literature on mathematical psychology is to be found in books (for example, Luce, 1959a; Restle, 1961a; Suppes and Atkinson, 1960) and in volumes of collected papers (Bush and Estes, 1959; Arrow, Karlin, and Suppes, 1960; Luce, 1960b; Criswell, Solomon, and Suppes, 1962; Atkinson, 1964). An excellent review of the field is available in the three volumes of the *Handbook of Mathematical Psychology* edited by Luce, Bush, and Galanter. The *Journal of Mathematical Psychology* was established in 1964 to communicate the increasing volume of research in this area.

As the table of contents of this book suggests, mathematical models have been applied to a broad range of experimental problems. The following sample may suffice to indicate the diversity of situations studied: discrimination learning; escape and avoidance conditioning; learning set and reversal learning set; concept identification; probability learning; imitation learning in children; free verbal recall; rote serial learning; paired-associate learning; continuous-time probability learning; immediate memory; response latency distributions in instrumental conditioning; multiperson interactions; impression formation; reinforcement of a continuum of responses; stimulus generalization; displacement and conflict; learning of miniature logic systems by children; aspects of second language acquisition; and optimum teaching procedures. The area is expanding rapidly, and there are many exciting new developments. It seems likely that mathematical psychology eventually will prove useful in many areas of psychology.

A final word. Psychologists familiar with the theories of Hull, Tolman, and Guthrie are sometimes puzzled when they first encounter a mathematical model for learning. Generally, the model is stated quite simply, without attaching a list of postulates about drive level, amount and delay of reinforcement, stimulus intensity, and so forth. In most applications of models, these classical variables have not been the topic of the investigation and are presumed fixed throughout a given experiment. Such variables may well influence the estimated parameter values of the model (for example, the a_j and b_j of Eq. 1.3); they are like initial-state descriptions that are used but not derived from the theory. In some instances, one is interested in testing a particular theory about the learning parameters as they relate to experimental manipulations. Thus, Estes (1958) has explored hypotheses about drive effects by applying stimulus sampling theory; Estes and Suppes (1959b) and Clayton (1964) have investigated hypotheses about the effect of amount and delay of reward; Anderson (1959a) investigated the interval between the conditioned and unconditioned stimulus; and Atkinson and Estes (1963) showed how stimulus intensity and generalization can be handled in stimulus sampling theory. At a minimum such hypotheses are expected to account for the well-known experimental results under consideration. The purpose of this discussion is to point out that hypotheses concerning classical experimental variables can be and have been formulated and tested in the context of mathematical learning theories. In this sense, there is a great deal of continuity between the older theories of learning and present-day stochastic models.

CHAPTER 2

CONCEPT IDENTIFICATION

Psychologists have done much research on the topics of thinking and problem-solving in human subjects. These studies try to specify the cognitive processes a person utilizes in solving one or another type of problem; they also try to determine how the likelihood of the person's using certain modes of attack and solution changes as variables such as the mental set and chronological age are varied. One practical difficulty encountered in research on problem-solving is the lack of a systematic analysis of what processes are involved in any arbitrarily selected problem with which we confront the subject. An infinite variety of problem types could be constructed and used as experimental materials; undoubtedly, different cognitive processes are used to solve different types of problems. One could compile a weighty catalog listing the different types of problems studied experimentally, the variables manipulated, and the results obtained. For many people, such a catalog would not represent scientific knowledge any more than do the listings in a telephone directory. They would object that the catalog would give little aid in understanding why the facts were as they were. If understanding in this sense is the end-product of scientific research, then some conceptual or theoretical analysis of the experimental procedure and results is required.

The effect of this belief upon practicing researchers is, historically, to channel their research efforts predominantly to those kinds of experimental situations for which cogent conceptual analyses already exist. In this regard, studies of concept identification have acquired prominence within the general area of research on thinking and problem-solving. Because problems of concept identification are complicated, psychologists are willing to assume that important cognitive processes of the person must be brought to bear in solving such problems; yet, they are also simple enough so that the psychologist can feel partly satisfied with the conceptual-theoretical analysis he gives of the subject's behavior during the solution of one of these problems. The theoretical analyses suggest a wide range of independent variables that can be manipulated within the context of an experiment on concept identification. Since the theory also suggests what should be the effect of manipulations of these variables, the related experimental research is conducted to verify or disprove the theoretical analysis. Historically, this is the reason for the large amount of research on concept identification, and for the relatively meager amount of research on other types of problems in the general area of thinking and problem-solving.

Experiments on concept identification usually have the following format: the experimenter constructs a complicated assemblage of stimulus patterns that could be classified in a variety of different ways. The experimenter decides to classify these patterns by some specific rule, and then he sets out to teach this rule to the subject by certain training procedures (short of telling the subject what the rule is). The specific training procedure may be varied. All the patterns may be displayed at once, segregated into their respective classes; and after perusing them, the subject tries to infer the rule that generated the segregation. Or the patterns may all be shown unsegregated; the subject selects particular ones and requests information about their classification; the task here is for the subject to arrive at the classification rule by using the smallest number of requests for information (since some patterns may give more information than others about the correct classification). These procedures expose all the patterns at all times during the experiment, and the subject need not rely upon his memory for specific patterns. An alternative method of collecting data requires the subject to rely upon his memory since he sees only one pattern at a time. After seeing the pattern, the subject tries to classify it correctly. Following his attempted classification (response), the experimenter informs him of the correct classification for the pattern. It is this latter procedure that we shall discuss in this chapter. For a review of results obtained by the full information procedures listed above, see books by Bruner, Goodnow, and Austin (1956) and Hunt (1962).

To introduce some historical perspective, let us mention that the concept identification task with memory load is quite similar to what is called discrimination learning (cf. Kimble, 1961). Such classificatory behavior may be described by saying that certain labeling responses come under the control of critical discriminative stimuli (for example, the color of the patterns) but show generalization to patterns varying in noncritical aspects (for example, the same classificatory response is evoked by a red pattern whether it be large or small). A large amount of work, experimental and theoretical, has been concerned with describing how such discriminative performances develop with training; a fair portion of the experimental work has been done with animals (rats, cats, monkeys). In the main, there have been two approaches or schools of thought concerning the appropriate way to formulate what is learned and how it is learned in such discrimination tasks. One of these will be called the "stimulus-response-reinforcement" point of view; the other the "hypothesis" point of view. The former position is best represented in papers by Hull (1930), Spence (1936), Wickens (1954), and Burke and Estes (1957); the latter, in papers by Lashley (1929), Krechevsky (1932), and more recently by Restle (1962) and Levine (1963).

In the S-R reinforcement view, each time response R_1 is reinforced in the presence of a given pattern of stimuli, each component of that pattern develops some associative tendency (habit) to elicit R_1. Similarly, when response R_1 is not reinforced to a pattern, some inhibitory tendencies are developed to R_1 from each constituent element of the pattern (alternatively, R_1 becomes disassociated from the element if it were previously conditioned to it). In this system, then, over successive practice trials, the strength of the reinforced response in the presence of the critical stimulus component continues to grow, whereas the habit differential of R_1 versus R_2 to noncritical (irrelevant) cues approaches some stable, low level. After some training, perfect discriminative performance is attained when the habit differential of the critical element favoring the correct response is sufficient to offset any opposing habit differential due to the irrelevant elements in any particular stimulus pattern. According to this classical theory, (a) all stimuli impinging on the sensorium influence the response selected with their relative influence depending on their reinforcement history and (b) the habit growth of particular elements is gradual and cumulative.

According to the "hypothesis" point of view, sensory information is filtered by some type of selector mechanism, and the setting of this selector determines at any moment which stimulus components are effective in specifying the response and in acquiring associative connections to the response reinforced. The selector acts as an "attention device," and the setting of the selector determines which stimulus dimensions will be attended to out of the entire pattern. The trial outcomes, nonreward in particular, may change the setting of the selector as well as the responses associated to the elements selected. By a trial-and-check process (mechanisms can be provided), the filter eventually zeros in on the critical dimensions, correct responses are connected to these dimensions, and the problem is solved. This typical system can be discussed in several ways: Krechevsky, Levine, and Restle use the expression "hypothesis testing" by the subject; Lawrence (1963) and Sutherland (1959) use the expression employed above; namely, filtering of the input and the development of response associations to the elements of the stimulus selected by the filter.

Many experiments have been performed with the goal of establishing empirical support for one or the other theoretical position. It is not possible to review even the major lines of research in this brief space; suffice it to say that evidence can be adduced for both positions under appropriate experimental conditions. In general, the consensus appears to be that a postulate of some kind of orientation, adaptation, or filtering mechanism is needed to explain a variety of results (a conclusion hardly surprising to the layman). An unresolved question is whether all the selection required occurs at the periphery of the organism, through receptor adjustments (for example, focusing the eyes on a part of the visual field), which actions themselves are modified by the usual laws of reinforcement (for example, see Atkinson, 1960a, 1961a; Ehrenfreund, 1948; and Wyckoff, 1952) or whether it is necessary to postulate that some filtering goes on at higher centers of the brain. The neurophysiological evidence appears to indicate that filtering of sensory information can occur at a variety of relay stations along the path from the receptor to the sensory cortex.

In contrast to the theories regarding animal discrimination learning, theories about human learning have, with some notable exceptions (for example, Baum, 1954; Bourne and Restle, 1959; and Hull, 1920), been discussed within the framework of a hypothesis-testing approach or some simple variant of it. The model developed later in this chapter is of this genre, since it describes the subject as selecting certain cues for attention and associating particular classificatory responses to the cues so selected. At a formal level, the model is very similar to that developed by Restle (1962) from a strict hypothesis-testing point of view. The papers by Restle and one by Bower and Trabasso (1964) are recommended collateral reading to this chapter. These papers contain more empirical content than can be packed into a chapter like the present one, whose aim is an introduction to concept-learning models.

2.1 A VOCABULARY FOR DESCRIBING CONCEPT IDENTIFICATION EXPERIMENTS

To begin exposition of our procedure and the type of results it generates, we first introduce some necessary vocabulary. Suppose that the stimulus patterns are constructed from two-valued (binary) stimulus attributes. The word *attribute* will refer to aspects like the shape of the stimulus object, its color, size, its position on the display, the number of objects, the presence or absence of borders, and so forth. We also use the term *stimulus dimension* interchangeably with the term attribute. Over the series of patterns, a given attribute may have several values: thus, the colors red and green would be the *values* of the color dimension. An attribute will be called a "cue" if more than one value of it appears over a series of stimuli requiring different classificatory responses.

In abstract terms, then, we could characterize our stimulus patterns by noting that they involve the stimulus dimensions $D_1, D_2, \ldots, D_n$ and the numbers of values of each dimension are $v_1, v_2, \ldots, v_n$. The number of different stimulus patterns possible is the product $v_1 v_2 v_3 \cdots v_n$. In the application we shall consider, each dimension has exactly two values (binary). Thus, with n independent dimensions, the number of possible patterns is $2 \times 2 \cdots (n$ times$)$ or 2^n. This is an exponential function that quickly becomes large: for $n = 3$ there are 8 patterns; for $n = 6$, there are 64 patterns; for $n = 12$, there are 4096 patterns.

A classification rule consists of a partition on this assemblage of 2^n patterns. Thus, the rule "green objects belong to class 1, red objects to class 2" partitions the 2^n patterns into two classes, with 2^{n-1} patterns belonging to class 1 and 2^{n-1} patterns belonging to class 2. This classification is mutually exclusive (i.e., no pattern belongs to both classes) and exhaustive [i.e., every pattern of the series belongs to one of the classes, since $2^{n-1} + 2^{n-1} = 2(2^{n-1}) = 2^n$]. A variety of classification rules can be thought of: some of these are symmetric (that is, the same number of patterns belong in each class); others are asymmetric (that is, different numbers in the two classes). An example of an asymmetric concept would be: "green squares are in class 1, everything else in class 2," with respective class sizes of 2^{n-2} and $3(2^{n-2})$.

The next notion to be discussed is that of the *validity* of a cue. A cue is valid to the extent that use of the values of that dimension can lead to correct responses. Thus, if all red objects belong to class 1 and green objects to class 2, then color would be called a completely valid, or relevant, cue. A cue is completely invalid (irrelevant) if it provides no basis for classifying patterns better than random guessing. Thus, if half the class 1 objects are circular and half triangular (and similarly for the class 2 objects), then form would be an irrelevant cue (zero validity). Another way to define "zero validity" is to say that the contingency correlation between the values of a dimension and the correct classification is zero. Cases of intermediate or partial validity arise whenever a cue has a correlation between zero and unity with the correct classification. For example, one might construct a series in which three fourths of the large figures belong to class 1 and one fourth to class 2, whereas the reverse proportions hold for small figures. The 2 × 2 table for a given binary attribute may be represented as follows, where the entries a, b, c, d denote the number of stimulus patterns falling in the four cells:

$$\text{Values of attribute} \begin{array}{c} \\ 1 \\ 2 \end{array} \begin{array}{cc} \text{Class} \\ 1 \quad 2 \\ \begin{bmatrix} a & b \\ c & d \end{bmatrix} \end{array}.$$

For such a 2 × 2 table, the contingency correlation φ is calculated by the formula

$$\varphi = \frac{ad - bc}{\sqrt{(a + b)(c + d)(a + c)(b + d)}}.$$

Table 2.1 gives examples of a relevant, an irrelevant, and a partially valid cue for a five dimensional problem involving $2^5 = 32$ patterns.

Table 2.1   Examples of a Relevant, Irrelevant, and Partially
Valid Cue for a Five-dimensional Problem

Relevant Cue $\varphi = +1.00$			Irrelevant Cue $\varphi = 0.00$			Partially Valid Cue $\varphi = 0.50$		
	Class			Class			Class	
	1	2		1	2		1	2
red	16	0	circle	8	8	large	12	4
blue	0	16	square	8	8	small	4	12

The Data Reduction Process

A word should be said about the way the data are collected and reduced. Table 2.2 illustrates the first eight trials for a hypothetical subject who is learning a two-category problem with one relevant dimension and two irrelevant dimensions, and responses A and B. The stimuli are composed of two forms (circle, square), two colors (black, white), and two numbers of objects (one or two), giving $2^3 = 8$ patterns. Color is relevant, with the assignments "black $= A$" and "white $= B$." Form and number are irrelevant cues. The stimuli are displayed one at a time in random order. After the subject's guess, he is informed of the correct answer. His response is coded as one if it is an error and zero if it is correct. In such experiments, each subject is usually trained until he solves the problem. Operationally, this means that training is continued until the subject meets some stringent criterion of success, such as a run of ten or more consecutive correct responses.

The primary datum obtained from each subject, then, is a sequence of ones and zeros. The characteristic of these sequences is that they end with a one followed by ten zeros (or whatever the criterion is). From an experiment in which N subjects learn the same problem to a criterion, we will have a sample of N sequences of ones and zeros. The purpose of the theory is to account for the quantitative characteristics of this sample of

Table 2.2   Hypothetical Subject's Data on the First Eight Trials of a Two-category Problem

Trial No.	Stimulus	Subject's Response	Correct Response	Coded Response Sequence
1.	●	A	A	0
2.	□ □	B	B	0
3.	□	A	B	1
4.	● ●	B	A	1
5.	○	A	B	1
6.	■	B	A	1
7.	○ ○	B	B	0
8.	■ ■	B	A	1

N sequences. We should recognize at the outset that our data-reduction method discards certain kinds of information. Thus, from the sequence of ones and zeros, we cannot infer what stimulus pattern was shown, what was the actual response, whether an error was of one type or another, and so on. This model is gross in the sense that it does not attempt to account for such information. The model supposes that the patterns are presented to each subject in a different random order, and it predicts the probability that a randomly selected subject will be correct in his response to the nth pattern in this series. In so doing, it suppresses information about the exact pattern shown, the exact response, and the prior sequence of stimuli and reinforcements that this particular subject has seen. In fact, one might argue that the predictions of the theory are accurate because it is predicting the average performance of the group of N subjects, and in taking this average, the effects due to the particular variables mentioned above are balanced out. Other approaches (for instance, computer simulation of a subject's behavior; Hunt, 1962) attempt to do more than this but have achieved only limited success; however, their discussion is beyond the range of this chapter.

2.2 THE THEORY

In two-category problems of the type illustrated above, we suppose that the primary task of the subject is to learn what cue is relevant for the classification. Once he has identified the relevant cue, we will suppose that he always attends to it, bases his responses on it, and is consistently correct. But how does he come to identify the relevant cue? We will suppose that he selects single cues (out of the entire array of possible cues) for testing. We suppose furthermore that this cue selection is random in a particular sense to be explained below. If the cue selected leads to a correct response, we suppose that the subject continues using that cue on the next trial. If the selected cue leads to an error, then the subject randomly resamples from the total pool of possible cues and uses the newly sampled cue to respond on the next trial. In resampling, he may of course select again the cue he has just discarded. The way the experiment is run ensures that a response based on any irrelevant cue has a probability near $\frac{1}{2}$ of being correct. Once the relevant cue is selected and connected to the correct responses, the probability of a correct response is 1.

Some cues in the situation are more obvious than others. That is, the subject is more likely to attend to certain cues than to others. To represent such features of the stimulus selection process, we associate with each cue a weight w_i representing the obviousness, distinctiveness, salience, or attention-value of cue i. The relative weight of the relevant cue defines a structural parameter:

$$ c = \frac{w_r}{w_r + \sum_i w_i}. $$

The sum in the denominator is over the weights of all the irrelevant cues in the problem. We will let c represent the probability that, in searching through the attributes, the subject selects the relevant cue for testing.

Following an error, the subject samples an attribute and associates the response reinforced on the trial with the particular value of that attribute present on the trial. To illustrate, suppose the stimulus is "two black circles," the subject response "B," and the experimenter says, "No, A is correct." At that moment, the subject allegedly samples from the cue population. Suppose he decides to look at the shape attribute. The shape on the pattern shown is "circles," the correct answer was "A." So the subject sets up the assignments "Circle $= A$, and Noncircle (square) $= B$." Such a tentative statement of the relevant cue and the response assignments is the subject's *hypothesis*. Thus, when the stimulus pattern for the next trial is shown, the subject is set to encode it on the basis of its shape and to

number of points in our sample space, corresponding to all integer values of n, the trial on which the transition from $\bar{S}$ to S occurs. We assume that there is some probabilistic process generating the outcomes, and our model seeks to capture the generation rules of this process. In particular, assuming the model is true, it permits us to calculate the probability of any particular outcome (trial sequence of states) of our experiment. How this is done is not immediately relevant and will be illustrated later. Important here is simply the assertion that a model of the state generating process permits us to associate with each possible outcome its probability of occurrence.

Thus, we have a sample space of outcomes (trial sequences of states), each having an associated probability of occurrence. Various *events* may be defined on this sample space. Specifying a particular event defines a set of outcomes; that is, a subset of points in the sample space. For example, "the process is in state $\bar{S}$ at the beginning of trial 10" defines such an event; we denote this event by the symbol $\bar{S}_{10}$. For each outcome we can decide whether or not this event occurs. The probability of an event is just the sum of the probabilities of the sample points that are members of the set defined by that event. If two events A and B are *mutually exclusive* (share no common sample points), then the probability of the compound event "A or B" is the sum of the probabilities of the individual A and B events, and the probability of the joint event "A and B" is the product of the two single event probabilities. For our example, the events $\bar{S}_{10}$ and $\bar{S}_{15}$ are not mutually exclusive. In fact, the sample points associated with the $\bar{S}_{15}$ event are all contained within (form a subset of) the set of points associated with the $\bar{S}_{10}$ event. In everyday terms, if the process is in state $\bar{S}$ on trial 15, then it must have been in state $\bar{S}$ on all preceding trials, including trial 10.

The next notion to be discussed is that of a *random variable*. A random variable is a function $X(u)$ defined over the sample space of a probabilistic process, where u is an arbitrary point in the sample space. Thus, in defining a random variable, we specify a rule which assigns a number X to every point in the sample space. Often there is some confusion because what is called a random variable is actually a function, but the term is kept because it has been widely used for a long time. One reason the term "random variable" creates confusion is that the functional dependence of the number X on the sample point u is conventionally suppressed in the notation. Thus, we speak of the random variable X, where it is understood that we mean the function $X(u)$ in the sense defined above.

To give an example, later we will be interested in the number of trials a subject is in state $\bar{S}$ before entering state S. We would set up a random variable to represent this number of trials, and give it some arbitrary label

(Y, for instance). For each point in the sample space (trial sequence of states), we identify the trial of the last occurrence of state $\bar{S}$ and set Y equal to that number. In this manner, each sample point will have a value of Y attached to it. The possible values of Y are the positive integers 1, 2, 3, ... Specifying a value of Y (say, $Y = 5$) is equivalent to defining the event "the last occurrence of state $\bar{S}$ is on trial 5"; the probability of this event is obtained in the usual manner, by adding up the probabilities associated with those sample points where the event occurs. If, for some arbitrary value n, we derive the probability of the event $Y = n$, written as $Pr(Y = n)$, we have obtained the *probability distribution* of the random variable Y. The statement of a probability distribution is a shorthand form for telling us the probability of all events of the sort $Y = n$ for any n.

Bernoulli Trials and Markov Chains

Any sequence of trial outcomes that can be analyzed in probabilistic terms is called a stochastic process. We will be concerned here with defining and illustrating two kinds of stochastic processes: the independent trials (Bernoulli) process and the Markov chain process. Suppose there is a small set of possible outcomes of each trial. Examples would be successive outcomes of tossing a coin (H or T) or rolling a die (1 through 6). Define a function f_n whose values are the possible outcomes on trial n (For instance, $f_n = H$ or T in the coin tossing experiment). Then the sequence of outcome functions f_1, f_2, f_3, . . . is an *independent trials (Bernoulli) process* if the probabilities that f_n takes on its particular values are independent of the outcomes of the preceding trials and are independent of the trial number n. That is, we have *stationarity* in the sense that all outcome functions f_n have the same probability distribution. Sequences of outcomes from tossing a coin or rolling a die are examples of independent trials processes.

A sequence of outcome functions f_n is a *Markov chain* if the probability distribution of the nth outcome function depends on the outcome of the directly preceding trial (that is, the value of f_{n-1}) but is independent of the outcomes of all former trials. To illustrate, let i represent the trial outcome, and suppose that i can assume the values 1, 2, or 3. Let $f_n = i$ represent the event that the outcome of trial n was i. Then a Markov chain is specified by conditional probabilities of the form $Pr(f_n = j \mid f_{n-1} = i)$, where i and j can take on the values 1, 2, or 3.* We call the values of

---

* A vertical line is used for writing conditional probabilities. The expression $Pr(A \mid B)$ is read as "the probability of A conditional upon B" or "the conditional probability of A given that B has occurred."

the outcome function f_n the "states" of the Markov chain; $Pr(f_n = j\,|\,f_{n-1} = i)$ is the conditional probability that if the chain is in state i on trial $n - 1$, it will be in state j on trial n. If these state-to-state transition probabilities are constant over all trials, then the Markov chain is said to be *homogeneous*; that is, we can write

$$Pr(f_n = j\,|\,f_{n-1} = i) = p_{ij}.$$

If the transition probabilities depend on the trial number, the chain is said to be *inhomogeneous*. An intuitive way to characterize a Markov chain is to say that the process has no memory for its past history and knows only the current state that it occupies. Alternatively, the state on the next trial is determined only by the state presently occupied and is independent of the history by which the present state was reached; this is sometimes called the "independence of path" condition for Markov chains.

As mentioned above, a homogeneous Markov chain is specified by the transition probabilities p_{ij}. These are most easily summarized in a matrix; the rows of the matrix are the possible states on trial n, and the columns the possible states on trial $n + 1$. The matrix for our three-state process (where f_n can take on the values 1, 2, or 3) is as follows:

State on trial
$n + 1$
(value of f_{n+1})

$$
\begin{array}{cc}
\text{State on trial } n \\
(\text{value of } f_n)
\end{array}
\begin{array}{c}
1 \\
2 \\
3
\end{array}
\begin{bmatrix}
p_{11} & p_{12} & p_{13} \\
p_{21} & p_{22} & p_{23} \\
p_{31} & p_{32} & p_{33}
\end{bmatrix}.
$$

The entry p_{ij} in the ith row and jth column gives the probability of a transition to state j on trial $n + 1$, conditional on being in state i on trial n. The entries in each row characterize a conditional probability distribution. For example, the three entries p_{21}, p_{22}, p_{23} in the second row specify the probability of being in states 1, 2, or 3 on trial $n + 1$ conditional upon occupancy of state 2 on trial n. Because the set of entries in each row of the matrix specifies a (conditional) probability distribution, each row sum is 1. A matrix of this type is called a *stochastic matrix*. Another piece of information needed about a Markov chain is which state it starts in on trial 1. This information may be provided in the form of an initial probability distribution; with probability p_i the process starts off in state i on trial 1. Given this information, we are able to calculate the probability of any particular trial-sequence of states by multiplying the appropriate transition probabilities together. To illustrate with the three-state process above, the probability of the 4-trial sequence 3, 2, 1, 3 would be $p_3 p_{32} p_{21} p_{13}$, where p_3 is the probability of starting in state 3 on trial 1.

Markov chains are of three types: *absorbing, ergodic,* or *periodic.* The type can be determined from the matrix of transition probabilities. For our immediate purposes, we need discuss only absorbing chains. Ergodic chains are discussed and applied to data in Chapters 7, 8, and 9; periodic chains are not required for the topics covered in this book. An absorbing Markov chain is a chain that has one or more *absorbing states.* State i is absorbing if $p_{ii} = 1$; that is, once state i is entered, the process remains there for the remainder of the experiment.

Suppose, in the three-state matrix above, that $p_{11} = 1$ and both p_{21} and p_{32} were nonzero. This means that it is possible to enter state 1 from either state 2 or 3, but a transition out of 1 cannot occur. It is obvious that such a process eventually will be absorbed in state 1. For such absorbing chains the relevant questions involve how many trials are necessary before the process is absorbed, the number of trials in each of the transient states, and so forth. There are standard techniques for computing a variety of such statistics for absorbing chains (Kemeny and Snell, 1960). When there are two or more absorbing states, interest centers on the probability that the process is absorbed at a particular absorbing state. A chain with two absorbing states is illustrated in Chapter 4.

Transition Matrix for the Concept Identification Model

Having introduced these notions about Markov chains, let us apply them to the process of immediate interest; namely, the trial-sequence of $\bar{S}$ and S states in the concept identification model. The state on trial n will be denoted $\bar{S}_n$ or S_n, and the corresponding transition matrix is as follows:

$$\begin{array}{c} \\ S_n \\ \bar{S}_n \end{array} \begin{array}{cc} S_{n+1} & \bar{S}_{n+1} \\ \begin{bmatrix} 1 & 0 \\ qc & 1 - qc \end{bmatrix} \end{array}.$$

The rationale for these transition probabilities was given in the preceding section. The 1 in the upper left-hand corner identifies S as an absorbing state. If qc is greater than zero, then the transition from $\bar{S}$ to S will eventually occur and the process will be absorbed in state S. By assumption, the process begins in state $\bar{S}$ on trial 1. To calculate the probability of the sequence of states, for example, $\bar{S}_1, \bar{S}_2, \bar{S}_3, S_4, S_5, \ldots$ we multiply the transition probabilities involved to obtain

$$1 \cdot (1 - qc) \cdot (1 - qc) \cdot qc \cdot 1 \cdot 1 \cdot 1 \cdots = (1 - qc)^2 qc.$$

If we let the random variable Y denote the number of trials that the process is in state $\bar{S}$ before it shifts to S, then the sequence illustrated above assigns the value 3 to Y. Thus, we have

$$Pr(Y = 3) = Pr(\bar{S}_1, \bar{S}_2, \bar{S}_3, S_4 \cdots) = (1 - qc)^2 qc.$$

It can be shown that the probability distribution of Y is

$$Pr(Y = n) = (1 - qc)^{n-1} qc \qquad\qquad (n \geq 1).$$

The method for verifying this result will be illustrated later in connection with Eq. 2.4. The function $Pr(Y = n)$ will be discussed in another context later and is given here simply to illustrate a probability distribution from our Markov chain.

To summarize, the concept identification model leads us to represent the process as a two-state absorbing Markov chain. However, it is important to realize that although this Markov chain specifies the trial-sequence of states $\bar{S}$ and S, in the ordinary experiment these states are not observed. What we do observe is the subject's sequence of class-ificatory responses, and these are coded as correct (0) or incorrect (1). The responses bear only a probabilistic relation to the sequence of states S and $\bar{S}$. This relation is specified by the following *response axioms:*

1. *If the subject begins the trial in state $\bar{S}$, then his response on that trial is correct with probability p and is incorrect with probability $q = 1 - p$.*
2. *If the subject begins the trial in state S, then his response on that trial is correct with probability 1.*

By virtue of these response axioms, statements about the sequence of states for the Markov process can be translated into statements about the subject's observable responses. How this is done will be illustrated in Sec. 2.4. An interesting point here is that although the sequence of states S and $\bar{S}$ form a Markov chain, the sequence of observable responses do not, unless $p = 0$.

2.3 ANALYSIS OF PRESOLUTION DATA

We have characterized the subject as being in one of the two states, S or $\bar{S}$, on each trial; this is equivalent to saying that he has one of two values of response probability, p or 1, on each trial. He begins with a correct response probability of p, stays at that level for a randomly determined number of trials, and then on a single trial shifts to a response probability of 1. Moreover, the model says that an error occurs on that trial on which the shift from $\bar{S}$ to S occurs. Because the shift is to a state where the correct response probability is 1, there can be no further errors following this shift. Hence, during all those trials up to and including a subject's last error, he is in state $\bar{S}$; following his last error, he is in state S.

This theoretical description has some very strong implications about the sequence of responses a subject makes prior to his last error (Suppes and Ginsberg, 1963). For convenience, we will refer to these as presolution trials. The model implies that the sequence of presolution trials constitutes a Bernoulli series of observations. This means that (a) the probability of a correct response remains constant at the value p over the entire series of presolution trials, and (b) the outcomes of successive trials are statistically independent (that is, the probability of a correct response on a presolution trial is the same regardless of the past history of responses). As noted on p. 36, the first characteristic is called *stationarity* since estimates of response probability over presolution trials are assumed to be constant or stationary, and the second characteristic is called *independence*. Thus, the model leads us to expect that the sequence of presolution trials generated by a subject should approximate a stationary series of independent Bernoulli observations with probability p of a correct response. These are predictions that can be directly tested.

Tests for Stationarity of Presolution Responses

We now consider some tests for stationarity. There are a number of ways one can try to decide whether or not subjects display any change in their performance over the series of presolution trials. Each method leads naturally to a statistical test of the null hypothesis, which specifies that response probabilities are constant over presolution trials.

Let us begin by providing some illustrative data to work with, so that we will have clearly in mind what is being referred to. Suppose that we have run ten subjects on a concept-learning task. By the data reduction procedure illustrated earlier, we obtain a string of ones (errors) and zeros (correct responses) from each subject. Each subject is trained until he meets a criterion of solution, such as ten consecutive correct answers. Table 2.3 gives the string of responses up through and including the last error for ten hypothetical subjects. To keep the table of manageable size, we suppose that all subjects have solved the problem by the tenth trial; in actual data, of course, some subjects may take considerably longer to solve the problem.

The relevant summary statistics for each subject are given in the right-hand column of the table. These include the number of errors, the

Table 2.3   Artificial Data

Subject	Trial Number										Total Errors	Total Correct	Proportion Correct	First Half	Second Half	Frequency Difference
	1	2	3	4	5	6	7	8	9	10						
1	0	0	1	1	0	1	1	0	1	1	6	4	4/10	2/4	1/4	−1
2	1	1	1	0	0	1	0	0	0	1	5	5	5/10	1/4	3/4	+2
3	1	0	0	1	1						3	2	2/5	1/2	1/2	0
4	0	1									1	1	1/2	*	*	*
5	0	0	1	1	0	1	0	1	0	1	4	4	4/8	2/3	2/3	0
6	1	0	0	0	1	0	1				3	4	4/7	2/3	2/3	0
7	1	1	0	0	1						3	2	2/5	0/2	2/2	+2
8	0	1	1	0	0	0	1	1			4	4	4/8	1/3	2/3	+1
9	0	0	0	1	1	0	0	1	1		4	5	5/9	3/4	2/4	−1
10	0	0	1	0	1						2	3	3/5	2/2	1/2	−1
											35	34	34/69	14/27	16/27	+2
													49.4	51.8	59.3	

Before last error:

	1	2	3	4	5	6	7	8	9	10	
Correct	6	6	4	5	4	3	3	2	1	0	34
Opportunities	10	9	9	9	6	6	5	3	2	0	59
Per cent correct	60	67	44	55	67	50	60	67	50	*	57.6

number of correct responses, and the percentage of successes. The next two columns give the number of successes divided by the number of responses in the first and second halves of each subject's presolution trials. It should be noted that in making these calculations, the last error of the subject is excluded. After this last error is excluded, the remaining trials are divided in half, discarding an odd trial in the middle of the series if necessary. For subject 4, only one response remained after discarding the last error; hence, for him there is no proper definition of the first and second halves of the presolution trials. The rightmost column gives the difference in successes between the second and first halves of a subject's prelearning trials. Other summary statistics easily obtained from the table are the average number of errors per subject ($3.5 = \frac{35}{10}$), the average number of successes before the last error ($3.4 = \frac{34}{10}$), and the average trial number on which the last error occurs ($6.9 = \frac{69}{10}$). The row at the bottom of the table gives the sums for each trial of the number of correct responses and of the number of opportunities for a correct response before the subject's last error. Thus, the number of subjects contributing (opportunities) declines over trials as progressively more subjects solve the problem. At the end of these rows, we have written the sum of the number of successes (34) and the number of opportunities (59). The total number of opportunities (59) plus the number of sequences (10) is equal to the sum of the number of successes and errors, including the last error (69). Excluding the last error, the overall proportion of successes prior to the last error is $\frac{34}{59} = 0.576$. When we include the trial of the last error for each subject, this proportion is $\frac{34}{69} = 0.494$.

The first test for stationarity uses the column sums in the bottom row of the table, that is, the observed number of successes and opportunities prior to but excluding the last error for each subject. The question to be answered is whether this trial-sequence of response proportions is stationary. Using the overall proportion of successes prior to the last error (0.576) and the number of opportunities on each trial, we generate a prediction for each trial of the number of successes and errors. Thus, the null hypothesis is essentially that on each trial 57.6 per cent of the observations will be successes, and 42.4 per cent will be errors. Now, these observed numbers will exhibit some statistical fluctuations from the predicted values. To assess whether the deviations are large enough to discredit the null hypothesis of stationarity, we apply a χ^2 test. In applying a χ^2 test, it is advisable to group together enough adjacent trials so that all expected (predicted) frequencies are five or greater. This has been done in Table 2.4.

In Table 2.4, the expected number of correct responses in a cell is 0.576 times the number of observations for those trials. The expected number of errors in the cells of the bottom rows is the error probability

$(1 - 0.576 = 0.424)$ times the number of observations. For example, considering trials 1 and 2 together, the expected number of correct responses is 10.94. This is obtained by noting that there are 19 observations on trials 1 and 2 (see Table 2.3) and then multiplying 0.576 times 19; the expected number of errors on trials 1 and 2 is $19 - 10.94 = 8.06$. For each of the eight cells of Table 2.4, we calculate the quantity $(O - E)^2/E$, where O and E are the observed and expected frequencies, respectively. Then the calculated quantity is the squared difference between observed and expected frequencies divided by the expected frequency. These

Table 2.4   Predicted and Observed Frequencies over Trials

		Trials			
		1 and 2	3 and 4	5 and 6	7, 8, and 9
Correct	Observed (O)	12	9	7	6
	Expected (E)	10.94	10.37	6.91	5.76
	$\dfrac{(O - E)^2}{E}$	0.1027	0.1809	0.0012	0.0100
Errors	Observed (O)	7	9	5	4
	Expected (E)	8.06	7.63	5.09	4.24
	$\dfrac{(O - E)^2}{E}$	0.1394	0.2460	0.0016	0.0136

quantities are listed in Table 2.4. The sum of these quantities over the eight cells is 0.6954. Under the null hypothesis, the sum of these $(O - E)^2/E$ scores should have a χ^2 distribution with three degrees of freedom. The three degrees of freedom are found by determining the number of constraints on the entries in the eight cells of Table 2.4. First, the observed and expected quantities in each column must add up to the same value; namely, the number of observations for that trial block. Thus, the four column sums impose four constraints. The last constraint is that the overall percentage of successes is the same for the observed and expected scores; that is, we estimated the proportion 0.576 from the observed scores and used this in generating the expected frequencies. Therefore, there are a total of five constraints imposed on the eight-cell table, leaving three degrees of freedom. Referring to a χ^2 table with three degrees of freedom, a value of 0.6954 would not permit us to reject the null hypothesis of stationarity.

One might object to the foregoing test for stationarity because it involves the implicit assumption that all sequences are generated by the identical process. But suppose that subjects really differ; in particular, suppose that faster learners have high probabilities of correct responding which improve over trials, whereas slower learners begin with lower probabilities which also increase over trials. By the foregoing method of pooling, the fast learners contribute most of the data on early trials, whereas the slow learners are weighted more on later trials. Because of this differential weighting of slower subjects, it is possible that the pooled averages might appear constant over trials although each individual subject actually improves over trials.

This argument suggests that we need a statistic sensitive to the trends within each individual's response sequence. One simple test that meets this requirement compares the number of successes in the first and second halves of each subject's series of presolution trials. If each individual is improving over his trials, then we will find that the number of successes in the second half is larger than the number in the first half, except for sampling variability. On the other hand, if the response probability is the same in both halves, then the numbers of successes in the two halves should be equal.

The relevant statistics for making this comparison are shown in the last three columns of Table 2.3. There the number of successes in the first half was 14 out of 27 opportunities, and in the second half it was 16 out of 27. A simple test for whether the success probability is the same in the first and second halves is to perform a paired t-test on the difference scores in the last column of Table 2.3. This test essentially asks whether the mean difference score is reliably different from zero (cf. Hays, 1963). For the present case, the mean difference of $\frac{2}{10} = 0.20$ is too small to cause us to reject the hypothesis of no difference ($t = 0.20/0.36 = 0.56$, $df = 9$). Thus this test supports the previous test on stationarity of the presolution response sequences.

This method of dividing each subject's prelearning trials into equal parts can be extended to any number of divisions. For example, we might divide the trial sequence into four successive parts and look for trends in response probabilities over the four successive "quartiles." If there are N trials before the last error, then there will be $N/4$ trials in each quartile if N is a multiple of four. If N is not a multiple of four, some decision has to be made about how to treat the 1, 2, or 3 odd trials. Various methods are discussed by Hilgard (1938) and Suppes and Ginsberg (1963). After dividing each subject's protocol into equal parts, we then sum over subjects to obtain estimates of response probability in each part. These analyses are called Vincentizing methods, and the curve constructed is called a Vincent curve, after the woman who first proposed this method of plotting learning data (Vincent, 1912).

We have discussed the model's prediction of stationarity in simple two-category concept learning tasks and have described methods to test for stationarity. Perhaps it is appropriate in concluding this section to mention that the predicted stationarity has indeed been consistently found in empirical studies of this learning task and is a replicable phenomenon. For example, Bower and Trabasso (1964) report relatively flat stationarity curves from a number of different experiments, and other investigators have found the same results. One example of such results is

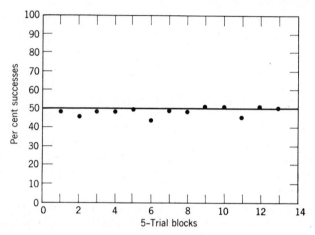

Fig. 2.1 Stationarity data: percentage of successes prior to the last error plotted in blocks of five trials.

reproduced in Fig. 2.1. We wish to emphasize that the model predicts stationary presolution performance only for the simple two-category task involving binary cues. If the task is complicated by increasing the number of values of the relevant dimension (and hence the number of classificatory responses), stationarity is no longer predicted (cf. Appendix A in Bower and Trabasso, 1964). Similarly, if the correct classifications are made to depend upon the joint values of two or more dimensions, then stationarity is no longer predicted, nor is it found. The theory discussed in this chapter can be extended to handle such compound concept learning data, but to introduce the modifications here would lead us too far afield.

Test for Independence of Presolution Responses

A second major assumption of the model is that successive presolution responses will be statistically independent. This means that for a given subject's protocol the probability of a success on any presolution trial is the same regardless of whether a success or failure occurred on the preceding trial. In a sense, independence of successive responses is a counter-intuitive assumption for learning experiments; it is commonly believed that making a correct response implies that you know more (and will so indicate on the next trial) than if you had responded incorrectly. Although this is generally a valid inference, one cannot be sure that it holds for the presolution trials in the present concept-learning task.

At this point it is necessary to introduce some notation for the subject's response. We define a random variable x_n that represents the response of a particular subject on some arbitrary trial n of the experiment; specifically, the value of x_n will be 1 if an error occurred on trial n and 0 otherwise.* Put in equation form

$$x_n = \begin{cases} 1, \text{ if the subject made an error on trial } n \\ 0, \text{ if the subject was correct on trial } n. \end{cases}$$

In terms of this notation, we can write the probability of an error on trial n as $Pr(x_n = 1)$; clearly, $Pr(x_n = 1) + Pr(x_n = 0) = 1$. In these terms, then, each subject generates a particular trial-sequence of values of the random variables $x_1, x_2, x_3, \ldots$. These are the sequences of ones and zeros mentioned earlier.

With this notation at hand, we now turn to the question of whether successes and errors are occurring independently in the presolution response sequences. Effectively, we must compare two conditional probabilities to decide this matter. One is the probability of a success conditional upon the occurrence of a success on the previous trial; this is written as $Pr(x_{n+1} = 0 \mid x_n = 0)$, where n and $n + 1$ denote any two adjacent presolution trials. The second is the probability of a success conditional upon the occurrence of an error on the previous trial; namely, $Pr(x_{n+1} = 0 \mid x_n = 1)$. Our test for independence essentially reduces to deciding whether these two conditional probabilities estimated from the data are equal. If they are equal, then the probability of a success on any trial is independent of the response on the prior trial.

We will use a χ^2 test to answer this question of independence of presolution responses (cf. Suppes and Ginsberg, 1963). Since the conditional probabilities refer to the dependence between the responses

---

* Recall that a random variable was defined as a function $X(u)$ over the sample space of a random experiment. The random variable x_n introduced here is defined for a sample space, where each point is a trial-sequence of correct and incorrect responses. That is, sample spaces can be defined over response sequences, as well as over the state sequences described on p. 35. Given a point in the sample space, the function x_n assigns a value of 1 if an error occurred on trial n for that point and 0 otherwise.

on two adjacent trials, we tabulate the frequency of all response pairs over all pairs of adjacent presolution trials. That is, we count the number of times a success or error follows a success and, similarly, the number of times a success or error follows an error. In these counts, we may include the transition from the next-to-last presolution response to the last error. To illustrate this counting, consider subject 9 from Table 2.3. His sequence of responses was coded as 00011001 1. In this case, a 1 is followed by a 1 two times and by a 0 one time; a 0 is followed by a 1 twice and by another 0 three times. These response frequencies may be arranged in a 2 × 2 table as follows:

		Response on Current Trial	
		1	0
Response on prior trial	1	2	1
	0	2	3

We obtain a 2 × 2 table like this for each subject. Usually the cell entries for individuals are too small for statistical tests, so we sum the corresponding entries of all the individual tables. For the presolution data of the ten subjects given in Table 2.3, we obtain the pooled results given in

Table 2.5   Presolution Transition Frequencies

		Trial $n + 1$		
		1	0	
Trial n	1	12	13	25
	0	19	15	34
		31	28	59

Table 2.5. From this table of frequency data, we estimate the following conditional probabilities:

$$Pr(x_{n+1} = 0 \mid x_n = 1) = \tfrac{13}{25} = 0.520$$

(2.1) $$Pr(x_{n+1} = 0 \mid x_n = 0) = \tfrac{15}{34} = 0.432.$$

The overall probability of a correct response, disregarding the prior response, is

(2.2) $$Pr(x_{n+1} = 0) = \tfrac{28}{59} = 0.474.$$

The question to be decided is whether the conditional probabilities in Eq. 2.1 differ significantly from each other. Our method for testing whether the difference is significant involves computing a χ^2 for the 2 × 2 table. For this test, we predict the cell entries in Table 2.5 by assuming that the responses are independent; the null hypothesis is that the true conditional success probabilities in Eq. 2.1 are the same and are equal to the mean success probability of 0.474 in Eq. 2.2. Taking the total frequency of errors on trial n (25 here), we calculate the expected successes on trial $n + 1$ (25 × 0.474 = 11.85) and the expected errors on the next trial (25 × 0.526 = 13.15). In a similar fashion, the expected successes and

Table 2.6   Predicted and Observed Presolution Transition Data

Observed	Expected	$\dfrac{(O - E)^2}{E}$	Observed	Expected	$\dfrac{(O - E)^2}{E}$
12	13.15	0.101	13	11.85	0.112
19	17.85	0.068	15	16.15	0.075

errors following a success (34 cases) also are calculated. The expected and observed values are displayed together in Table 2.6. For each pair of observed and expected values, we calculate $(O - E)^2/E$. Summing the values of $(O - E)^2/E$ over the four cells yields

$$\chi^2 = 0.101 + 0.112 + 0.068 + 0.075 = 0.356.$$

The $(O - E)^2/E$ score in each cell is a χ^2 variable with one degree of freedom. Without any constraints the sum of these four variates would have a χ^2 distribution with four degrees of freedom. However, we have imposed three constraints: (1) the entries in the first row must sum to 25, (2) the entries in the second row must sum to 34, and (3) the sum of expected frequencies in the second column must be 28. With these constraints, once the entry in one of the cells is specified, the remaining three cells are uniquely determined. Hence, we are left with only one degree of freedom. Thus our procedure generates a χ^2 with one degree of freedom. If we consult a χ^2 table, a value of $\chi^2 = 0.356$ with one degree of freedom does not permit rejection of the null hypothesis that successive errors and successes occur independently.

To illustrate this property of independence in actual data, we cite Table 2.7. Here are displayed transition frequencies pooled over a number of two-category concept learning experiments reported by Bower and Trabasso (1964). The large number of observations provides for reliable estimates of the conditional probabilities and for a strong test of independence. The conditional probability of a success was 0.504 following a success and 0.502 following an error. The near-equality of these two values indicates that the assumption of independence is plausible ($\chi^2 = 0.046$).

The tests that have just been outlined for stationarity and independence of presolution responses provide the basic information to determine whether these responses can be represented as a Bernoulli series. There are, of course, further tests of Bernoulli properties that could be carried out on these data, such as predicting specific sequences of responses or predicting the (binomial) probability of the number of errors in blocks of

Table 2.7   Pooled Transition Frequencies

		Trial $n + 1$	
		1	0
Trial n	1	2501	2524
	0	2507	2552

K presolution trials (cf. Suppes and Ginsberg, 1963). However, these additional tests are ancillary to the basic information on stationarity and independence.

This concludes our discussion of presolution analyses. The analyses exhibited here provide information about one of the critical assumptions in the concept identification model, namely, that prior to solution, the subject generates a stationary series of independent responses. It should be noted that none of these presolution analyses depends upon assumptions about how or why solution occurs. We turn now to stating assumptions about how concept learning occurs and to deriving some implications of these assumptions. In the context of an experiment, these implications are evaluated as numerical predictions of various statistics of the data. By this method we determine whether the model's assumptions are realistic.

2.4   MATHEMATICAL DERIVATIONS FROM THE MODEL

We now use the model to derive predictions regarding statistics obtained from the observable response sequences. To review briefly, the subject begins in state $\bar{S}$ on trial 1, and makes an error with probability q on every trial that he is in $\bar{S}$. Each time he makes an error, he has probability c of shifting into state S, where he will make no further errors.

The first quantity to be derived is the probability of an error on trial n of the experiment; we let q_n denote this probability; that is, $q_n = Pr(x_n = 1)$. For an individual subject, the probability of an error on any particular trial is either q (if he is in state $\bar{S}$) or 0 (if he is in state S). In other words, the error probability is itself a random variable, taking on value q or 0. The likelihood that the error probability takes on the value q on trial n is the probability that a subject is in state $\bar{S}$ on trial n, namely, $Pr(\bar{S}_n)$; and the likelihood that it equals 0 is $Pr(S_n)$. The expected value of a random variable is the sum of each value times its probability of occurrence. Hence, the probability of an error on trial n is

$$(2.3) \qquad q_n = q \cdot Pr(\bar{S}_n) + 0 \cdot Pr(S_n) = qPr(\bar{S}_n).$$

Thus to compute q_n we need to determine $Pr(\bar{S}_n)$. To begin, by assumption the subject starts in $\bar{S}$ on trial 1, so $Pr(\bar{S}_1) = 1$. The likelihood that he is still in $\bar{S}$ at the beginning of trial 2 is the probability, $1 - qc$, that he did not leave $\bar{S}$ on trial 1; so

$$Pr(\bar{S}_2) = Pr(\bar{S}_1)(1 - qc) = 1 - qc.$$

The probability that he is in state $\bar{S}$ on trial 3 is the product of the likelihood of $\bar{S}_2$ and of not leaving on that trial, or

$$Pr(\bar{S}_3) = Pr(\bar{S}_2)(1 - qc) = (1 - qc)^2.$$

The probability of still being in state $\bar{S}$ on trial 4 is

$$Pr(\bar{S}_4) = Pr(\bar{S}_3)(1 - qc) = (1 - qc)^3.$$

By now it should be clear how the successive values of $Pr(\bar{S}_n)$ are generated; multiply the previous-trial value of $Pr(\bar{S}_n)$ by the constant $(1 - qc)$, which results in increasing the exponent of the $(1 - qc)$ term by one. We may conjecture that the general result is

$$(2.4) \qquad Pr(\bar{S}_n) = (1 - qc)^{n-1}.$$

The reader may check that Eq. 2.4 is consistent with the values calculated for $n = 1, 2, 3$, and 4. We shall use a proof by induction to show that it is true for any n.

The essentials of an inductive proof are these: (a) show that the conjectured solution holds for $n = 1$ (we have already done so), and (b) assuming that it holds for some arbitrary value n, prove that it holds as well for $n + 1$. If both steps can be satisfied, then the conjecture is proved. For our case, the proof is trivial. Assume that Eq. 2.4 holds for $Pr(\bar{S}_n)$. To obtain $Pr(\bar{S}_{n+1})$, we note that the subject must be in $\bar{S}$ on trial n [which by the induction hypothesis is $(1 - qc)^{n-1}$] and remain in $\bar{S}$ for the next trial, with probability $1 - qc$. Hence,

$$(2.5) \qquad \begin{aligned} Pr(\bar{S}_{n+1}) &= Pr(\bar{S}_n)(1 - qc) \\ &= (1 - qc)^{n-1}(1 - qc) \\ &= (1 - qc)^n. \end{aligned}$$

The last line is consistent with the conjecture in Eq. 2.4 if we replace n by $n + 1$. Therefore, Eq. 2.4 is proved.

Equation 2.5 is an example of a *linear difference equation* of the general form

$$y_{n+1} = Gy_n,$$

where G is a constant (and equals $1 - qc$ for our special case) and y_n is a dependent variable defined on the nonnegative integers. The solution to this difference equation is

$$y_n = G^{n-1}y_1$$

and is arrived at in the same way we established Eq. 2.4. We will not digress here to discuss difference equations further since they play no essential role in this chapter. They are introduced in more detail in Sec. 5.3, where they are fundamental to the derivations.

Having found $Pr(\bar{S}_n)$, we multiply by q to obtain the probability of an error on trial n; i.e.,

$$(2.6) \qquad \begin{aligned} q_n = Pr(x_n = 1) &= Pr(x_n = 1 \mid \bar{S}_n)Pr(\bar{S}_n) \\ &= q(1 - qc)^{n-1}. \end{aligned}$$

So that the reader may visualize this function, we have plotted it in Fig. 2.2 with q_n on the ordinate and the trial number, n, on the abscissa. For this example, $q = 0.50$ and $1 - qc = 0.80$. The values of q_n generate an exponential decay curve having negative acceleration. The successive values of q_n for $n = 1, 2, 3, 4, \ldots$ are 0.500, 0.400, 0.320, 0.256, etc. Successive differences between adjacent terms decrease in the order 0.100, 0.080, 0.064; hence the label "negative acceleration."

The *asymptotic probability* of an error is defined as the limit of q_n as n becomes large. The limit in this case equals zero since the quantity $1 - qc$ when raised to higher powers approaches zero; that is,

$$\lim_{n \to \infty} q_n = \lim_{n \to \infty} q(1 - qc)^{n-1} = 0.$$

It is instructive to point out an interesting contrast here. The reader will have noted that the average q_n curve in Fig. 2.2 is a smooth decreasing function. This is to be contrasted with the fact that the model supposes that the error-probability curve for each subject is a step function, starting at q on trial 1, staying flat for some random number of trials, then dropping abruptly to zero. This small paradox is resolved when we notice that q_n is calculated on the basis of predicting the probability that learning has not yet occurred by trial n, and this latter probability is a smooth function of trials. Alternatively, the smooth q_n curve in Fig. 2.2 may be considered

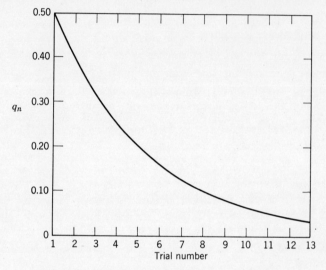

Fig. 2.2   A graph of the function $q_n = 0.5(0.8)^{n-1}$.

the result of averaging together many step-functions, where the trial of the step is distributed according to $qc(1 - qc)^{n-1}$. It is known that if we average together the performance of a group of subjects learning a concept problem, the group average proportion of errors changes over trials much as depicted in Fig. 2.2, even though presolution analyses reveal stationary probabilities prior to the last error for each subject. In this case the group average learning curve is not representative of the learning curve for individual subjects. Despite this possibly misleading feature, the mean learning curve is still a useful index of group performance, and the model should be able to predict it with accuracy.

Sums of Geometric Series

In practice, there is frequent occasion to plot learning curves in blocks of trials rather than in terms of single trials. This renders the learning curve more informative, especially when learning is very slow or there are only a few subjects contributing observations on each trial. Blocking of trials is employed to smooth out variability in the empirical estimates of performance probabilities. Since the model predicts q_n for any trial, it may also be made to predict the curve obtained by averaging observations over blocks of trials. To illustrate the computation, let us suppose trials are to be divided into blocks of length k. We let m index the trial block and let $Q(m)$ represent the average error probability in block m. The value of $Q(1)$ is obtained as follows:

$$Q(1) = \frac{q_1 + q_2 + \cdots + q_k}{k} = \frac{1}{k}\left[\sum_{i=1}^{k} q(1 - qc)^{i-1}\right] = \frac{q}{k}\left[\sum_{i=1}^{k}(1 - qc)^{i-1}\right].$$

We meet here for the first time in this text a small mathematical problem—how to obtain an explicit expression for the sum of a geometric series. Since this series occurs repeatedly throughout the book, it is essential to digress momentarily to consider sums of geometric series. The series

(2.7a) $$\mathscr{S} = \sum_{n=1}^{k} r^{n-1} = 1 + r + r^2 + \cdots + r^{k-1}$$

is called a geometric series with ratio r. The sum of the series is found by multiplying the series by r and subtracting the series $r\mathscr{S}$ from the series $\mathscr{S}$. In this subtraction, all terms cancel except for the $1 - r^k$ entries:

$$\mathscr{S} = 1 + r + r^2 + \cdots + r^{k-2} + r^{k-1}$$
$$\underline{- r\mathscr{S} = \quad - (r + r^2 + \cdots + r^{k-2} + r^{k-1} + r^k)}$$
$$\mathscr{S} - r\mathscr{S} = 1 - r^k$$

Solving for $\mathscr{S}$ in the last line,

(2.7b) $$\mathscr{S} = \frac{1 - r^k}{1 - r}.$$

We note that the expression for $\mathscr{S}$ is indeterminate if $r = 1$. Of course, from the definition of $\mathscr{S}$, we have $\mathscr{S} = k$ when $r = 1$. In numerous cases encountered later, the series has an infinite number of terms. If $0 < r < 1$ so that r^k approaches zero for large k, then the sum of the series has a limit; namely,

$$\sum_{n=1}^{\infty} r^{n-1} = \lim_{k \to \infty} \frac{1 - r^k}{1 - r} = \frac{1}{1 - r}.$$

We wish to solve one more series sum since it too will be used throughout this book. The series to be summed is

$$\mathscr{S} = \sum_{n=1}^{k} nr^{n-1} = 1 + 2r + 3r^2 + 4r^3 + \cdots + kr^{k-1}.$$

To solve for this series sum, we try the trick of multiplying $\mathscr{S}$ by r, and subtracting $r\mathscr{S}$ from $\mathscr{S}$. The operation is:

$$\mathscr{S} = 1 + 2r + 3r^2 + 4r^3 + \cdots + kr^{k-1}$$
$$-r\mathscr{S} = \quad - [r + 2r^2 + 3r^3 + \cdots + (k-1)r^{k-1} + kr^k]$$
$$\mathscr{S} - r\mathscr{S} = (1 - r)\mathscr{S} = 1 + r + r^2 + r^3 + \cdots + r^{k-1} - kr^k.$$

This expression is still not sufficiently reduced. So we reapply the same device: we multiply $(1 - r)\mathscr{S}$ by r and subtract this $r(1 - r)\mathscr{S}$ from $(1 - r)\mathscr{S}$. This yields

$$(1 - r)\mathscr{S} = 1 + r + r^2 + r^3 + \cdots + r^{k-1} - kr^k$$
$$-r(1 - r)\mathscr{S} = \quad - [r + r^2 + r^3 + \cdots + r^{k-1} + r^k - kr^{k+1}]$$
$$(1 - r)^2\mathscr{S} = 1 - r^k - kr^k + kr^{k+1}$$
$$= 1 - r^k[1 + k(1 - r)]$$

or

$$\mathscr{S} = \frac{1}{(1 - r)^2} - \frac{r^k[1 + k(1 - r)]}{(1 - r)^2}.$$

The limit of this series sum as k approaches infinity is

$$\lim_{k \to \infty} \mathscr{S} = \frac{1}{(1 - r)^2} - \frac{1}{(1 - r)^2}\left[\lim_{k \to \infty} r^k + (1 - r) \lim_{k \to \infty} kr^k\right].$$

Now terms of the form kr^k converge to zero for large values of k, when $0 < r < 1$. Hence, the limit may be written as

$$(2.8) \qquad \sum_{n=1}^{\infty} nr^{n-1} = \frac{1}{(1 - r)^2}.$$

The trick used here to sum geometric series is standard and should be well learned: multiply the series by its ratio, and subtract the product from the original series. Applying the trick one time worked in solving $\sum r^{n-1}$. To solve $\sum nr^{n-1}$, the same algebraic operation had to be applied twice in succession. To solve $\sum n^2 r^{n-1}$ requires applying the tactic three times in succession, etc.

With this information on geometric series at hand, let us return now to out initial expression for $Q(1)$. To repeat, it is

$$Q(1) = \frac{q}{k}\left[\sum_{i=1}^{k} (1 - qc)^{i-1}\right].$$

Here we have a geometric series like Eq. 2.7a with ratio $r = 1 - qc$. So by Eq. 2.7b the sum of this series is

$$Q(1) = \frac{q}{k}\frac{[1 - (1 - qc)^k]}{[1 - (1 - qc)]} = \frac{1 - (1 - qc)^k}{kc}.$$

To obtain the average error probability over the second block of trials, denoted $Q(2)$, we average the error probabilities from trials $k + 1$ through $2k$, as follows:

$$Q(2) = \frac{q_{k+1} + q_{k+2} + \cdots + q_{2k}}{k} = \frac{1}{k}\left[\sum_{i=k+1}^{2k} q(1 - qc)^{i-1}\right].$$

We make the following simplification:

(2.9) $Q(2) = \dfrac{q}{k}[(1 - qc)^k + (1 - qc)^{k+1} + \cdots + (1 - qc)^{2k-1}]$

$\qquad\qquad = (1 - qc)^k\left[\dfrac{q}{k}\sum_{i=1}^{k}(1 - qc)^{i-1}\right]$

$\qquad\qquad = (1 - qc)^k Q(1).$

That is, the term inside the brackets is just $Q(1)$ obtained previously. Equation 2.9 is an example of a linear difference equation of the form

$$Q(m + 1) = G Q(m)$$

where $G = (1 - qc)^k$. A difference equation of this type was encountered previously in Eq. 2.5, and its solution was shown to be

(2.10) $Q(m) = Q(1)G^{m-1} = Q(1)[(1 - qc)^k]^{m-1}.$

Thus, the block-sized mean learning curve is also a negatively accelerated decay curve, starting at $Q(1)$ and decreasing at the rate of $(1 - qc)^k$ from block to block.

Distribution of Total Errors

We continue our derivations of predictions from the model. One useful summary statistic of a subject's performance is the total number of errors he makes before reaching the criterion of learning. This statistic has a simple relationship to the learning parameter c; it also provides a convenient means for estimating c for a given set of data.

Let T be a random variable representing the total number of errors made by a subject. Since the subject begins in state $\bar{S}$ and an error is required before the subject has an opportunity to move into state S, it is clear that T has to be one or larger;* thus, the possible values of T are

---

* An alternate way to start off the subject is to suppose that with probability c he begins with the correct hypothesis; if so, he solves without making any errors. The distribution of T under this assumption is $Pr(T = k) = c(1 - c)^k$ for $k = 0, 1, 2, \ldots$, having mean $(1 - c)/c$. Bower and Trabasso (1964) found, however, that this latter formula led to poorer predictions in cue additivity experiments than did the one used in the text. Various arguments can be given for either variant of the "starting" assumptions, but this minor point will not be discussed further here.

the positive integers 1, 2, 3, ... Deriving the probability distribution of T consists of using the model to find the probability that T will take on each of its possible values.

The derivation is simple because it hinges upon two central assumptions: first, that opportunities for learning occur only on error trials and that success trials are without effect; second, the probability that any given error is the subject's final error (i.e., he learns on that trial) is a constant c. Thus, the probability that $T = 1$ is the likelihood that the subject learns on the trial of his first error, which is c. The probability that $T = 2$ is the joint likelihood that the subject fails to learn (with probability $1 - c$) on his first error and then learns on his second error (with probability c). The product of the probabilities of these two events is $c(1 - c)$, which is $Pr(T = 2)$. By continuing in this manner, it may be seen that $Pr(T = k)$ is the likelihood that the subject fails to learn on his first $k - 1$ errors [with probability $(1 - c)^{k-1}$] but then learns on his kth error, with probability c. Thus, the distribution of T may be written as

$$(2.11) \qquad Pr(T = k) = c(1 - c)^{k-1}, \qquad \text{(for } k \geqslant 1\text{).}$$

The distribution function expressed in Eq. 2.11 is called the geometric distribution; alternatively, the random variable T is said to be geometrically distributed. Its name derives from the fact that the successive terms of $Pr(T = k)$ are the same as successive terms of a geometric series, where each term is obtained by multiplying the preceding term by a constant ($1 - c$ in this case). A plot of $Pr(T = k)$ against k generates an exponential decay curve. A quick first test of whether the expression in Eq. 2.11 is a distribution function is to see if its terms sum to unity. The reader may quickly verify that the sum from $k = 1$ to ∞ of $Pr(T = k)$ does indeed equal one.

Moments of a Probability Distribution

Some descriptive measures of the distribution of a random variable are its expected value and its mean squared value. The mean squared value is also called the second raw moment of the distribution. The expected value of any random variable X is written as $E(X)$ and is defined as

$$E(X) = \sum_k k \, Pr(X = k),$$

where the sum is over all possible values of k for which $Pr(X = k)$ is defined. Thus, the expected value is the sum of the products of the values of the random variable times the probabilities that it takes on those values.

More generally, if we consider any function $g(X)$ of a random variable X, the expected value of $g(X)$ is defined as

$$E[g(X)] = \sum_k g(k)Pr(X = k).$$

The raw moments of a probability distribution are obtained when $g(k)$ equals an integer power of k. The rth raw moment is the expectation of the function $g(k) = k^r$.* The raw moments are descriptive of a distribution function in the sense that the moments uniquely determine the distribution. In principle, by knowing all moments, we could analytically determine the distribution function from which they were derived.

Letting T be the total errors random variable, we have for the expected total errors

$$E(T) = \sum_{k=1}^{\infty} k\, Pr(T = k) = \sum_{k=1}^{\infty} kc(1 - c)^{k-1} = c \sum_{k=1}^{\infty} k(1 - c)^{k-1}.$$

We encounter here a sum of the form $\sum nr^{n-1}$ which was dealt with in Eq. 2.8. Applying that result to our present problem yields

$$(2.12) \qquad E(T) = c \sum_{k=1}^{\infty} k(1 - c)^{k-1} = \frac{1}{c}.$$

Thus, if the probability of learning after each error is c, then the average number of errors before learning occurs is $1/c$.

The second raw moment of T is

$$E(T^2) = \sum_{k=1}^{\infty} k^2 c(1 - c)^{k-1} = \frac{c(2 - c)}{c^3} = \frac{2 - c}{c^2}.$$

Here we encounter a sum of the form $\sum n^2 r^{n-1}$. Applying the "differencing" procedure three times in succession (as illustrated preceding Eq. 2.8) yields the solution $(1 + r)/(1 - r)^3$ for the limit of the series sum. This solution has been substituted in deriving the equation above. The statistic commonly computed is not the second raw moment of a distribution, but rather its variance. For any random variable X the variance is the expected value of the function

$$g(X) = [X - E(X)]^2.$$

---

* The expectation operator, $E(\cdot)$, is a linear operator in the sense that it possesses the following two properties: if X and Y are any two random variables, and a is some constant, then

$$E(aX) = aE(X)$$

and

$$E(X + Y) = E(X) + E(Y).$$

By our definition of the expectation operator, for any constant a, $E(a) = a$.

This is the average value of the squared deviations about the mean of the distribution. By using the linearity property of an expectation operator, we may prove the following relationship between the variance, denoted $\text{Var}(X)$, and the first and second raw moments of a distribution:

$$\begin{aligned}
\text{Var}(X) = E[(X - E(X))^2] &= E[X^2 - 2E(X) \cdot X + E(X)^2] \\
&= E(X^2) - E[2E(X) \cdot X] + E[E(X)^2] \\
&= E(X^2) - 2E(X) \cdot E(X) + E(X)^2 \\
&= E(X^2) - E(X)^2.
\end{aligned}$$

This shows that the variance equals the second raw moment minus the square of the first moment. Applying this formula to our problem yields

$$\text{Var}(T) = \frac{2 - c}{c^2} - \left(\frac{1}{c}\right)^2 = \frac{1 - c}{c^2}.$$

The standard deviation of a random variable X, denoted $\sigma(X)$, is defined as the square root of its variance. For the concept learning model,

$$(2.13) \qquad \sigma(T) = \sqrt{\text{Var}(T)} = \frac{\sqrt{1 - c}}{c} = E(T)\sqrt{1 - c}.$$

The relationship specified in Eq. 2.13 between the mean and standard deviation of T provides a quick and rough index of whether the data may be adequately represented by a geometric distribution. In most of the concept learning experiments, c is small (between 0.05 and 0.10), so that $\sqrt{1 - c}$ is near one. In this case, the standard deviation should be large but slightly less than the mean value. When this prediction is upheld by the data, we have some preliminary confidence that the empirical distribution of the random variable will be fairly well approximated by the geometric function.

We illustrate this point by referring to some data reported by Bower and Trabasso (1964, pp. 72 to 77). A total of 46 college students learned a two-category concept identification problem to a criterion of ten consecutive correct responses. The stimuli were geometric patterns varying in six dimensions; the color of the figure (red or blue) was the relevant attribute determining the classification. For further details, the original report should be consulted. The mean total errors (that is, the average over the 46 subjects) was 11.45 and the standard deviation was 11.02. We will set the observed mean errors, denoted $\bar{T}$, equal to the theoretical expression, $E(T)$, (cf. Eq. 2.12) and solve this equation for an estimate of the parameter c. We use the notation $\hat{c}$ to denote an estimate of c.

$$\hat{c} = \frac{1}{\bar{T}} = \frac{1}{11.45} = 0.0873.$$

Using this estimate of c, we are now in a position to make an independent prediction of the observed standard deviation of the probability distribution of total errors. The prediction is

$$\sigma(T) = E(T)\sqrt{1 - c} = 11.45\sqrt{0.9127} = 10.96.$$

In this case the predicted standard deviation is very close to the observed value of 11.02.

The entire distribution of total errors can be predicted by using Eq. 2.11 and the estimate of $\hat{c} = 0.0873$. The measure graphed in Fig. 2.3 is the

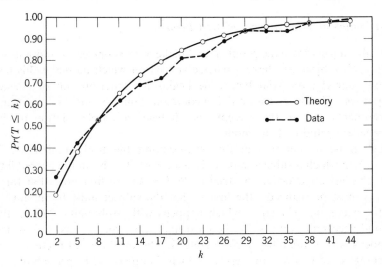

Fig. 2.3 Cumulative distribution of T, total errors per subject item, plotted in class intervals of three errors.

cumulative probability that T is less than or equal to k, for k of 2, 5, 8, ... To obtain a theoretical expression for this cumulative total, we sum Eq. 2.11 from 1 to k, namely,

$$Pr(T \le k) = \sum_{n=1}^{k} Pr(T = n) = c \sum_{n=1}^{k} (1 - c)^{n-1}.$$

This expression is c multiplied by the sum of the first k terms of a geometric series. Substituting for this sum using Eq. 2.7 yields

$$Pr(T \le k) = c \frac{[1 - (1 - c)^k]}{[1 - (1 - c)]} = 1 - (1 - c)^k.$$

With $\hat{c} = 0.0873$, this function is plotted in Fig. 2.3 for k of 2, 5, 8, ...

The goodness-of-fit of the predicted to the observed cumulative distribution may be evaluated in several ways. A simple test is the Kolmogorov-Smirnov one-sample statistic; one compares the maximum discrepancy of predicted and observed values with a tabled value (cf. Siegel, 1956, p. 251). The tables give the probability of obtaining various-sized discrepancies on the null hypothesis that the observed and predicted cumulative distributions are identical. For the cumulative distributions shown in Fig. 2.3, the maximal discrepancy is 0.082 (occurring on trial 16), which is not large enough to reject the null hypothesis in this instance.

Distribution of Trial Number of Last Error

If all subjects solve the problem and make at least one error in doing so, then each subject will have a particular trial on which he makes his last error; namely, the trial before he begins his criterion run of correct responses. "Trials to criterion" is a common summary statistic in learning experiments and, in the present case, it bears a simple relation to the parameters q and c of the model.

Let L be a random variable representing the trial number (1, 2, 3, . . .) on which a subject makes his last error. To obtain the probability that the last error occurs on trial k, $Pr(L = k)$, we first note that three events must be realized: the first is that the subject must be in state $\bar{S}$ at the beginning of trial k, which happens with probability $Pr(\bar{S}_k)$; the second necessary event is that he must make an error on this trial, which happens with probability q given state $\bar{S}$; the third crucial event is that learning occurs after the error, which happens with probability c. Multiplying these three event probabilities yields the probability that the last error occurs on trial k; namely,

$$(2.14) \quad \begin{aligned} Pr(L = k) &= Pr(\bar{S}_k)Pr(x_k = 1 \mid \bar{S}_k)Pr(S_{k+1} \mid \bar{S}_k \ \& \ x_k = 1) \\ &= Pr(\bar{S}_k)qc \\ &= qc(1 - qc)^{k-1}. \end{aligned}$$

Equation 2.14 shows that L has a geometric distribution as did the total errors statistic T. However, for L the geometric ratio is $1 - qc$ rather than $1 - c$. Hence, to find the mean and standard deviation of L we replace c by qc in Eqs. 2.12 and 2.13:

$$(2.15) \quad \begin{aligned} E(L) &= \frac{1}{qc} = \frac{1}{q} E(T), \\ \sigma(L) &= E(L)\sqrt{1 - qc}. \end{aligned}$$

We note that the expected trial of last error is $1/q$ times the mean total errors. For the Bower-Trabasso experiment mentioned above, the observed mean trial of last error was 22.89 with a standard deviation of 22.39. Using an a priori value of $q = 0.50$ (since it is a two-category experiment) and the previously calculated estimate $c = 0.087$, Eq. 2.15 predicts a mean of 22.90 and a standard deviation of 22.41. The predictions in this instance are quite accurate.

Distribution of the Number of Successes Between Adjacent Errors

Consider any two adjacent errors, say the nth and $(n + 1)$st. Intervening between these two adjacent errors there may be 0, 1, 2, ... correct responses. We wish to derive the probability of a run of exactly j successes intervening between two adjacent errors. This is a useful statistic because a large number of observations can be obtained on it from a set of data, so the empirical distribution is quite stable.

Define H as the number of successes intervening between two adjacent errors, having possible values of 0, 1, 2, ... To derive the probability that there are j successes between two errors, we begin with the subject making an error on some arbitrary trial. Now, with probability c he learns on that trial, so he will not make another error; such cases are excluded since another error does not occur. But in the remaining $1 - c$ percentage of the cases, learning fails to occur on this error trial so that a next error is inevitable and H is defined. Within the subset of sequences that are going to have a next error, the probability that the error occurs on the very next trial (that is, $H = 0$) is q. Letting $p = 1 - q$, the probability of a success followed by an error is pq; of two successes then an error is p^2q; and so forth. The probability of a run of j successes and then an error is just p^jq. Note that the parameter c does not enter here because the model supposes that no learning is possible on these intervening success trials. Hence, the H distribution is

$$(2.16) \qquad Pr(H = j) = p^jq, \qquad \text{(for } j \geqslant 0\text{)}.$$

We note that H has a geometric distribution with ratio p. Significantly, the H-distribution does not depend upon the trial number on which the leading error occurs. That is, the length of a success run between any two adjacent errors is expected to be constant regardless of whether the errors occur early or late in training.

The mean and standard deviation of H may be obtained by standard methods and are

$$E(H) = \frac{1 - q}{q}$$

$$\text{Var}(H) = \frac{1 - q}{q^2}.$$

Note that the expression for Var(H) depends on q in exactly the same way that Var(T) depended on c. For the experiment mentioned above, q was 0.50. The obtained and predicted distributions of H are shown in Fig. 2.4. The two distributions are hardly distinguishable. The observed mean value of H was 1.00 with $p/q = 1$ predicted; the observed standard deviation was 1.48 with 1.42 predicted. The fit between observed and predicted values is excellent.

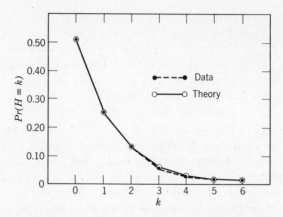

Fig. 2.4   Distribution of the number of successes between adjacent errors.

Although the derivation of H has been carried out for successes between two adjacent errors, it may be noted that the expression is equally valid when related to the number of successes before the very first error. The crucial item in the derivation is that the subject is in state $\bar{S}$ at the start of the H-counting procedure. This is assumed to be the case at the beginning of the experiment on trial 1 before the first error; for the nth error later, the inference rests on the fact that the H-counting procedure applies only if an $(n + 1)$st error occurs later. Because of the identity of the expected distributions, successes before the first error and between later adjacent errors are pooled in constructing the empirical frequency histogram of H. To illustrate how the H distribution is tabulated, suppose a subject gives us the sequence 100110100 . . . (all the rest zeros). The H-values are: a 0 before the first error, a 2 between the first and second errors, a 0 between the second and third errors, and a 1 between the third and fourth errors. Thus, the event $H = 0$ is tallied twice, $H = 1$ once, and $H = 2$ once, making four tallies for this subject's protocol.

It was noted earlier that H is a useful random variable to count because many observations can be obtained for it. A subject who makes n errors before learning contributes only one observation to the empirical T and

L distributions, yet he contributes n observations to the empirical H distribution. For the Bower-Trabasso data with 46 subjects, there are 46 observations for the T distribution in Fig. 2.3 but a total of 527 observations for the H distribution in Fig. 2.4.

2.5 SEQUENTIAL STATISTICS

Each subject contributes a specific sequence of ones and zeros. Sequential statistics yield useful information about the dependencies existing between events (responses) in the specific sequence in which they occur. Sequential statistics yield information such as the following: (a) the conditional probability of an error following an error, (b) the extent to which the errors tend to occur in a few long strings (runs) rather than in many short strings, (c) the influence of the response on trial n upon the response on trial $n + k$, and so forth. Such sequential dependencies are the basic components of a stochastic process, whereas overall statistics like the learning curve, total errors, etc., are more or less derivative from these basic components. Traditionally, psychologists have not examined sequential statistics because the necessary conceptual tools for their analysis were not available. However, with the advent of information theory and stochastic learning theories, the importance of sequential statistics has been recognized, and useful models are expected to deliver accurate predictions of these aspects of the data. In the following, we will use the concept learning model to derive predictive equations for several of these sequential statistics.

We will begin by deriving the conditional probability of an error following an error since this quantity plays a central role in the derivations which follow. Let us suppose that we observe an error on trial n, and wish to know the probability that another error will occur on trial $n + 1$ in this protocol. The error on trial n tells us that the subject was in state $\bar{S}$ at the beginning of trial n. After an error in state $\bar{S}$, the probability that the subject remains in state $\bar{S}$ for trial $n + 1$ is $1 - c$. If he is still in state $\bar{S}$ on trial $n + 1$, then his likelihood of an error on that trial is q. Thus the probability of an error on trial $n + 1$ conditional upon an error on trial n is

$$Pr(x_{n+1} = 1 \mid x_n = 1) = (1 - c)q = \alpha.$$

Here the symbol α has been introduced for brevity. If the model is correct, then this conditional probability of an error following an error is a constant independent of the trial number n. This happens because our Markov process is "ahistorical" in a certain respect: regardless of the subject's past responses or the number of prior trials, his error on a given trial tells us that he is still in state $\bar{S}$, and according to the model that is the only information needed to predict response probability on the following trial.

Furthermore, the model predicts that the conditional probability of an error following two or more consecutive errors is the same as that following a single error, namely, α. That this prediction is somewhat counter-intuitive is illustrated by comparing the following two cases: subject A runs off nine consecutive errors, whereas subject B runs off eight consecutive successes and then makes an error on trial 9. The model predicts that the two subjects have an equal probability, α, of making an error on trial 10, whereas common sense leads to the opposite expectation. Our data indicate that at least for the illustrative experiment the model is right and common sense is wrong on this point. The important point brought out by the predicted identity of these two cases is that in terms of the model the error on trial 9 gives us all the information that can be gathered from the subject's past responses. That error tells us that both subjects are in state $\bar{S}$ on trial 9; the responses prior to that provide no additional information.

From the above, it also follows that the conditional probability of j consecutive errors following a given error is just α^j. To sketch this proof for $j = 2$, the following reasoning applies:

(2.17)

$$Pr(x_{n+2} = 1 \ \& \ x_{n+1} = 1 \mid x_n = 1)$$
$$= Pr(x_{n+2} = 1 \mid x_{n+1} = 1 \ \& \ x_n = 1) \cdot Pr(x_{n+1} = 1 \mid x_n = 1)$$
$$= Pr(x_{n+2} = 1 \mid x_{n+1} = 1)Pr(x_{n+1} = 1 \mid x_n = 1)$$
$$= \alpha \cdot \alpha = \alpha^2.$$

The basis for the derivation in Eq. 2.17 is that the probability of an error on trial $n + 2$ conditional upon errors on trials $n + 1$ and n is the same as the error probability on trial $n + 2$ conditional only upon the error on trial $n + 1$. Because the probability of an error following an error is a constant independent of the trial number, both terms in the lower line of Eq. 2.17 are simply α. The derivation of the probability of j errors following an error proceeds in analogous fashion. The general result that has been established will be given an equation number for later reference;

(2.18) $Pr(x_{n+j} = 1 \ \& \ x_{n+j-1} = 1 \ \& \cdots \& \ x_{n+1} = 1 \mid x_n = 1) = \alpha^j.$

The result in Eq. 2.18 will be used in the next derivation. The quantity we wish to predict is the mean number of times we observe j consecutive errors during the entire course of learning. Let us begin by defining a random variable, $u_{j,n}$, to represent the event "an error on trial n followed by $j - 1$ consecutive errors." More formally, $u_{j,n}$ is defined as the product of the x_n's running over j trials, from n to $n + j - 1$; namely,

(2.19) $u_{j,n} = x_n \cdot x_{n+1} \cdots x_{n+j-1}.$

Each of the x_n's is a random variable with value one or zero. Thus, $u_{j,n}$ is also a random variable with values one and zero; $u_{j,n}$ takes on the value one if all the x's in Eq. 2.19 have value one; if any x_i is zero, then the entire product has the value zero. We sometimes say that $u_{j,n}$ is a *counter variable*, counting the occurrence of a string of j errors, just as x_n is a counter variable for trial n.

As a random variable, $u_{j,n}$ will have an expected value. Earlier we noted that the expectation of a dichotomous variable with values one and zero is just the probability that it takes on the value of one:

$$E(u_{j,n}) = 0 \cdot Pr(u_{j,n} = 0) + 1 \cdot Pr(u_{j,n} = 1) = Pr(u_{j,n} = 1).$$

Consequently, to find the expectation we need to find the probability that $u_{j,n} = 1$. In this regard, the result in Eq. 2.18 is most helpful. The probability that $u_{j,n} = 1$ is calculated as follows:

(2.20) $Pr(u_{j,n} = 1) = Pr(j - 1 \text{ further errors} \mid x_n = 1)Pr(x_n = 1)$

$$= \alpha^{j-1}q_n.$$

The second term on the right of Eq. 2.20 is just the mean error probability on trial n; the first term is the conditional probability of $j - 1$ errors following an error, which from Eq. 2.18 is α^{j-1}.

The purpose of our derivation here is to find the predicted mean number of times we observe j consecutive errors throughout the entire course of learning. In other words, we are interested in the sum of the $u_{j,n}$ over all trials. Define u_j as the sum over all trials; namely,

$$u_j = \sum_{n=1}^{\infty} u_{j,n}.$$

Thus, u_1 counts the total number of errors (i.e., $u_1 = T$), u_2 counts the number of pairs of adjacent errors, u_3 the number of triples or 3-tuples of errors, etc. The general name is a "j-tuple" of errors. To illustrate the overlapping method by which the u_j's are counted, consider their values for the learning protocol 11010011111010... (all the rest correct). For this sequence, $u_1 = 9$, $u_2 = 5$, $u_3 = 3$, $u_4 = 2$, $u_5 = 1$, and all other u_j's are zero. Note that the u_j's are counted in an overlapping manner.

The variable u_j has an unknown probability distribution, and it would be a difficult task to derive it. However, it is still possible to derive the expectation of u_j even though we do not know its distribution function. This circumstance arises because u_j is the sum of random variables

($u_{j,n}$'s) whose mean values are known (Eq. 2.20). A theorem of the probability calculus is that the expected value of a sum of random variables equals the sum of their separate expected values:

$$E(u_j) = E\left[\sum_{n=1}^{\infty} u_{j,n}\right] = \sum_{n=1}^{\infty} E(u_{j,n}).$$

From Eq. 2.20, we have an expression for the expected values of the $u_{j,n}$'s. Substituting these values into the above, we obtain

(2.21)
$$\begin{aligned} E(u_j) &= \sum_{n=1}^{\infty} q_n \alpha^{j-1} = \alpha^{j-1} \sum_{n=1}^{\infty} q(1 - qc)^{n-1} \\ &= \frac{\alpha^{j-1}}{c} \\ &= E(u_1)\alpha^{j-1}. \end{aligned}$$

In Eq. 2.21 the term $1/c$ is the expected total errors, which we have called $E(u_1)$. Thus, the mean number of 2-tuples is α times the mean number of errors; of 3-tuples is α^2 times the number of errors; etc. Equation 2.21 may be used to predict the average u_j values once c and q have been estimated from the data, and these predictions may then be compared to the observed mean values.

Error Run Statistics

An alternate set of sequential statistics is that pertaining to runs of errors. A run is defined as any number of consecutive errors preceded and followed by a correct response. Error runs may be of different lengths, and we let r_j be the number of runs of exactly j errors in a single response sequence. The number of runs of any length will be called R; thus,

$$R = \sum_{j} r_j.$$

To illustrate, in the protocol 11010111110 . . . , there is one error run of length 1, one of length 2, and one of length 5. The total number of runs of any length, R, is three in this case.

The values of r_j and R bear a simple relationship to the u_j's discussed previously. The relationships are

(2.22)
$$R = u_1 - u_2$$
$$r_j = u_j - 2u_{j+1} + u_{j+2}.$$

The reader may check these relationships for the sample protocol above. Proof of the results in Eq. 2.22 are given by Bush (1959); his proof, although easy to follow, is too lengthy to reproduce here.

Since the expected values of the u_j's have been derived in Eq. 2.21, the expected values of R and r_j are readily determined through Eq. 2.22. The results are

(2.23)
$$E(R) = E(u_1) - E(u_2) = E(u_1)(1 - \alpha)$$
$$E(r_j) = E(u_1)\alpha^{j-1}(1 - \alpha)^2.$$

We illustrate predictions of α, R, and r_j for the concept experiment discussed earlier. For the parameters $q = 0.50$ and $\hat{c} = 0.087$, the predicted probability of an error following an error on the preceding trial is $q(1 - c) = 0.457$. The observed probability of an error following an error was 0.460. The observed mean values of error runs of various lengths were: $r_1 = 3.11$, $r_2 = 1.72$, $r_3 = 0.76$, $r_4 = 0.39$, whereas the corresponding values predicted by Eq. 2.23 are 3.34, 1.55, 0.71 and 0.33. The total number of error runs was 6.17, whereas Eq. 2.23 predicts 6.18. Thus, in this case, the model accurately predicts these sequential statistics.

Other Sequential Statistics

The number of sequential statistics that one could tabulate is practically unlimited. The more commonly selected statistics are error runs and "autocorrelations" of lag k. This latter is defined as the number of pairs of errors occurring k trials apart without regard to the nature of the intervening responses in that subject's sequence. Formally, the autocorrelation statistic c_k is defined as

(2.24)
$$c_k = \sum_{n=1}^{\infty} x_n x_{n+k}.$$

So defined, c_k is a counter variable adding up the number of times errors occur k trials apart. Note that c_k does indeed count error pairs, since $x_n x_{n+k} = 1$ if $x_n = x_{n+k} = 1$ and $x_n x_{n+k} = 0$ otherwise. Its conventional label, "autocorrelation," is actually a misnomer since it is not a correlation and can have values larger than unity. However, it does summarize the same kind of information that is involved in an autocorrelation, namely, the effect (correlation) of the response on one trial upon the response k trials later.

In order to find the expectation of c_k, we must rewrite the product inside the summation sign in Eq. 2.24. Since $x_n x_{n+k}$ equals zero unless both $x_n = 1$ and $x_{n+k} = 1$, we have

$$E(c_k) = \sum_{n=1}^{\infty} E(x_n x_{n+k}) = \sum_{n=1}^{\infty} Pr(x_n = 1 \ \& \ x_{n+k} = 1).$$

Now the problem is to find $Pr(x_n = 1 \ \& \ x_{n+k} = 1)$. We do this by specifying the chain of events which must occur in order than the event "$x_n = 1 \ \& \ x_{n+k} = 1$" can be realized. The diagram in Fig. 2.5 shows the chain of

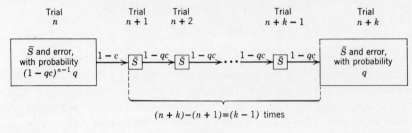

$$(n + k) - (n + 1) = (k - 1) \text{ times}$$

Figure 2.5

events for trials n through $n + k$. The product of the probabilities of the events in the figure is the desired quantity $Pr(x_n = 1 \ \& \ x_{n+k} = 1)$, so

$$Pr(x_n = 1 \ \& \ x_{n+k} = 1) = (1 - qc)^{n-1} q^2 (1 - c)(1 - qc)^{k-1}.$$

Inserting this result into Eq. 2.24 and summing over n yields

$$(2.25) \qquad E(c_k) = \sum_{n=1}^{\infty} Pr(x_n = 1 \ \& \ x_{n+k} = 1)$$

$$= \frac{q(1 - c)(1 - qc)^{k-1}}{c}$$

$$= E(u_2)(1 - qc)^{k-1}.$$

Equation 2.25 tells us that the influence of the error on trial n decreases as we move farther away (increase k) from that trial. For the concept experiment mentioned earlier, the observed mean values of $E(c_1)$, $E(c_2)$, and $E(c_3)$ were 5.28, 4.87, and 4.70; the corresponding predictions from Eq. 2.25 are 5.23, 4.95, and 4.70, respectively.

As stated before, the possible sequential statistics are unlimited. However, despite the fact that many can be defined, they tend not to be independent of the more basic statistics regarding error j-tuples and autocorrelations. Novel sequential statistics are expressible as various sums and/or products of the x_n's and in the final analysis they usually turn out to be some algebraic function of the u_j and c_k statistics. To illustrate this nonindependence, we give three examples:

(1) Success-error pairs k trials apart:

$$E[\sum(1 - x_n)x_{n+k}] = (1 - qc)^k u_1 - c_k = \frac{c_{k+1}}{\alpha} - c_k$$

(2) Error-success-error triples:

$$E[\sum x_n(1 - x_{n+1})x_{n+2}] = c_2 - u_3$$

(3) Alternations of successes and failures:

$$E[\sum x_n(1 - x_{n+1}) + (1 - x_n)x_{n+1}] = 2u_1 - x_1 - 2u_2 = 2R - x_1.$$

These examples illustrate that the u_j and c_k can be viewed as the basic sequential statistics.

This concludes our derivation of implications from the model. Many other statistics can be predicted by the model. However, there is little use in piling up more comparisons between predicted and observed quantities. In practice, if the model accurately predicts the statistics enumerated above, then it will also fit practically any others our ingenuity can devise. It is clear that the returns in information both in terms of information about the data itself and about the model's fit diminish rapidly as more predictions are made.

The fundamental statistics of importance to the concept model are (1) stationarity and independence prior to the last error and (2) the distribution of total errors or trial number of last error. If these statistics conform to the predictions of the model, then we have found in practice that the remaining statistics accord well with predictions.

2.6 ESTIMATION OF PARAMETERS

We discuss now a topic that has been postponed in the preceding pages, namely, the estimation from data of the parameters q and c. Because the problem of parameter estimation is an important one in mathematical psychology, we have devoted Chapter 9 to a discussion of the topic. In this section our immediate objective is to show how the estimates of q and c are derived and to discuss some of their properties. For a fuller understanding of the specific procedures, the reader may consult Chapter 9. The derivation of our estimates of q and c will involve at one point the notion of a derivative of a function. Introduction of derivatives is unavoidable, and readers unfamiliar with the differential calculus will be asked to accept the results as stated.

We utilize the method of *maximum likelihood* to estimate our parameters c and q. The rationale for the method is simple and direct. We first write, in terms of the model, an expression for the probability (likelihood) of getting the data that are actually obtained in a particular experiment. The expression for the likelihood of the observed data will be some function of the parameters q and c. The procedure is then to select estimates of q and c that maximize the likelihood function.

We begin by writing the likelihood of the sequence of responses obtained for some arbitrary subject i. Let

$$x_n^{(i)} = \begin{cases} 1, \text{ if subject } i \text{ is incorrect on trial } n \\ 0, \text{ if subject } i \text{ is correct on trial } n. \end{cases}$$

Thus, the observations for subject i is a denumerable vector

$$[x_1^{(i)} x_2^{(i)} x_3^{(i)} \cdots],$$

where $x_n^{(i)} = 0$ or 1 accordingly as the ith subject's response on trial n is correct or incorrect. The symbol $l_i(p, c)$ will denote the probability of obtaining the response sequence observed given parameter values p and c, that is, the likelihood function. From the model we can write

(2.26)
$$\begin{aligned} l_i(p, c) &= Pr(x_1^{(i)} x_2^{(i)} x_3^{(i)} \cdots) \\ &= p^{z_i} q^{T_i} (1 - c)^{T_i - 1} c. \end{aligned}$$

The righthand side of Eq. 2.26 summarizes the subject's response sequence by two numbers: T_i, his total number of errors, and z_i, the number of successes before his last error. Because the model supposes that responses prior to the last error are independent, all possible sequences of z_i successes and T_i errors have the same probability, and therefore we may ignore the actual order in which the successes and failures occurred. Since order is immaterial, the statistics z_i and T_i are sufficient (cf. Sec. 9.1); that is, these numbers summarize all the information in the response series relevant to the parameters of the stochastic process.

Now suppose that N subjects were run in the experiment, and that all of them solved the problem. The joint likelihood function for the N subjects is the product of the individual likelihood functions given in Eq. 2.26. In taking products, the exponents z_i and T_i are summed over subjects. Hence we use the abbreviations Z and T', where

$$Z = \sum_{i=1}^{N} z_i$$

$$T' = \sum_{i=1}^{N} T_i.$$

The joint likelihood function is then

(2.27)
$$\begin{aligned} L(p, c) &= \prod_{i=1}^{N} l_i(p, c) \\ &= p^Z (1 - p)^{T'} (1 - c)^{T' - N} c^N. \end{aligned}$$

The symbol $\prod_{i=1}^{N}$ is an abbreviated way of writing a product involving N factors; here it denotes the product $l_1 \cdot l_2 \cdot l_3 \cdot \cdots \cdot l_N$. Because z_i and T_i are sufficient statistics for each individual subject, Z and T' are also sufficient statistics for the pooled data from N subjects. Observe that c does not bear the subscript i because we assume that the population of subjects is homogeneous with respect to this parameter.

Our estimates of p and c will be those values which maximize L. Since this particular L expression can be factored into the product of a function depending only on p and another function depending only on c, L can be maximized with respect to one parameter without regard to the value of the other parameter.

It is convenient to find the maximum of the logarithm of L (denoted $\log L$) rather than the maximum of L itself. Because $\log L$ is a strictly monotonic-increasing function of L, the point at which $\log L$ is maximal is the same as that at which L is maximal. Thus, taking the log of the expression in Eq. 2.27 yields

(2.28)
$$\log L = Z \log p + T' \log(1 - p) + (T' - N) \log(1 - c) + N \log c.$$

First consider the estimate of c. If we were to plot $\log L$ versus c, the function would rise to some maximum point and then decline. The maximum point would be that point at which the slope of this curve was zero: the slope would be positive to the left of the maximum and negative to the right of the maximum. The slope of $\log L$ versus c is thus a function of c. We wish to find the value of c for which this slope function is zero. This slope function is the first partial derivative of $\log L$ with respect to c; namely,

(2.29)
$$\frac{\partial \log L}{\partial c} = \frac{N}{c} - \frac{(T' - N)}{1 - c}.$$

This is our slope function, and we wish to find that value of c for which this function is zero. Setting Eq. 2.29 equal to zero and solving for c yields

$$\frac{N}{c} = \frac{T' - N}{1 - c}.$$

Solving,

(2.30)
$$\hat{c} = \frac{N}{T'}.$$

We place the "hat" above c to indicate that this is an estimate of the parameter c. This result of our maximum likelihood procedure for estimating c is intuitively natural and agrees with our earlier estimate in Eq. 2.12.

In Sec. 9.2 we discuss how one derives an expression for the variance of a maximum likelihood estimate. We display the result here without proof:

$$\text{Var}(\hat{c}) = \frac{c^2(1 - \hat{c})}{N}.$$

For example, for the experiment discussed earlier, $N = 46$ and $T'/N = 11.45$. Thus,

$$\hat{c} = \frac{1}{11.45} = 0.0873,$$

$$\text{Var}(\hat{c}) = \frac{(0.0873)^2(0.9127)}{46} = 0.000154,$$

and the standard deviation of the c estimate is

$$\sigma(\hat{c}) = \sqrt{\text{Var}(\hat{c})}$$
$$= 0.0124.$$

The theory of maximum likelihood estimation tells us that, for moderately large N, the estimate will be normally distributed in an appropriate way with mean $\hat{c}$ and standard deviation $\sigma(\hat{c})$. These properties provide a simple way of testing particular hypotheses about the value of the parameter c. For example, suppose that from other considerations, we had predicted that the value of c in this experiment would be 0.12. Given that the experiment yielded an estimate of $\hat{c} = 0.0873$ with $\sigma(\hat{c}) = 0.0124$, we can use the normal distribution to calculate the probability that the true value of c is 0.12. Letting c_0 represent some hypothesized value, the variable

$$z = \frac{c_0 - \hat{c}}{\sigma(\hat{c})}$$

will be normally distributed with mean 0 and variance 1. For our particular example, $c_0 = 0.12$, so that $z = 2.64$. Looking up the value 2.64 in a table of normal deviates, we find that a value this large or larger is highly improbable. Thus, we are prone to reject the hypothesis that $c_0 = 0.12$. Here we have an illustration (albeit trivial in this case) of how knowledge of a maximum likelihood estimate and its variance enables us to test hypotheses regarding parameter values.

To complete this section on parameter estimation, we obtain the maximum likelihood estimate of p (or of $1 - q$). Referring to Eq. 2.28, we take the derivative of $\log L$ with respect to p:

$$\frac{\partial \log L}{\partial p} = \frac{Z}{p} - \frac{T'}{1 - p}.$$

Setting this result equal to zero and solving for p yields

$$\hat{p} = \frac{Z}{Z + T'}.$$

Dividing all terms by N yields the observed means per subject, which we denote by $\bar{Z}$ and $\bar{T}$. The expression in the denominator is then just the mean trial of the last error, since $\bar{L} = \bar{Z} + \bar{T}$. Hence, we have

$$\hat{p} = \frac{\bar{Z}}{\bar{L}}$$

and

(2.31)
$$\hat{q} = 1 - \hat{p} = \frac{\bar{T}}{\bar{L}}.$$

2.7 CONCLUDING COMMENT

Our primary purpose in this chapter has been to illustrate the following points: how a behavioral model is formulated and implications are derived from it, the types of data analyses that are relevant to the model including comparing predicted and observed quantities, and how to estimate parameters. Indeed, such topics are the focal points of this entire book. The intent was not to convince the reader that the model presented here is valid for a broad range of experiments or that it is the best possible way to conceptualize the behavioral process under study.

This text begins with a discussion of the concept identification model because in modern mathematical psychology it is one of the most elementary models that at the same time is serviceable. Establishing the validity and scope of a theoretical model is a continuing scientific task that goes through many stages before the model is thoroughly discredited or replaced by a new one. The model of two-category concept identification presented here is undoubtedly wrong in many details and is surely incomplete in the sense that important aspects of concept learning behavior are not presently incorporated in the model. The same can be said for practically any model. At this moment of writing, the model enjoys some degree of explanatory and predictive success for a limited range of experimental conditions, but the history of science assures us that the model's success is due mainly to our current lack of ingenuity in devising appropriate experiments to test its inadequacies. When these experiments are made, the theory probably will be revised or extended to handle them, or failing to do so, it will die a quiet death from neglect.

CHAPTER 3

PAIRED-ASSOCIATE LEARNING

The area of experimental psychology known as verbal learning encompasses a wide range of topics, and among the most actively investigated of these topics is paired-associate learning. Of course, the question of how people form associations has excited the curiosity of scientists for centuries, but it was not until the monumental work of Ebbinghaus (1885) that experimental techniques requisite to an adequate theory of association learning were introduced. Since that date, and especially in the last few decades, the number of published experimental studies has increased enormously. In this chapter we shall not attempt even a brief review of the empirical literature on association learning; much of this work is not directly relevant to the theoretical exposition in this chapter. The reader wishing to acquire a broader knowledge of the area can refer to any of the appropriate books and journals on verbal learning (for example, McGeoch and Irion, 1952; Deese, 1958; Cofer, 1961; and Cofer and Musgrave, 1963).

A major reason for the vigorous search to discover fundamental laws of association learning is that many psychologists regard complex verbal skills as hierarchies or chains of elemental stimulus-response (S-R) associations. In this chapter the emphasis is on how subjects learn the individual associations under simplified, controlled experimental conditions. Mathematical models established from considerations at this molecular level might well serve as the basis for later quantitative theories about more elaborate learning phenomena.

Let us, then, specify the type of experimental procedure by which data on association learning are collected. The models presented here are designed for data gathered by the traditional method of *paired-associates*, so it is pertinent to describe a standard paired-associate procedure next.

The subject is presented with a list of *S-R* pairs, one pair at a time. For example, one pair in the list might be Γ-2. Here Γ (gamma) is called the *stimulus member* of the pair, and 2 is called the *response member*. The stimulus and response members might be words, nonsense syllables, digits, or other symbols. In the *anticipation method* the stimulus member of the pair is presented for a short interval of time before the response member. The subject's task is to learn to anticipate the response member by saying it (or writing it, or pressing a button) when the stimulus appears. Thus the subject would learn to say "two" when he sees the stimulus Γ.

Ordinarily the items are presented visually. Each stimulus term might be printed on a card, with the experimenter manually displaying the cards one at a time to the subject. Or he might use a memory-drum apparatus, with one window for exposing the stimulus member and a second window for exposing the response member. When the subject responds to the presentation of the stimulus member, the experimenter records the response and then presents the correct response member of the pair, thereby informing the subject of the appropriate answer. Each time the subject is informed of the correct response we shall say that a *reinforcement* has been given. After a short time interval (for example, 4 seconds), a second pair from the list is presented, and the procedure is repeated until each pair has been presented once. This constitutes one *trial* on each stimulus-response pair. To prevent the subject from memorizing the presentation order, the pairs are presented in a different (random) order on each trial. The trials continue in this fashion until some predetermined stopping point has been reached. Generally trials on a particular list terminate when the subject's performance attains a specified criterion of learning, such as three successive errorless trials on all items in the list. In some experiments a fixed number of trials may be given, regardless of how far learning has progressed. Certain other procedural details can vary from one study to another, but the description above characterizes the typical paired-associate experiments.

The Traditional View of Paired-Associate Learning

In order to gain some perspective on the models discussed in this chapter, we begin by reviewing what we consider to be the traditional theoretical viewpoint that dominates much of the research on verbal learning. As we will see later, this approach is quite different from the one adopted here.

Over the years, a prevailing conception has emerged about how paired-associate learning should be characterized. Roughly speaking, this viewpoint is an incremental type of stimulus-response associationism, with an emphasis upon response competition (interference) as the major source of difficulty in such learning. This theoretical approach is explicated in the next few pages. It is a confederation of many ideas, and not all workers in verbal learning subscribe to all parts as described here. However, most workers would probably agree on something close to the system described below. For references, see Postman (1963), Underwood and Keppel (1962), and McGeoch and Irion (1952).

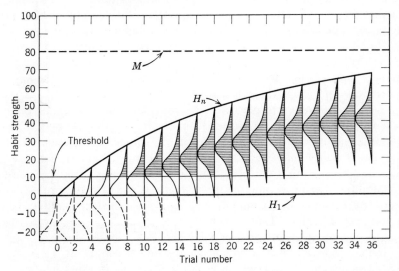

Fig. 3.1 Diagram showing the gradual movement of the zone of reaction-potential oscillation (up-ended bell-shaped area) across the threshold (adapted from Figure 71 in Hull, 1943).

The incremental process used is frequently that of Hull (1943). The associative connection (habit, $_sH_r$) between a stimulus and its reinforced response is assumed to vary in strength from zero to a maximum, increasing toward its maximum with each reinforced trial in a negatively accelerated fashion. If H_n represents the habit strength of an S-R connection on trial n, then the growth function for habit is assumed to be

$$H_n = M - (M - H_1)b^{n-1},$$

where M is the maximum strength of the habit, b is its rate of growth, and H_1 is the initial value.

Figure 3.1 displays the hypothesized accumulation of habit strength to an S-R connection resulting from successive reinforced trials. Inserted into Fig. 3.1 are two mechanisms assumed by Hull. One of these is the threshold for response evocation; it was assumed that the habit had to exceed a threshold value before the response could occur. In practice, this threshold is assumed to vary with the nature of the task: there may be one threshold for overt production (recall) of the response to its stimulus and a different threshold for simply recognizing that the S-R pair has been presented before. In brief, the threshold for recall would be assumed to be higher than that for recognition. The second mechanism graphed in Fig. 3.1 is what Hull called "oscillatory inhibition." The true habit of an S-R connection was, on any trial, subjected to a randomly varying amount of inhibition, subtracting from the strength effective on that trial. The determinants of this oscillating inhibition were not specified by Hull, but others have assumed that it represents the effect of variability in the focal stimulus, in the stimulus-reception process, or in the contextual stimuli. This random factor varies from moment to moment, yielding a distribution of values (the bell-shaped distributions in Fig. 3.1). At the moment the stimulus is presented, a particular value of inhibition is effective that must be subtracted from the true habit strength. The response rule of the theory is simple: if the momentary effective habit strength is above threshold, the response occurs; otherwise not. This rule enables one to transform habit into statements about response probability. The probability of the response is equal to the probability that the subtraction of the inhibition variable from the true habit yields a suprathreshold value. This probability is represented in Fig. 3.1 by the shaded portion of the distribution lying above the threshold line.

Hull's response rule is essentially that proposed earlier by Thurstone (1927) for handling psychophysical judgments. The threshold notion is taken over directly; the distribution of oscillatory inhibition is similar to Thurstone's notion of "discriminal dispersion." The threshold and oscillation functions have no observable counterparts; they are simply calculational devices, permitting one to translate the intervening variable of habit strength into statements about an observable quantity, namely, response probability. Figure 3.2 displays the type of probability curve generated by the mechanism in Fig. 3.1; in this case, the learning curve is S-shaped.

Hull was concerned with various measures of habit strength in addition to response probability. First, it was postulated that habit strength was inversely related to response latency. Second, the stronger the habit, the more effectively the primary response could compete with interfering responses. Thus, the greater the habit established to the S_1-R_1 connection, the more training required to bring the performance of a new connection, S_1-R_2, to a given criterion level (so-called "negative transfer"). Viewed within a competition-of-response framework of forgetting (cf. McGeoch and Irion, 1952), response decrements over time in the R_1 probability are ascribed to new learning or recovery of different responses R_2, R_3, . . . , to the S_1 stimulus. Thus, the stronger the primary S_1-R_1 habit, the less forgetting will occur over an interval of time. These other measures of habit strength (latency, retention, etc.) may continue to improve with practice on the initial S_1-R_1 habit well after response probability has reached unity. The continued increase in habit may be seen in Fig. 3.1. This point is used, for example, to interpret the beneficial effect of overlearning upon retention of a learned response.

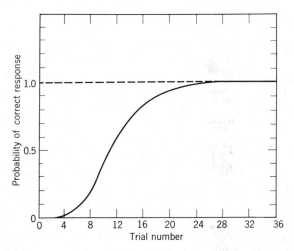

Fig. 3.2 Graph showing a theoretical function for the probability of a correct response. Note the sigmoid shape of the learning curve as contrasted with the corresponding H_n function in Figure 3.1 (adapted from Figure 72 in Hull, 1943).

This theory is flexible. There are five unspecified parameters in Fig. 3.1 that can be varied to generate a variety of curve forms of the type illustrated in Fig. 3.2. The five parameters are (1) the initial value of habit, (2) the rate at which habit increases over trials, (3) the value of the threshold, (4) the maximum value to which habit will grow, and (5) the variance of the oscillation function. If the initial habit is high or if the threshold is low, then the resulting probability curve will display initial negative acceleration, rather than the initial positive acceleration seen in Fig. 3.2. If the range of the oscillation function is larger than the difference between the threshold and the habit maximum, then nonunity asymptotes will be obtained. If the rate of learning is large relative to the range of oscillation, then the resultant probability curve will approximate a step-function, going from zero to unity on some one trial after training commences. Because of the flexibility introduced by the surplus of arbitrary parameters the theory is difficult to disprove, which may account for its survival value.

Hull's theory describes the formation of an S-R connection, where the response term may be considered as a single, functional unit. But the nominal response (for example, the trigram XPK) may itself be a novel chain of units to be learned. In paired-associate learning with consonant trigram response terms, the largest portion of the subject's learning time is probably taken up with response integration. Typically, a majority of his errors represent failures to respond, or incomplete or garbled versions of the appropriate response. To perform effectively, the subject must recall the units of the response (letters), the serial order in which they occur, and must overcome confusions with and interference from other novel strings of letters that are being learned concurrently to other stimuli in the list. The most potent factor controlling response learning is the meaningfulness and/or pronounceability of the specific letter sequences involved. Underwood and Schulz (1960), who have investigated factors in response learning, suggest that response learning be kept conceptually distinct from the S-R association phase of paired-associate learning. It is not altogether clear how to formulate this response learning phase in terms of the Hullian theory discussed above. Several decompositions are possible. For example, each reinforcement of the response XPK to its appropriate stimulus term may add increments to three element-habits, to respond with the letter X, the letter P, and the letter K to the stimulus. Some additional habit would be needed to describe order learning; that is, that the letters go in the serial order XPK. Hull's analyses of serial response learning (Hull, 1952) can be used to account for the order learning, but it seems impossibly complex in this context.

Even when the response terms are integrated units, the theory as presented is an oversimplification of the apparatus needed to make it relevant to paired-associate learning. The discussion above refers to the learning of a single stimulus-response connection in isolation. The normal paired-associate situation involves many stimulus-response pairs being learned concurrently. It was Eleanor Gibson (1940) who first viewed verbal learning situations as requiring the formation and discrimination of multiple S-R connections along with the inhibition of generalized response tendencies. In brief, during concurrent training on S_1-R_1 and S_2-R_2, the S_2-R_2 habit may show "stimulus generalization" to S_1. The occurrence of a response to the wrong stimulus is called an intrusion error, and such errors are attributed to stimulus generalization. Since the occurrence of R_2 to stimulus S_1 is not reinforced, inhibition will be conditioned to the generalized S_1-R_2 habit (see Hull, 1943; Gibson, 1940). Similarly, since inhibition is conditioned to making R_1 in the presence of stimulus S_2, there will be some stimulus generalization of this R_1 inhibition from S_2 back to S_1. To summarize the total picture, for multiple S-R learning then, in calculating the course of performance on the pair S_1-R_1, one must consider (1) the generalized tendencies (habits) for S_1 to evoke incorrect responses R_2, R_3, . . . due to stimulus generalization, (2) the inhibition not to give responses R_2, R_3, . . . to S_1, and (3) the summated generalized inhibition (at S_1) of response R_1 to stimuli S_2, S_3, ... Also the response rule is changed because, to S_1, the subject has a net habit ($_sH_r$ minus the sum of the generalized inhibitions) to make R_1 and generalized net habits to make R_2, R_3, . . . , and these net habits oscillate independently of one another. It is assumed that when stimulus S_1 is presented, whichever net habit is momentarily dominant determines the response, provided that habit is suprathreshold.

As one might forsee, when these modifications are added to handle multiple S-R learning, the theory becomes unwieldy and the number of unknown parameters may well exceed the number of observations taken in an ordinary experiment. Some theorists (for example, Runquist, 1962) have attempted to make enough simplifying assumptions so that the system can be applied to simple paired-associate data, but the quantitative predictions of the system have not been very rewarding. Despite these complexities, the theoretical system has been used in practice as a qualitative device for explaining and ordering experimental results. Because the theory has such a rich collection of concepts, it has proved quite serviceable in interpreting a broad range of facts about verbal learning. A variety of qualitative predictions apparently follow from the theory. The qualifier "apparently" is inserted because the steps in the derivation from the expanded system are not spelled out in detail. In a few cases, the prediction from the system seems sufficiently obvious that the details are hardly needed; in many others, given the complexity of the system, its predictions are simply ambiguous unless the details can be provided.

Another Approach to Paired-Associate Learning

We are left in a peculiar state of affairs. We have a traditional theory which is rich in concepts but (in its attempt to be comprehensive) has become so complex that quantitative predictions are virtually impossible to obtain. The theory in a typical application has so many unknown parameters to be estimated that a quantitative description of paired-associate data seems defeated before it starts. This state of affairs was bound to lead to some dissatisfaction among quantitatively oriented psychologists working on verbal learning.

But can anything be done about this dissatisfaction? Yes, something can be done on a modest scale. The first strategy employed by mathematical psychologists in formulating models for verbal learning was to curtail drastically the scope of the theorizing. Comprehensiveness is foregone: an attempt is made to focus on only a few variables, and the experimental arrangements are constructed to minimize the influence of other factors not under consideration. Thus, one is led to work with "miniature theories" or small-scale models for various pieces of the verbal learning puzzle. The common criticism of such efforts, their lack of completeness or comprehensiveness, is true by design but is viewed by these workers as the current price to be paid for tractable theories. After restricting the scope of application of the theory, the second strategy in recent mathematical theorizing has been to begin with axioms that are as simple and elementary as possible. The models to be presented in this chapter are examples involving such simple learning assumptions. This bent for simplicity in the axioms comes from two considerations. First, for a model to be a viable, useful instrument for describing data quantitatively, it must be mathematically workable; that is, we want to be able to derive parameter estimators and a variety of predictions without undue labor. Second, it is possible that the data are simpler than the traditional theory supposes and that one may achieve an adequate explanation with the simple ideas. If a simple theory accounts for, say, 95 per cent of the variance in the data from the class of experiments to which it is applicable, there is little force to the argument that the model should be further complicated to handle these experiments.

To summarize, then, current mathematical models applied to verbal learning are miniature systems, based on relatively simple assumptions, and are applied to fairly restricted classes of experimental situations. The models to be discussed in this chapter are limited to the association phase of paired-associate learning. In an attempt to isolate this process for study, the S-R pairs to be learned are selected so as to minimize the stimulus-discrimination and response-learning aspects. Highly discriminable stimuli (such as different Greek letters) are used. Response learning is precluded by using a small set of integrated functional units that are known by the subject in advance of the experiment (for example, the first three digits). When only, say, three responses are used, the experimenter might assign each as "correct" for more than one stimulus in the list. For example, with twenty-one stimuli and three response terms, each response would be assigned to seven of the stimuli. Since both the experiments and models focus on the association stage, we use the word "learning" henceforth to refer to the formation of the stimulus-response associations.

There is one additional consideration that restricts the mathematical learning theorist's choice of paired-associate material. When applying models to the data, it is convenient to append to the model the assumption that the S-R pairs are equally difficult to learn. The experimenter makes this assumption tenable by randomly assigning the correct response member to each stimulus before beginning the experiment. For the same reason, all stimuli are drawn from a common pool (for example, all might be Greek letters).* By the arbitrary construction of S-R pairs, the experimenter increases the likelihood that none of the associations were learned prior to the start of the experiment.

Bower's experiment (1961 a), which is one of the principal sources of paired-associate learning data for our analysis, utilized the following procedure. Twenty-nine subjects (college students) learned a list of ten items to a criterion of two consecutive errorless trials. The stimuli were different pairs of consonant letters; the responses were the integers 1 and 2, each response being assigned as correct to a randomly selected five stimuli for each subject. A response was obtained from the subject on each presentation of an item, and he was informed of the correct answer following his response.

As was the case with the concept identification model, the paired-associate learning models to be discussed in this chapter consider the responses only as correct or incorrect; information about which response occurred when the error was recorded is discarded. Again, we code a correct response as a zero and an error as a one. The coded sequence of responses over successive trials to a particular stimulus by a particular subject will be called a *subject-item sequence*.

The models attempt to predict the statistical features of the coded subject-item sequences. Following the pattern of the preceding chapter, we shall be concerned with how well the models fit the observed distribution of total errors per subject-item sequence, the mean trial number of last error, and so on.

We begin with the one-element model for paired-associate learning. After some intuitive rationales, the axioms of the model are stated. Then in Sec. 3.2 the axioms are used to derive equations for the various statistics of interest. Next, in Sec. 3.3 the model is evaluated by seeing how well it fits paired-associate learning data. In Sec. 3.4 we develop the simple linear model, which is in one sense the antithesis of the one-element model; the accuracy of this model is compared with that of the one-element model by fitting both to the same paired-associate learning data. Subsequent sections of this chapter deal with more elaborate models.

---

* Item heterogeneity is a factor that obscures the testing of the underlying assumptions of a model. If care is not taken in constructing the items, it is sometimes difficult to know whether inaccurate predictions reflect a basic flaw in the model or merely indicate that the homogeneity assumption is untenable.

3.1 THE ONE-ELEMENT MODEL

There are three principal reasons why we shall emphasize the one-element model (sometimes referred to as the all-or-none model) in this chapter. In the first place, this model has had an important role in the recent development of mathematical learning theories. Second, the simple mathematical structure of the model enables us to illustrate the derivational techniques in a straightforward manner. Finally, the one-element model is similar to the concept identification model in Chapter 2; therefore the reader will already be familiar with some of the methods of derivation.

Intuitive Rationales

Let us begin by stating an intuitive rationale for the all-or-none model. The axioms of a paired-associate learning model include hypothesized answers to the following questions: When the subject is shown a stimulus member concurrently with its response member, how may we characterize his learning of the stimulus-response association? In other words, how do reinforced presentations enable the subject to learn to anticipate the response member when at some later time he sees the stimulus member alone? As its name implies, the all-or-none model answers these questions by assuming that a single reinforcement of a previously unlearned pair produces either complete learning of the association, or no learning whatever. This assumption implies that an association cannot be learned partially or gradually. Since reinforcement occurs on each trial, it is reasonable to suppose that a formerly unlearned item can become learned on any trial, regardless of the response on that trial. Herein the model differs from the concept identification model, which assumed that learning was possible only after errors. Once the stimulus-response association has been formed, it is assumed to be preserved throughout the remainder of the experiment. It is assumed that the subject gives the correct response on every trial after the stimulus member has become associated to its proper response.

Prior to learning, the subject is regarded as guessing. Exactly what assumptions should we make about the subject's scheme for guessing? This is really a peripheral question, because derivations can be carried out without specifying the subject's mode of guessing. Then, at the last step, we can append any of several auxiliary guessing mechanisms or rules to the basic model. The virtue of proceeding in this fashion is that if the model fails we can separate the learning process from the guessing system and see which is at fault. If at the outset a particular guessing scheme had been assumed, it would have been more difficult to interpret deviations of predicted from observed values.

To maintain the logical distinction between the physical paired-associate stimulus and its counterpart in the model, we shall refer to the latter as a "stimulus element." We shall use the terms "all-or-none" and "one-element" synonymously, and "conditioning" will be used interchangeably with "association learning."

Stated formally, for a single subject and item the assumptions of the one-element model are as follows:

Axioms

1. *The stimulus member of each paired-associate item in the list can be represented mathematically by a single hypothetical stimulus element.*
2. *Each time a particular stimulus is presented to the subject, he samples the stimulus element.*
3. *On each trial the element is in exactly one of two learning states. Either the element is in state C (associated to the correct response) or the element is in state $\bar{C}$ (not associated to the correct response).*
4. *On each reinforced trial, the probability of a transition of the element from $\bar{C}$ to C is c; the probability of a transition from C to C is one.* (Let us paraphrase this axiom as follows. If the subject has not formed the association prior to the current reinforcement of this association, he now forms it with probability *c*. If the association was formed prior to the current reinforcement, it is preserved with probability one.)
5. *If the stimulus element is in state C when the subject responds, he makes the correct response with probability one. If the stimulus element is in state $\bar{C}$ when the subject responds, he guesses the correct response with probability g.*
6. *At the beginning of the experiment, the element is in the unconditioned state $\bar{C}$.*

Comments and Alternative Interpretations

Let us comment on these assumptions before deriving some of their consequences. Axiom 1 treats the paired-associate stimulus as a single element. One might protest this representation by pointing out that a typical verbal stimulus has not one but several components (for example, letters) and hence should be identified with several elements. But when the stimuli are highly discriminable, as in the present experiments, there is ample justification for assuming only one element per stimulus. The distinctiveness enables the subject to associate his response to the stimulus ensemble as a whole; he need not associate the response separately to the individual constituents. In the technical literature, the unitary element is sometimes called a *pattern*, to connote responding on the basis of the entire pattern of stimulation. For experiments with substantial and varying degrees of overlap among stimuli (for example, shared letters), it would be more natural to assume several elements per stimulus. The word "samples" in Axiom 2 can be interpreted to mean that the subject attends to the item each time it is presented. That is, factors leading to a failure of attention to the stimulus item (boredom, fatigue, etc.) are being ignored in this formulation of the model. Because the conventional verbal learning procedure soon becomes a somewhat dull, monotonous task for the subject, the research on watchkeeping or vigilance (cf. Broadbent, 1958) suggests that occasional blocks or moments of inattention will probably occur. Thus, the sampling assumption of perfect attention treats only an ideal case, which is justifiable because it is approximately correct and because it simplifies the analysis.*

Axioms 3, 4, and 5 give the model its all-or-none characteristics. These axioms could be empirically inappropriate, for they might lead to predictions that are discrepant from paired-associate learning data. Putting it differently, the all-or-none feature generates specific predictions which, upon casual inspection, are neither obviously correct nor obviously incorrect. So before the model is investigated in detail, we do not know whether its predictions will be upheld by the data. Axiom 4 implies that for a given subject the parameter c is a constant. This parameter is assumed to be independent of the trial number and of the past history of responses given to that stimulus. By implication, c also is not a function of the past response histories of other items in the list. This latter restriction could be modified for application to experiments where the items were manifestly not independent (e.g., in cases of highly similar stimuli).

Another important aspect of the model is that the probability of a transition from the conditioned state C to the unconditioned state $\bar{C}$ is zero; the model assumes that an association is not forgotten after it has been learned. We shall have more to say on this point later. Axiom 5, which establishes the connection between learning and responding, says that while the stimulus is in $\bar{C}$, the probability of a correct response is equal

---

* Axiom 2 is really superfluous in our model, because it has the same effect on each trial. We include it to explicate the perceptual interpretation given here and to anticipate the N-element stimulus sampling theory in Chapter 8. That general theory is more flexible than the one-element model in handling perceptual factors, for when $N > 1$, we can assume that only some of the available elements are sampled on a particular trial.

to the probability that the subject guesses correctly. Axiom 6 asserts that no learning of the association has occurred prior to the start of the experiment. This seems a reasonable assumption for the present context, since at the start of the experiment the experimenter randomly assigns a response as "correct" for each stimulus.

Such an analysis of individual axioms is helpful in understanding a model and in comparing it with one's intuitive conception of the learning process. By assuming that only a single process governs paired-associate learning, much desirable mathematical simplicity is achieved in the one-element model. When the predictions of this model are accurate we can conclude that it is unnecessary to introduce assumptions which complicate the model. For instance, when the model is accurate, there is no need to assume that the conditioning parameter c varies from trial to trial or that forgetting occurs to any significant degree. However, in situations where the model fails, the problem is to decide how it can be improved. Often only one or two axioms are amiss. Likewise, in extending a model to new experimental situations, we can sometimes retain many of the original axioms (for example, see Crothers, 1964).

The reader may note that the axioms constitute an extremely elementary model of the association process, making it analogous to a simple two-way switch that is either open or closed. The only free parameter in the system is c, the probability that an unlearned association becomes learned with the next reinforcement. Despite the simplicity of the model, there are still several alternative conceptions of the association process that are consistent with the axioms of the model. One possibility is to suppose that at the moment the subject studies the S-R pair, that pair is either fully learned or no learning at all takes place; in the latter case, an immediate retest with the same stimulus would show only chance performance, according to this first interpretation. Data on immediate recall by Peterson and Peterson (1962) and Murdock (1961, 1963) suggest, however, that this interpretation is not empirically correct. In particular, recall probabilities are virtually unity on a test given immediately following a study trial on an S-R pair. The recall probability declines as other S-R pairs are tested and studied before the first pair is retested. Murdock, for example, found that this "short-term" recall probability induced by a single presentation of an S-R pair declined to its asymptote after about four or five intervening items had been presented.

These data on short-term recall suggest the following alternative interpretation of the all-or-none model: at the moment an S-R pair is studied, with probability c it goes into a long-term memory storage system, where it is invulnerable to interference from intervening items; with probability $1 - c$ the S-R pair goes into a short-term memory-store.

Items in the short-term store can be retrieved for immediate recall. However, the short-term store is of limited capacity, and other S-R items that come in may erase or eliminate any item residing in this store. Thus, items placed in the short-term store might be remembered for a short time (that is, after a few intervening items) but are very likely to be forgotten after many interpolated items. For the usual paired-associate experiments involving lists of 10 to 20 pairs, this interpretation would imply that if an S-R pair is not put into the long-term store at the time it is studied, then in all likelihood it will be forgotten by the time it comes up for a test on the next trial. In theory, the small residual probability that an item is still in the short-term store at the time of testing would appear, upon gross analysis, as a slight average increase in the guessing probability, g. In summary, then, this interpretation says that all S-R pairs are "conditioned" at the time of presentation but that a proportion $1 - c$ of the pairs will be forgotten due to interference prior to the next test.

Note that when these two conceptions are applied to the customary paired-associate experiments, they each have the same formal representation; namely, the all-or-none model. This is not an uncommon happening in mathematical psychology, that different theoretical ideas yield the same mathematical representation or model for a particular set of experimental conditions. One differentiates between the ideas by devising experimental situations where the models for the ideas differ and where the differential predictions can be tested against the data. Our purpose in this section has been to show the reader how an abstract model can summarize some reasonable psychological notions about how such a process operates.

3.2 DERIVATIONS FROM THE ONE-ELEMENT MODEL

All the derivations are executed for a single item. We assume that the model makes predictions for a typical sequence from a pool of subject-item sequences with identical c parameters. It is convenient further to assume that this idealized pool is adequately approximated by the particular subject-item sequences to which we are applying the model. This latter assumption is more or less justified by constructing the items so as to be equally difficult. When the items have been so selected, we assume that the single-item predictions generalize to all items and subjects. At other times we might investigate the consequences of taking different parameter values for different subsets of items or subjects.

Our ultimate interest is in what the one-element model implies about responding, but since these predictions depend entirely on the learning state of the subject when he responds, the first step is to study the statistical properties of the states $\bar{C}$ and C. According to Axioms 3 and 4, state-to-state transitions for a given subject-item from one trial to the next can be represented by the following transition matrix.

$$
(3.1) \quad
\begin{array}{c}
\\
C_n \\
\bar{C}_n
\end{array}
\begin{array}{cc}
C_{n+1} & \bar{C}_{n+1} \\
\left[\begin{array}{cc} 1 & 0 \\ c & 1-c \end{array} \right]
\end{array}
\qquad
\begin{array}{c}
Pr(\text{correct response} \mid \text{row state}) \\
1 \\
g
\end{array}
$$

Here C_n and $\bar{C}_n$ denote the events "state C on trial n" and "state $\bar{C}$ on trial n," respectively. The bottom row of this transition matrix represents the first statement in Axiom 4, and the top row expresses the second part of that axiom. The column on the right indicates for each state on trial n the probability of a correct response on that trial, as specified by Axiom 5. As indicated in that column, we shall denote by g the probability of a correct guess if the subject is currently in $\bar{C}$.

From Eq. 3.1 we see that the expressions for the one-element model will be functions of its parameters c and g. However, in the present experimental applications we shall estimate g in advance from the number of response alternatives available to the subject. Then the equations will be functions of the single parameter c, which must be estimated from the data.

The one-element model summarized in Eq. 3.1 has two fundamental properties, and these properties will be used repeatedly in carrying out the derivations. The first feature is that errors can occur only in the unconditioned state $\bar{C}$, so whenever the subject makes an error we know his state is $\bar{C}$. The second fact is that the one-element model, like the concept identification model, is a homogeneous Markov chain. The chain is Markovian because the conditioning state on trial $n + 1$ depends only on the state on trial n, but not on events before trial n (see the transition matrix in Eq. 3.1). The chain is homogeneous because the transition probabilities are independent of the trial number. If c in Eq. 3.1 were replaced by c_n (indicating that c is a function of n), then we would have a nonhomogeneous Markov chain.

State Probabilities on Trial n

We begin the derivations by finding the probability that the subject is still in the unconditioned state $\bar{C}$ at the start of trial n. This probability is written as $Pr(\bar{C}_n)$. Likewise, $Pr(C_n)$ denotes the probability that the subject is in state C on trial n. It is sufficient to derive only $Pr(\bar{C}_n)$, because on any trial the item must either be in $\bar{C}$ or in C, so

$$Pr(C_n) = 1 - Pr(\bar{C}_n).$$

We can take advantage of Eq. 2.4 of the concept model to guess what the solution for $Pr(\bar{C}_n)$ will be. Recall that in the notation of Chapter 2 the probability of staying in the initial state from one trial to the next equaled $1 - qc$. Equation 2.4 of that chapter gave $Pr(\bar{S}_n) = (1 - qc)^{n-1}$. The one-element model assumes that the probability of staying in the initial state from one trial to the next equals $1 - c$. Hence by changing notation we anticipate that $Pr(\bar{C}_n) = (1 - c)^{n-1}$. Next we verify this conjecture.

According to Axiom 6, the item is in the unconditioned state $\bar{C}$ at the start of the experiment, so $Pr(\bar{C}_1) = 1$. By Eq. 3.1, the first reinforcement brings about a transition from $\bar{C}$ to C with probability c. Therefore, $Pr(C_2) = c$ and $Pr(\bar{C}_2) = 1 - c$. With this information, let us use a *tree diagram* to find $Pr(\bar{C}_3)$. Although the diagram is not essential to the proof in the present simple problem, familiarity with this method will aid in understanding more complex derivations encountered later.

We digress for a moment to describe a tree diagram. Figure 3.3 gives the diagram to be used in finding $Pr(\bar{C}_3)$. The diagram consists of nodes (represented by the symbols $\bar{C}$ and C) connected by arrows. In this instance, the nodes represent learning states, because we are interested in finding state probabilities. Nodes are drawn for successive trials, reading from left to right in the figure. Connections between nodes signify possible state transitions from one trial to the next. Above each arrow appears the corresponding transition probability as specified by Eq. 3.1. Each possible way of tracing out a path from the node on trial 1 to a node on trial 3 defines a *branch* (or path) of the tree. The tree in Fig. 3.3 has three branches. A branch probability is the product of the probabilities of the events traced out in forming that branch. That is, the branch probability is the product of the probabilities above the arrows that make up that branch. The right side of Fig. 3.3 gives the branch probabilities for this tree.

Once the branch probabilities are known, it is a simple matter to compute the probability of being in a particular state on trial 3. We simply sum the probabilities of all branches which end in the appropriate state on trial 3. So in Fig. 3.3, $Pr(C_3) = c + (1 - c)c = 2c - c^2$, and $Pr(\bar{C}_3) = (1 - c)^2$.

We now know that $Pr(\bar{C}_1) = 1 = (1 - c)^0$, $Pr(\bar{C}_2) = (1 - c) = (1 - c)^1$, and $Pr(\bar{C}_3) = (1 - c)^2$. Can we infer the expression for $Pr(\bar{C}_n)$ for an arbitrary value of n? The rule seems to be that the exponent of $1 - c$ is one less than the trial number, so we write the solution as

$$(3.2) \qquad Pr(\bar{C}_n) = (1 - c)^{n-1}.$$

This result verifies the conjecture previously made by comparing the one-element model with the concept identification model. If the reader can visualize an n-trial extension of the branch diagram in Fig. 3.3, it will be clear that $(1 - c)^{n-1}$ is just the product of the probabilities along the lower branch of the tree. Notice that when $n = 1, 2$, and 3, respectively, we indeed obtain from Eq. 3.2 the equations given above for $Pr(\bar{C}_1)$, $Pr(\bar{C}_2)$, and $Pr(\bar{C}_3)$.

A more direct way of arriving at Eq. 3.2 is to observe that the subject is in $\bar{C}$ on trial n only if each of the preceding $n - 1$ reinforcements has failed to produce association learning. The probability of no learning on a single

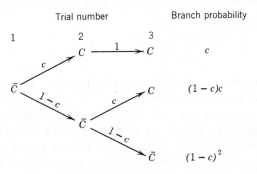

Fig. 3.3   Tree diagram for states on trials 1 to 3.

trial is $1 - c$, so the probability of no learning over the preceding $n - 1$ trials is

$$Pr(\bar{C}_n) = \overbrace{(1 - c)(1 - c)(1 - c) \cdots (1 - c)}^{n - 1 \text{ times}} = (1 - c)^{n-1}.$$

This result verifies Eq. 3.2. Then it follows at once that

(3.3) $$Pr(C_n) = 1 - (1 - c)^{n-1}.$$

Mean Learning Curve

Having found the state probabilities on any trial n, we are now able to write an equation for the average probability of an error on trial n. As in Chapter 2, it is convenient to introduce a response indicator random variable x_n in the following way:

$$x_n = \begin{cases} 1 & \text{if an error occurs for this subject-item sequence on trial } n, \\ 0 & \text{if a correct response occurs for this subject-item sequence on trial } n. \end{cases}$$

Hence $Pr(x_n = 1)$ denotes the probability of an error on trial n. Since errors can occur only in $\bar{C}$, $Pr(x_n = 1)$ is the joint probability that the subject is in $\bar{C}$ on trial n and makes an error:

(3.4) $$Pr(x_n = 1) = Pr(\bar{C}_n)(1 - g) = (1 - c)^{n-1}(1 - g).$$

This equation implies that $Pr(x_n = 1)$ approaches 0 in the limit, because $(1 - c)^{n-1}$ goes to 0 as n becomes large. Hence the expected asymptotic proportion incorrect is 0; the subject should eventually reach any criterion of consecutive correct responses. Data indicating asymptotes significantly different from 0 per cent incorrect would contradict the model. Equation 3.4 also tells us that the ratio of the probability of an error on trial $n + 1$ to the probability of an error on trial n should be a constant, $1 - c$. That is,

$$\frac{Pr(x_{n+1} = 1)}{Pr(x_n = 1)} = 1 - c.$$

Hence if the observed ratios depart seriously from the predicted invariance, this would be evidence against the model.

The reader will note that the $Pr(x_n = 1)$ derived in Eq. 3.4 is the average or expected probability of an error, but this average value is, in fact, not identical to the error probability for any particular subject-item sequence. Any particular subject-item sequence on trial n has an error probability of $1 - g$ or 0, depending on whether learning has or has not occurred before trial n. The way the average value of the error probability changes with trials reflects the increasing likelihood over trials that the error probability for a single subject-item has jumped to 0 after starting at $1 - g$.

Total Error Statistics

Now that we know the expected probability of an error on any trial n, it is easy to find the expected total errors per subject-item in any number, N, of trials. The limit of this quantity as N approaches infinity will be the expected total errors per subject-item before perfect learning. Of course, subjects never encounter an infinite sequence of trials. But this idealization is approximated experimentally by continuing the trials until some stringent criterion of successive correct responses has been attained on each item. The run of correct responses is assumed to imply only a negligible probability that the item is still in the unconditioned state. Hence if the experiment had been continued, the number of errors on post-criterion trials would have been virtually zero. So we regard the criterion run as the start of an infinite burst of correct responses in the protocol. This approximation is quite satisfactory in practice, since care is taken to make the criterion sufficiently strict that the chances are slight of reaching it merely by guessing. In the first part of the following derivation we give the result for finite N, so that applications can be made to experiments where subjects did not reach criterion. Instead of deriving the distribution of total errors and then taking the expectation of this distribution (as was done in deriving Eq. 2.12), we shall find the expected total errors in the first N trials by summing from $n = 1$ to N the expected probability of an error on trial n.

By definition, the random variable x_n registers a one for each error and a zero for each correct response. Therefore, T_N, the total errors on a single item in N trials, will be

$$T_N = \sum_{n=1}^{N} x_n.$$

Because the x_n's are random variables, their sum, T_N, is also a random variable, having a distribution with an expected value. The expected total errors in N trials will be found by taking expectations of both sides of the above equation:

$$E(T_N) = E\left(\sum_{n=1}^{N} x_n\right).$$

We rewrite the right side of this equation by using the rule that the expectation of the sum of random variables is equal to the sum of the expectations:

(3.5)
$$E\left(\sum_{n=1}^{N} x_n\right) = \sum_{n=1}^{N} E(x_n).$$

Now the expectation of the random variable x_n is

$$E(x_n) = 0 \cdot Pr(x_n = 0) + 1 \cdot Pr(x_n = 1) = Pr(x_n = 1).$$

Substituting this result into Eq. 3.5 yields

$$E\left(\sum_{n=1}^{N} x_n\right) = \sum_{n=1}^{N} Pr(x_n = 1).$$

Next we replace $Pr(x_n = 1)$ by means of Eq. 3.4:

$$E\left(\sum_{n=1}^{N} x_n\right) = \sum_{n=1}^{N} (1 - c)^{n-1}(1 - g).$$

The final step is to carry out the summation over n. We take the factor $1 - g$ outside the summation sign and write the sum of the first N terms of the geometric series:

$$E\left(\sum_{n=1}^{N} x_n\right) = (1 - g)\sum_{n=1}^{N}(1 - c)^{n-1}$$

$$= \frac{(1 - g)[1 - (1 - c)^N]}{1 - (1 - c)}.$$

Replacing the left-hand term by $E(T_N)$,

$$(3.6) \qquad E(T_N) = \frac{(1 - g)[1 - (1 - c)^N]}{c}.$$

To find the expected total errors per subject-item, we take the limit as $N \rightarrow \infty$ of the right side of Eq. 3.6. Denoting this limit as $E(T)$,

$$(3.7) \qquad E(T) = \lim_{N \to \infty} \left\{ \frac{(1 - g)}{c} [1 - (1 - c)^N] \right\} = \frac{(1 - g)}{c}.$$

If we examine Eq. 3.7, we find that the expression is intuitively sensible. Since c is the probability of learning per trial, the number of trials before learning occurs will average out to be $1/c$. During each of these $1/c$ trials, the subject will make an error with probability $1 - g$, because he is guessing prior to learning. Hence, the mean total errors is just the mean number of guessing trials, $1/c$, times the likelihood of an error on each such trial, $1 - g$.

Next we shall obtain the probability that in an infinite sequence of trials the subject makes exactly k errors on a given item. We denote this quantity as $Pr(T = k)$, where k can be any nonnegative integer. By Eq. 3.7 we already know the expectation of this random variable T. In the one-element model, the trial of last error is not necessarily identical to the trial on which learning occurs, because the subject may guess correctly for several trials after his last error and before learning on a correct-response trial. Consequently the derivation is more complicated than that given in Sec. 2.4 for the concept identification model.

First we derive $Pr(T = 0)$. What are the ways in which the event "$T = 0$" can occur? The first way is if the subject guesses correctly on trial 1 and then learns on that trial. This path has probability gc. The second way in which the event "$T = 0$" can occur is if the subject guesses correctly on trial 1, fails to learn on that trial, again guesses correctly on trial 2, and then learns on trial 2. This branch and its associated probability are

	Trial 1		Trial 2	
	Correct	Fail to	Correct	Learn
	Guess	Learn	Guess	
Pr(Branch 2) =	g	$\cdot (1 - c) \cdot$	g	$\cdot \quad c \quad = g(1 - c)gc.$

Likewise the third branch corresponds to correct guesses on trials 1, 2, and 3, with the subject failing to learn on trials 1 and 2, then learning on trial 3. This branch has probability

$$g(1 - c) \cdot g(1 - c) \cdot gc = [g(1 - c)]^2gc.$$

Table 3.1 summarizes our results to this point.

Table 3.1 does not indicate all the ways in which "$T = 0$" can occur, because for any positive integer i, there is some probability that the subject guesses correctly on trials 1 through i and then learns on trial i. Let the ith branch by which "$T = 0$" can occur be the event "$T = 0$ and learn on trial i." The rows of Table 3.1 summarize the first three branches, and

Table 3.1   First Three Branches by which the Event
"$T = 0$" can Occur

Correct Guess(es) on Trial Number(s)	Trial Number on which Learning Occurs	Branch Probability
1	1	gc
1, 2	2	$g(1 - c)gc$
1, 2, 3	3	$[g(1 - c)]^2gc$

the third column of the table gives us the probabilities of these branches. In each row of the table, the exponent of $g(1 - c)$ in the branch probability expressions is one less than the trial number on which learning occurs. That is, for $i = 1, 2$, and 3, the exponent of $g(1 - c)$ in the ith branch is $i - 1$. We conjecture that this pattern holds for *any* value of i, i.e., that

(3.8) $Pr(T = 0 \text{ \& learn on trial } i) = Pr(\text{Branch } i)$

$$= [g(1 - c)]^{i-1}gc.$$

The above conjecture can be verified by rearranging the terms in the last part of Eq. 3.8:

$$Pr(\text{Branch } i) = g^i(1 - c)^{i-1}c.$$

In this form it is clear that the event "$T = 0$ and learn on trial i" occurs if the subject guesses correctly on each of his first i trials, fails to learn on each of trials 1 through $i - 1$, and learns on trial i.

Applying the rule that the event probability is the sum of the appropriate branch probabilities, we have

$$Pr(T = 0) = \sum_{i=1}^{\infty} Pr(T = 0 \text{ \& learn on trial } i) = \sum_{i=1}^{\infty} Pr(\text{Branch } i).$$

Substituting into the right-hand term from Eq. 3.8,

$$Pr(T = 0) = \sum_{i=1}^{\infty} [g(1 - c)]^{i-1} gc.$$

Summing the geometric series yields

$$Pr(T = 0) = gc \sum_{i=1}^{\infty} [g(1 - c)]^{i-1} = \frac{gc}{1 - g(1 - c)}.$$

For convenience in the next stage of the derivation we define b by the equation

(3.9)
$$b = \frac{c}{1 - g(1 - c)}.$$

Then from the above equation for $Pr(T = 0)$,

(3.10)
$$Pr(T = 0) = gb.$$

From Eq. 3.10 we can see that b equals the probability of no further errors after a guess (i.e., after a response in state $\bar{C}$).

Our definition of b permits a simple derivation of $Pr(T = k)$. The probability of no further errors after an error is b, so $1 - b$ is the probability that the event "no further errors after an error" *fails* to occur. Now in order for there to be exactly k errors, the first must occur (with probability $1 - gb$). After each of errors $1, 2, \ldots, k - 1$ the event "no further errors after an error" must fail to occur [with probability $(1 - b)^{k-1}$], and then with probability b this event must occur after the kth error. Hence, for $k \geq 1$

(3.11)
$$Pr(T = k) = (1 - gb)(1 - b)^{k-1}b$$
$$= \frac{(1 - b)^k b}{1 - c}.$$

Having found the distribution of total errors per subject item, we can calculate its mean:

$$E(T) = \sum_{k=1}^{\infty} k Pr(T = k) = \frac{(1 - b)b}{1 - c} \sum_{k=1}^{\infty} k(1 - b)^{k-1}.$$

But for $0 < x < 1$, $\sum_{k=1}^{\infty} kx^{k-1} = \frac{1}{(1 - x)^2}$. Hence, using this result with $x = 1 - b$ we obtain

(3.12)
$$E(T) = \frac{(1 - b)b}{1 - c} \cdot \frac{1}{b^2} = \frac{1}{1 - c}\left(\frac{1}{b} - 1\right).$$

From Eq. 3.9, $1/b = [1 - (1 - c)g]/c$, so

$$E(T) = \frac{1}{1 - c} \cdot \frac{(1 - c)(1 - g)}{c} = \frac{1 - g}{c}.$$

This result verifies Eq. 3.7, which was obtained from the expected probability of an error on trial n.

Equation 3.11 also provides a way to find the variance of total errors. Let us call this quantity $\text{Var}(T)$. Since T is a random variable, we have from Sec. 2.4 of the previous chapter

$$(3.13) \qquad \text{Var}(T) = E(T^2) - [E(T)]^2,$$

where $E(T^2)$ is the second row moment. By definition,

$$E(T^2) = \sum_{k=1}^{\infty} k^2 Pr(T = k).$$

Substituting for $Pr(T = k)$ from Eq. 3.11,

$$E(T^2) = \sum_{k=1}^{\infty} \frac{k^2 (1 - b)^k b}{1 - c} = \frac{(1 - b)b}{1 - c} \sum_{k=1}^{\infty} k^2 (1 - b)^{k-1}.$$

Now we use the fact that for $0 < x < 1$,

$$\sum_{k=1}^{\infty} k^2 x^{k-1} = \frac{1 + x}{(1 - x)^3}.$$

Continuing, with $x = 1 - b$,

$$E(T^2) = \frac{(1 - b)b}{1 - c} \left(\frac{2 - b}{b^3} \right) = \frac{(1 - b)(2 - b)}{(1 - c)b^2}.$$

But we proved in Eq. 3.12 that $E(T) = \dfrac{(1 - b)}{(1 - c)b}$, so

$$E(T^2) = E(T) \left(\frac{2 - b}{b} \right).$$

Putting this result into Eq. 3.13 gives

$$\text{Var}(T) = E(T) \left(\frac{2 - b}{b} \right) - [E(T)]^2$$

$$= E(T) \left[\frac{2}{b} - 2 + 1 - E(T) \right].$$

By a slight manipulation of Eq. 3.12, $2E(T)(1 - c) = \dfrac{2}{b} - 2$, so

$$(3.14) \qquad \text{Var}(T) = E(T)[E(T)(1 - 2c) + 1].$$

This completes the derivation. The ratio of the variance to the mean equals $E(T)(1 - 2c) + 1$. Therefore the condition for the variance to be greater than the mean is that $c < \frac{1}{2}$.

Trial Number of Last Error

In this section we find for any nonnegative integer k the probability that the subject makes his last error on a particular item on trial k. The trial number of last error (sometimes called the number of trials to criterion) is a natural statistic, used by experimenters to describe the speed of learning. Difficult learning tasks have a large number of trials before criterion. The statistic is derived here for a single subject-item, rather than with respect to an entire list of verbal items (which is the customary list-learning measure). We let the random variable L denote the trial number of last error for a particular subject-item sequence, and we wish to find the probability that the last error (in an effectively infinite sequence of trials) occurs on trial k; we denote this probability as $Pr(L = k)$. Because the error probability is zero in state C, it is certain that every sequence will indeed have a trial of last error. This clearly would not be the case if the error probabilities did not reach zero with continued training.

The last error occurs on trial k if (1) the subject is in $\bar{C}$ on trial k and makes an error, and (2) the subject makes no further errors after that trial. Event (1) has probability equal to

$$Pr(\bar{C}_k)(1 - g) = (1 - c)^{k-1}(1 - g).$$

The probability of event (2) is just the probability of no further errors after a response in $\bar{C}$, which by Eq. 3.9 equals b. Hence

(3.15) $$Pr(L = k) = (1 - c)^{k-1}(1 - g)b \qquad \text{(for } k \geq 1\text{)}.$$

Why is the result above incorrect for $k = 0$? Because in the $1 - g$ factor we have assumed that an error occurred on trial k. Let us define the event "$L = 0$" to mean that no errors occurred in the sequence. Therefore this event is identical to the event "$T = 0$," and so $Pr(L = 0)$ is gb, as given by Eq. 3.10.

For the expected trial number of last error, we refer to Eq. 3.15 and take expectations in the usual manner:

$$E(L) = \sum_{k=1}^{\infty} kPr(L = k) = \sum_{k=1}^{\infty} k(1 - c)^{k-1}(1 - g)b$$

$$= (1 - g)b \sum_{k=1}^{\infty} k(1 - c)^{k-1} = \frac{(1 - g)b}{c^2}.$$

This last equality comes from the fact that $\sum_{k=1}^{\infty} k(1 - c)^{k-1} = 1/c^2$. From Eq. 3.7 we have

$$(3.16) \qquad\qquad E(L) = E(T)\,\frac{b}{c}\,.$$

We note two things about this expression for the mean trial of the last error. First, we may write the $E(L)$ expression as

$$E(L) = \frac{1}{c}\left[\frac{1}{1 + c\,\dfrac{g}{1 - g}}\right].$$

This equation can be verified by using Eq. 3.9 to replace b in the equation $E(L) = (1 - g)b/c^2$. Both numerator and denominator of the resulting expression are then divided by $1 - g$. In this expression $1/c$ denotes the mean number of trials before learning occurs. The term in brackets is a fraction less than one which, when multiplied by $1/c$, tells us how much sooner the average trial of last error occurs than the average trial of learning. This fraction depends on g, the probability of guessing correctly. If g were zero so that the subject always erred before learning, then the mean trial of learning, the trial of the last error, the number of trials before the first success, and the total errors would all equal $1/c$. As g increases above zero, the mean trial of last error becomes progressively less than the mean trial of learning, $1/c$. A second comment is elicited by Eq. 3.16 when we take the ratio of total errors to trial of last error using the averages of both measures:

$$\frac{E(T)}{E(L)} = \frac{c}{b} = 1 - g + gc.$$

For the concept identification model in Chapter 2, which assumed that learning could occur only on error trials, this ratio of mean total errors to trial of last error was $1 - g$ (or q). In fact, this ratio was shown to be the maximum likelihood estimator of $1 - g$ for that model. For the present version of the one-element model, which assumes that learning can occur on error or on success trials, this ratio of mean errors to mean trials is biased above the true guessing error rate of $1 - g$ by a factor of gc. This correction factor essentially takes account of the fact that subjects may guess correctly for a few trials after their last error and before they learn (on a correct response trial).

Alternative Derivation of the Error Distribution

An alternative derivation of the distribution of errors uses the result obtained above for L. To find the probability of k errors, we suppose that the trial of last error is n $(n \geq k)$ and during the preceding $n - 1$ trials exactly $k - 1$ errors are observed. Since guessing occurs prior to the last error, the probability of $k - 1$ errors in $n - 1$ guesses is given by the binomial law,*

$$B(k - 1, n - 1) = \binom{n - 1}{k - 1}(1 - g)^{k-1}g^{n-k}.$$

Thus, $Pr(L = n) \cdot B(k - 1, n - 1)$ is the probability of one particular branch of the process that will give $T = k$. By fixing k and letting $n \geq k$ vary, we may add together the probabilities of all the possible branches where $T = k$. Thus,

$$Pr(T = k) = \sum_{n=k}^{\infty} Pr(L = n)B(k - 1, n - 1)$$

$$= \sum_{n=k}^{\infty} (1 - g)b(1 - c)^{n-1}\binom{n - 1}{k - 1}(1 - g)^{k-1}g^{n-k}.$$

By manipulating terms in this sum, it can be reduced to the form

$$Pr(T = k) = \frac{b}{1 - c}[(1 - g)(1 - c)]^k \sum_{i=0}^{\infty} \binom{k - 1 + i}{i}[g(1 - c)]^i.$$

For $0 < x < 1$, the series

$$\sum_{i=0}^{\infty} \binom{k - 1 + i}{i}x^i$$

has the sum $(1 - x)^{-k}$. If we substitute this result into our equation, the expression obtained is

$$Pr(T = k) = \frac{b}{1 - c}\left[\frac{(1 - g)(1 - c)}{1 - g(1 - c)}\right]^k \qquad \text{(for } k \geq 1).$$

---

* The factor $\binom{k}{i}$ is called a binomial coefficient, and in this problem gives the number of different ways by which i errors can occur in k trials. For positive integers i and k, the binomial coefficient is defined as

$$\binom{k}{i} = \begin{cases} \dfrac{k!}{i!\,(k - i)!} & \text{(for } i \leq k) \\ \\ 0 & \text{(for } i > k). \end{cases}$$

In this expression, $k!$ (read "k factorial") is the product of all integers from 1 through k, that is, $k! = 1 \cdot 2 \cdots (k - 1) \cdot k$, and $0! = 1$. For example,

$$\binom{6}{2} = \frac{6!}{2!\,4!} = \frac{1 \cdot 2 \cdot 3 \cdot 4 \cdot 5 \cdot 6}{1 \cdot 2 \cdot 1 \cdot 2 \cdot 3 \cdot 4} = \frac{30}{2} = 15.$$

The expression in brackets can be shown to equal $1 - b$; hence, we obtain the same result as that given in Eq. 3.11. This procedure may also be used to derive the distribution of the number of correct responses before the last error.

Response Sequences

None of the statistics considered so far (mean learning curve, distribution of total errors, distribution of trial of last error) tell us what the model predicts about sequential properties of the data. For example, the mean learning curve describes the likelihood of an error on trial n, but it does not indicate how this quantity is related to, say, the response on trial $n - 1$ in the same subject-item sequence. Likewise the total errors and trial of last error statistics do not provide information about intertrial dependencies in response probability. There are several reasons why it is desirable to have some prediction equations dealing with response sequences. For one thing, it often happens that by examining the accuracy of sequential predictions, we can decide between two models that describe other statistics with equal accuracy. Second, in some models certain predictions concerning sequential statistics hold regardless of the parameter values (these are called parameter-free predictions); such predictions provide the strongest possible tests of a model, and if the model fails the deficiency will be conspicuous. Parameter-free predictions are extremely valuable in evaluating the models, because discrepancies between predicted and observed values must reflect a flaw in the model and cannot be imputed to shortcomings in the method of parameter estimation.

The simplest sequential statistic to examine in the one-element model is the probability of an error on any trial, conditional on an error on the preceding trial in the same subject-item sequence. We denote this conditional probability by $Pr(x_{n+1} = 1 \mid x_n = 1)$. The fact that an error occurred on trial n tells us that the subject was in state $\bar{C}$ on that trial. For another error to occur on trial $n + 1$, the subject must remain in $\bar{C}$ (this event has probability $1 - c$) and guess incorrectly (this event has probability $1 - g$). Hence

$$(3.17) \qquad Pr(x_{n+1} = 1 \mid x_n = 1) = (1 - c)(1 - g).$$

From this equation, the parameter-free prediction is that

$$Pr(x_{n+1} = 1 \mid x_n = 1)$$

should be a constant independent of the trial index n. Later (Sec. 3.5) we shall cite data from several experiments in order to see whether the predicted constancy does indeed occur.

Another sequential statistic that we shall consider for the one-element model is the expected number of error runs of length j, denoted by $E(r_j)$. The manner of counting error runs in a response sequence of zeros and ones was illustrated in Sec. 2.12. Recall that, for example, the subject-item sequence $1011110101\ldots$ (all the rest zeros) includes one error run of length four, one error run of length two, and two error runs of length one. If the subject tended to persist in making an incorrect response, he would produce few runs of errors, but each run would be relatively long. Conversely, alternations between correct and incorrect responses would be

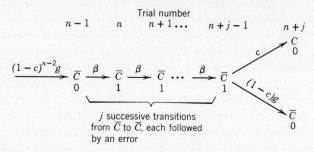

Fig. 3.4 Tree diagram for the event "an error run of length j beginning on trial n." The number 0 or 1 below each state symbol is the value of the random variable x_n on that trial.

manifest by many short error runs. Hence the error run statistic is a measure of the tendency to perseverate in making errors. We could use the method described in Chapter 2 to derive the expected number of error runs of length j; namely, first finding the equations for the j-tuples of errors and then apply Eq. 2.22 of that chapter to determine the r_j's from the j-tuples. However, that technique has been amply demonstrated, and since our ultimate interest is in the error runs we shall find these quantities directly, without resorting to the j-tuples.

The derivation begins by finding $Pr(r_{j,n})$, the probability of an error run of length j starting on trial n. An error run of length j begins on trial n if the subject is in $\bar{C}$ on trial $n-1$, guesses correctly, stays in $\bar{C}$ on each of the next j trials $n, n+1, n+2, \ldots, n+j-1$, makes an error on each of these trials, and then ends the error run by making a correct response on trial $n+j$. This event is diagrammed in Fig. 3.4. We have let β be the probability that the subject fails to leave $\bar{C}$ on a single trial and makes an error on the next trial. Therefore, from Eq. 3.17, $\beta = (1-c)(1-g)$. As the diagram shows, $(1-c)^{n-2}g$ is the probability of being in $\bar{C}$ on trial $n-1$ and guessing correctly on that trial. Next, $\beta^j = [(1-c)(1-g)]^j$ is the probability that the subject remains in $\bar{C}$ for each of the next j trials and makes an error on each trial. The correct response on trial $n + j$, which terminates the error run, can occur via either of two branches: with probability c the subject goes into state C immediately after the jth error in the run, and necessarily responds correctly on the next trial; or with probability $(1 - c)g$ he remains in $\bar{C}$ but guesses correctly on trial $n + j$.

Since $Pr(r_{j,n})$ is the sum of the probabilities of these two branches in Fig. 3.4,

$$Pr(r_{j,n}) = (1 - c)^{n-2}g\beta^j[c + (1 - c)g].$$

But $c + (1 - c)g = 1 - \beta$, so

$$(3.18) \qquad Pr(r_{j,n}) = (1 - c)^{n-2}g\beta^j(1 - \beta), \qquad (n \geq 2).$$

Equation 3.18 is incorrect for $n = 1$, because we assumed that a correct response occurred on trial $n - 1$. The necessary and sufficient conditions for an error run of length j to start on trial 1 are that the subject err on each of his first $j - 1$ trials, fail to learn after each error, commit another error on trial j, then respond correctly on trial $j + 1$, either via learning (state C) or via guessing (state $\bar{C}$). The probability of these joint events is

$$(3.19) \qquad Pr(r_{j,1}) = \beta^{j-1}(1 - g)(1 - \beta).$$

Finally, $E(r_j)$ is the sum from $n = 1$ to ∞ of $Pr(r_{j,n})$. In other words, the expected number of error runs of length j is the sum over n of the expected number of error runs of length j and starting on trial n. This latter quantity is easily seen to equal $Pr(r_{j,n})$. Taking the term for $n = 1$ from Eq. 3.19 and summing Eq. 3.18 from $n = 2$ to ∞ gives

$$E(r_j) = \beta^{j-1}(1 - g)(1 - \beta) + \sum_{n=2}^{\infty}(1 - c)^{n-2}g\beta^j(1 - \beta).$$

The sum of this series is

$$E(r_j) = \beta^{j-1}(1 - \beta)\left[1 - g + \frac{g\beta}{c}\right].$$

After multiplying the last term through by c and substituting $1 - \beta - g$ for $c(1 - g)$, we have

$$(3.20) \qquad E(r_j) = \beta^{j-1}(1 - \beta)^2 E(T).$$

From Eq. 3.20,

$$E(r_1) = \frac{(1 - \beta)^2(1 - g)}{c},$$

and so $E(r_j) = \beta^{j-1}E(r_1)$.

The expected total error runs of any length in a subject-item sequence is the sum from $j = 1$ to ∞ of the expected number of error runs of length

j. Denoting the expected total error runs as $E(R)$ and substituting from Eq. 3.20,

$$E(R) = \sum_{j=1}^{\infty} E(r_j)$$
$$= \sum_{j=1}^{\infty} \beta^{j-1}(1 - \beta)^2 E(T)$$
$$= E(T)(1 - \beta).$$

Let us pause a moment to consider the import of what the one-element model implies about the run structure of the sequential data. First, consider the mean length of a run of errors. The mean length of an error run is obtained by dividing mean total errors by mean runs, obtaining

$$\frac{E(T)}{E(R)} = \frac{1}{1 - \beta}.$$

This is an interesting relation because, by definition, $1 - \beta$ is the probability of a success on the next trial following an error. Given that the probability of a success following an error is $1 - \beta$, then it is sensible to expect that the average number of errors observed before a success would be $1/(1 - \beta)$. By the equation above, $1/(1 - \beta)$ is indeed the mean run length of errors. Second, consider the ratio of the expressions for mean runs of length j and runs of length $j - 1$. This ratio is

$$\frac{E(r_j)}{E(r_{j-1})} = \beta.$$

This ratio is expected to be constant over different values of j. The factor β is just the likelihood that, given $j - 1$ errors, one more error occurs before the success terminates a run of j errors. Because β is always less than one, we expect the number of error runs of length j to decrease monotonically with j, according to the function $E(r_j) = \beta^{j-1}E(r_1)$.

Presolution Responses

The one-element model makes a number of strong predictions about the statistical properties of a subject-item sequence prior to the last error in that sequence (Suppes and Ginsberg, 1963). These predictions are identical to those discussed in Sec. 2.2, a fact that is not surprising in view of the similarity of the concept identification and one-element paired-associate models. Prior to the last error, responses in a sequence are expected to form a Bernoulli sequence of independent trials with stationary probability, g, of a correct response on each trial.

Of particular interest in the present chapter is the stationarity prediction. Recall that it was derived by the following argument. Before his last error on an item, the subject must be in state $\bar{C}$ with respect to that item; we know this because, according to the model, errors never occur in C and the subject cannot return from C to $\bar{C}$. Granted, then, that the item is in $\bar{C}$ during the presolution trials, the probability of a correct response must be stationary over these trials and equal to g. Hence a Vincent curve of the observed presolution proportion correct should be a horizontal line with ordinate at g.

3.3   FIT OF THE ONE-ELEMENT MODEL TO PAIRED-ASSOCIATE DATA

Bower's experimental procedure was described at the beginning of this chapter. His stimulus-response pairs were constructed so as to be equally difficult. Hence as a working assumption we suppose that c is constant across items for a single subject. We further assume that c is the same for all subjects. This auxiliary assumption of homogeneous subject-item sequences is convenient because it permits pooling all subject-item sequences when computing the observed values of the various statistics. We emphasize that the homogeneity assumption is only convenient, not necessary, since we could proceed by estimating a different c value for each subject. We could construct statistical tests to evaluate the assumption of homogeneous c-values; these reduce essentially to assessing the inaccuracies of predictions generated by the common-c assumption. We could also say which statistics will be predicted inaccurately by the common-c model when there is heterogeneity. In general, common-c predictions of the mean learning curve and almost all sequential statistics are only slightly inaccurate if in fact there is significant item and/or subject differences. On the other hand, the common-c predictions will err more conspicuously in predicting probability distributions and variances of statistics like total errors and trial of last error. In effect, the common-c model would predict too little variance (in T or L) if the data were in fact averages taken over several one-element processes with different c parameters. The reader may convince himself of these assertions by performing some simple calculations of theoretical quantities averaged over two or more populations of protocols with different c values. For our present purposes, we may regard the homogeneity assumption as a convenient approximation that is satisfactory whenever it does not lead to markedly low predictions of variability between statistics of the sample of protocols [that is, Var(T) or Var(L)].

To return to Bower's experiment, the subjects had two response alternatives available on each trial. Therefore, we adopt the assumption that on each trial in $\bar{C}$ the probability of a correct guess, g, is $\frac{1}{2}$. (In general, suppose that r response alternatives are available to the subject. Under this condition it is usually assumed that while in $\bar{C}$ the subject guesses randomly from among r alternatives; that is, $g = 1/r$. The assumption that g depends only on the number of currently unlearned items also has been investigated.)

The only parameter that must be estimated from the data is c. Problems of parameter estimation are treated in Chapter 9. Here it suffices to remark that a suitable estimate of c can be obtained by setting the observed average total errors per subject-item equal to the corresponding theoretical expression. An advantage in using the expected total errors is that this statistic is based on the entire sequence of data from a subject-item and therefore is descriptive of overall performance. We let $\hat{c}$ represent the estimate of the parameter c.

All observed quantities to be reported were computed as explained in Chapter 2. In the experiment, the subject was terminated when he went through the list twice in succession without errors. However, in calculating data statistics, it is presumed that if the subject had been continued, he would have made all correct responses on later trials. There were 290 subject-item sequences (29 subjects × 10 items), and an average of 1.45 total errors per subject-item. From Eq. 3.7 with $g = \frac{1}{2}$,

$$1.45 = \frac{1 - \frac{1}{2}}{\hat{c}}.$$

Solving this equation gives $\hat{c} = 0.344$.

After inserting the estimate of c above into Eq. 3.4, the predicted proportion of incorrect responses on trial n was computed for $n = 1$, 2, ..., 10. The corresponding observed proportions were calculated from the frequency data. For example, the observed frequency of incorrect responses on trial 2 was 96, so the observed proportion incorrect on that trial equaled $96/290 = 0.331$. This value compares favorably with the predicted proportion: $(1 - c)(1 - g) = 0.656(0.500) = 0.328$. As Fig. 3.5 indicates, the agreement between observed and predicted learning curves is excellent.

The predicted distribution of total errors per subject-item sequence was calculated by using Eqs. 3.10 and 3.11. Figure 3.6 shows that the observed and predicted distributions agree fairly well. The comparison of the observed distribution of the trial number of last error with that predicted from Eqs. 3.10 and 3.15 is displayed in Fig. 3.7. The model is accurate except for k equal to 1 and 4. The predicted numbers of error runs of

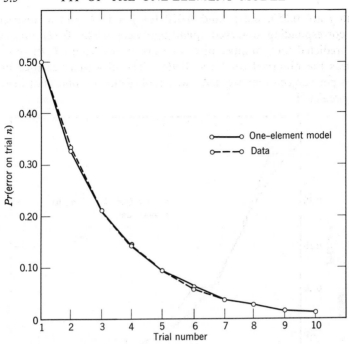

Fig. 3.5   The probability, q_n, of an error over successive trials.

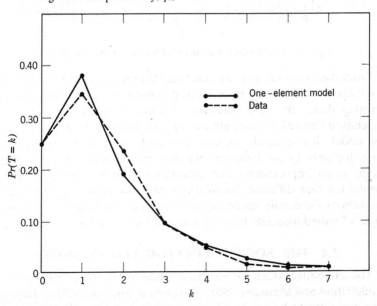

Fig. 3.6   Distribution of T_N, the total number of errors per subject-item sequence.

length j are 0.655, 0.215, and 0.070 for $j = 1$, 2, and 3, respectively. The corresponding observed quantities were 0.645, 0.221, and 0.058. The predicted total number of error runs of any length $E(R)$ was 0.975, whereas the observed total was 0.966. The observed variance in total errors per subject-item sequence was 1.88, which is somewhat below the 2.07 predicted.

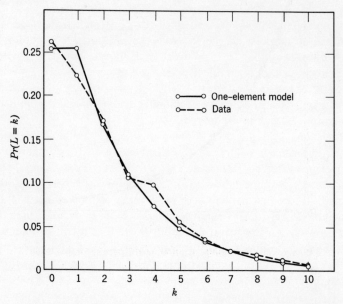

Fig. 3.7   Distribution of L, the trial number of the last failure.

From these comparisons, we conclude that the one-element model gives a satisfactory account of the statistical aspects of these paired-associate-learning data. By itself, however, this success does not warrant the conclusion that paired-associate learning occurs in the fashion assumed by the model. It is especially important to apply other models to these same data, for only by so doing can we determine whether the one-element model is an improvement over alternative versions. We have already mentioned that different formulations can sometimes lead to identical predictions for certain statistics, so it would be premature to dismiss the topic of paired-associate learning without testing additional models.

3.4   THE SINGLE-OPERATOR LINEAR MODEL

The alternative which we wish to consider is the single-operator linear model (Bush and Mosteller, 1955; Bush and Sternberg, 1959). The prediction equations to be developed here for this model were first presented in the Bush and Sternberg article. The linear operator model views learning as a direct change in response probability from one trial to the next. Thus, the response probability on trial $n + 1$ is obtained by a simple transformation of the response probability existing on trial n. We let q_n be the error probability on trial n, and the model generates a sequence of probabilities over trials, denoted $q_1, q_2, q_3, \ldots$. As the name implies, the linear operator model assumes that the operation transforming q_n into q_{n+1} is linear. The nature of this linear operator will be illustrated later. The single-operator linear model is characterized by the additional restriction that the same operator is applied to q_n on every trial. Linear operators are defined and discussed in a mathematically precise manner in Sec. 5.3. We shall not require operator notation to carry out the subsequent derivations in this chapter. Occasionally we shall refer to the single-operator linear model simply as the "linear model."

Before going into the derivations, we want to comment on why the single-operator linear model is an excellent candidate for comparison with the one-element model. The reason is that these two models differ sharply in their assumptions about how an individual stimulus-response association is learned. According to the linear model *each* reinforcement is assumed to bring about a decrement in the probability of an error. Learning, which occurs on each reinforced presentation, is gradual because a number of decrements in q_n are needed before this quantity is reduced to a near-zero value.* By contrast, we have seen that in the one-element model the effect of a single reinforcement is either to produce complete learning of the individual *S-R* association, or no learning at all. We would be wise to begin by discovering to what extent the data permit us to choose between these markedly different formulations, because we can expect less differentiation among models that are more similar to one another. Also, from a mathematical viewpoint, it is instructive to compare the single-operator linear and one-element models. The one-element model is a prototype of Markov models, whereas the single-operator model has the same status among linear models. Hence by comparing these two relatively simple versions we get some insight into the respective merits of linear and Markov models for paired-associate learning. Processes of both general types have played prominent roles in quantitative theorizing in other sciences, and it is not surprising that their counterparts arise in psychology. The popularity and success of linear and Markov models can be attributed in no small degree to the fact that they have convenient mathematical properties that simplify the task of performing derivations.

---

* The linear model is a probabilistic analog of the Hullian incremental learning theory discussed earlier.

Nonlinear transforms are generally less feasible because they create greater mathematical complexity. Likewise, it is often impossible to execute derivations for non-Markovian models.

Another advantage in contrasting the single-operator linear model with the one-element model arises from the fact that each model has the same number of parameters (one) to be estimated from the data. Comparisons between two models with unequal numbers of parameters (for example, a one-parameter model versus a three-parameter model) are worthwhile, but the evaluation is more difficult in such cases. If the model with more parameters is the more accurate, this outcome can be due to either of two factors. We would like to interpret its empirical confirmation as support for the particular axioms of the model. However, the superiority of the model with more parameters could be caused simply by its having sampled more of the data before making predictions.* We might answer this objection by appealing to the logic of statistical hypothesis testing; we can determine separately for each model whether its deviations from the data are significant, as indicated perhaps by a χ^2 test. As noted in Chapter 2, such tests of the null hypothesis involve subtracting one degree of freedom for each parameter estimated from the data. Therefore, in principle, the method adjusts for the number of parameters in a model. In concluding this section, let us indicate why this statistical compensation does not dissolve all the underlying problems of evaluating multiparameter models. The problem is that goodness-of-fit indices measure only discrepancies from a null hypothesis. They do not tell us how much improvement could reasonably be expected if we were to proceed by testing alternative models. There is no way to resolve this question short of formulating whatever plausible alternatives our ingenuity can devise. It seems to us that the utility of such comparisons is directly proportional to the number of parameters in the original model. That is, if a one-parameter model fits, it is usually difficult to propose an equally accurate alternative one-parameter model. But if the first model has three parameters, there is more latitude for concocting alternative versions. As mentioned in Chapter 1, we have included in this book a few comparisons of multiple-parameter models fitted to the same data. Even for

---

* When two models have the same number of parameters to be estimated, one usually uses the same observed statistics to estimate the parameters of both models. For example, in this chapter c in the one-element model and α in the linear model are both estimated by equating the observed and predicted total errors. Even this policy does not necessarily rule out the possibility that the estimation routine has given one model a spurious advantage over the other. Sternberg (1963, p. 95) has noted that different statistics may be optimal for estimating parameters in different models.

single-parameter models, comparative testing affords useful insights, as we shall now show.

Derivations from the Single-Operator Linear Model

Following the approach employed with the one-element model, we derive expressions for a sequence of responses to an individual paired-associate item by a single subject. It is convenient to proceed at the single-item level, because for present purposes the probability of a correct response to a particular stimulus is assumed to be independent of responses to other stimuli in the list. We retain the notation developed with the one-element model. Recall that the response indicator random variable x_n was defined as follows:

$$x_n = \begin{cases} 1 & \text{if an error occurs for this subject-item sequence on trial } n, \\ 0 & \text{if a correct response occurs for this subject-item sequence on trial } n. \end{cases}$$

Hence $Pr(x_n = 1)$ is the probability of an error on trial n. The expectation of the random variable x_n was shown to be $E(x_n) = Pr(x_n = 1)$.

The basic idea of the linear model is that each subject-item sequence is said to be a reflection of a trial-sequence of changing error probabilities denoted $q_1, q_2, q_3, \ldots$. With reinforced practice we expect, of course, that the q_n's will decrease toward zero over trials. The main assumption is that successive q-values in this sequence are related as follows:

(3.21) $$q_{n+1} = \alpha q_n.$$

In this expression, α is a fraction representing the extent to which the error probability on trial n is reduced as a result of the reinforcement on that trial. Small values of α produce large reductions in error probability from one trial to the next. The phrase "linear model" derives from the fact that q_{n+1} is a linear function of q_n.

To obtain somewhat firmer intuitions about the content of this basic assumption, consider the implied equation for changing the probability of the correct response. We let p_n represent the probability of the correct response on trial n, and obviously $p_n + q_n = 1$. Let us use Eq. 3.21 and the relation $p_{n+1} = 1 - q_{n+1}$ to obtain an expression for the change in p_n. The result from several substitutions goes as follows:

$$\begin{aligned} p_{n+1} &= 1 - q_{n+1} \\ &= 1 - \alpha(1 - p_n) \\ &= \alpha p_n + (1 - \alpha). \end{aligned}$$

This expression may be rewritten as

$$p_{n+1} = p_n + (1 - \alpha)(1 - p_n).$$

The next-to-last line may be interpreted as stating that p_{n+1} is a weighted average of p_n and one, where the weighting coefficients are α and $1 - \alpha$, respectively. The last line indicates that the probability of a correct response on trial $n + 1$ is the sum of (1) the prior value p_n, and (2) an increment which is a fraction of the difference between p_n and one (perfect responding). Also, the last line tells us that the incremental change in p_n will decrease as p_n approaches one, since the increment $(1 - \alpha)(1 - p_n)$ will approach zero as p_n approaches one. Thus, p_n will increase rapidly at first but more slowly for later trials, yielding a negatively accelerated growth curve.

Notice that Eq. 3.21 is formally identical to Eq. 2.5 of the concept-identification model. By the method of iteration employed there we obtain

$$(3.22) \qquad\qquad q_n = \alpha^{n-1} q_1,$$

where q_1 is the expected probability of an error on trial 1. The parameter q_1 should equal the probability of an error when the subject is guessing (in this model, the subject guesses only before his first reinforcement), so to be consistent we equate q_1 with $1 - g$ in the one-element model.

If in Eq. 3.22 we replace α by $1 - c$ and q_1 by $1 - g$, we obtain an expression identical to Eq. 3.4, the mean error probability derived from the one-element model. Since it is irrelevant what labels we attach to our parameters, we see that for this case the linear model and the one-element model yield the same expression for the mean learning curve. The coincidence is surprising because the basic conception of the learning process is quite different in the two models. The coincidence also tells us that other aspects of the data besides the mean learning curve must be examined if we want to distinguish between these two models. For the present case, this is a relatively easy matter since the two models differ in their predictions of a large number of aspects of the data. To illustrate the derivational techniques for the linear model, we consider the mean and variance of total errors, total runs of errors, and the mean number of pairs of errors that occur k trials apart.

A key assumption of the linear model in the derivations that follow is that the series of response indicator random variables, $x_1, x_2, x_3, \ldots,$ are all independent of one another. That is, the probability that x_n takes on the value one is the same regardless of what values were taken on by

x_{n-1}, x_{n-2}, ..., x_1. In formal notation, the independence assumption states that for any two trial indexes i and j,

$$Pr(x_i = 1 \mid x_j = 1) = Pr(x_i = 1 \mid x_j = 0) = Pr(x_i = 1).$$

Loosely speaking, the value of x_j is irrelevant information in determining the probability that x_i takes on the value one or zero. This independence property of the linear model is an implication of its sole assumption in Eq. 3.21. As noted in Eq. 3.22, the implication is that

$$q_n = q_1 \alpha^{n-1}.$$

From this result we know that q_n is a function only of the number of trials n and of nothing else such as the prior responses. This assumption may be contrasted with that of the one-element model in which the x_n's are not independent. For the one-element model, the conditional probability of an error on trial $n + 1$ depends strongly on whether an error or success occurred on trial n (see Eq. 3.17). Because the two models differ in this regard, we can expect the greatest differences in their predictions to show up in those statistics whose derivations from the linear model make use of the assumed independence of the x_n's. The variance of total errors and sequential statistics utilize the independence assumption in an obvious way, as we shall see presently.

Mean and Variance of Total Errors

Let T_N denote the total number of errors on a single subject-item sequence over the first N trials. From the definition of x_n, it follows that

$$T_N = \sum_{n=1}^{N} x_n.$$

That is, T_N is the sum of the N independent random variables x_n. Now there are no simple techniques known for deriving the probability distribution of T_N from the linear model. However, it is still feasible to obtain the mean and variance of T_N from its definition as the sum of the x_n's.

The expectation of T_N is found by taking expectations of both sides of the equation above:

$$E(T_N) = E\left(\sum_{n=1}^{N} x_n\right) = \sum_{n=1}^{N} E(x_n).$$

Recall that $E(x_n)$ is just the probability of an error on trial n, which is denoted as q_n. Next we replace q_n by Eq. 3.22 and sum the resulting geometric series:

(3.23) $$E(T_N) = \sum_{n=1}^{N} q_1 \alpha^{n-1} = \frac{q_1}{1 - \alpha}(1 - \alpha^N).$$

Now it is a simple matter to find the expected total errors in an infinite sequence of trials. Calling this quantity $E(T)$ and taking the limit as N approaches infinity of the right side of Eq. 3.23 gives

$$(3.24) \qquad E(T) = \lim_{N \to \infty} \frac{q_1}{1 - \alpha} (1 - \alpha^N) = \frac{q_1}{1 - \alpha}.$$

Equations 3.23 and 3.24 are formally identical to their counterparts in the one-element model (Eqs. 3.6 and 3.7). Of course, this fact is to be expected, because the models yielded identical equations for the probability of an error on a single trial.

To obtain the variance in total errors for an infinite number of trials we use the fact that for this model the x_n's are independent. Consequently, we can apply the theorem from probability calculus that the variance of the sum of independent random variables is equal to the sum of their individual variances. Thus, our expression for the variance of T is

$$\text{Var}(T) = \text{Var}\left(\sum_{n=1}^{\infty} x_n \right) = \sum_{n=1}^{\infty} \text{Var}(x_n).$$

But

$$\text{Var}(x_n) = E(x_n^2) - [E(x_n)]^2.$$

We know that $E(x_n) = q_n$. Because x_n takes on values of only one or zero, and since $1^2 = 1$ and $0^2 = 0$, it should be apparent that $E(x_n^2)$ will have the same value as $E(x_n)$, namely, q_n. Thus we may write the variance of x_n as

$$\text{Var}(x_n) = q_n - q_n^2 = q_n(1 - q_n).$$

We use this result to substitute back into the equation for $\text{Var}(T)$. Then we employ the model's assumption that q_n is equal to $q_1 \alpha^{n-1}$.

$$(3.25) \qquad \text{Var}(T) = \sum_{n=1}^{\infty} q_n(1 - q_n)$$

$$= \sum_{n=1}^{\infty} \left[\alpha^{n-1}q_1 - (\alpha^{n-1}q_1)^2 \right]$$

$$= q_1 \sum_{n=1}^{\infty} \alpha^{n-1} - q_1^2 \sum_{n=1}^{\infty} (\alpha^2)^{n-1}$$

$$= E(T) - \frac{q_1^2}{1 - \alpha^2}.$$

In the development above, we have substituted $E(T)$ for the sum of the q_n's. Also, we have interchanged the exponents, changing $(\alpha^{n-1})^2$ into $(\alpha^2)^{n-1}$, and then applying the standard method for summing a geometric series.

According to this model (see Eq. 3.25) the variance of total errors should always be less than the mean total errors. By contrast, the one-element model says (see Eq. 3.14) that $\text{Var}(T)$ is greater than $E(T)$ whenever $c < 0.5$. If $c = 1 - \alpha$ it is easily shown that $\text{Var}(T)$ for the linear model is always less than $\text{Var}(T)$ for the one-element model. Thus, prediction of $\text{Var}(T)$ in the data provides a differential test of the two models.

Mean Total Number of Error Runs

An error run was defined as a string of one or more successive errors followed by a correct response. Hence in an infinite sequence of trials the expected total number of error runs is equal to the expected number of response pairs consisting of an error followed by a correct response on the next trial. The probability that such a couplet occurs on trials n and $n + 1$ is $Pr(x_n = 1 \ \& \ x_{n+1} = 0)$, which equals $Pr(x_n = 1)Pr(x_{n+1} = 0)$, because the random variables are independent. We find the total error runs, $E(R)$, by summing this expression over n:

$$E(R) = \sum_{n=1}^{\infty} Pr(x_n = 1)Pr(x_{n+1} = 0) = \sum_{n=1}^{\infty} q_n(1 - q_{n+1}).$$

Substituting from Eqs. 3.24 and 3.22,

$$(3.26) \qquad E(R) = E(T) - \frac{\alpha q_1^2}{1 - \alpha^2}.$$

Note that the factor α in the numerator of the second term above distinguishes $E(R)$ from $\text{Var}(T)$.

"Autocorrelations" of Errors

As mentioned earlier, the statistic c_k is a count of the number of times an error is followed by an error k trials later, without regard to intervening responses. Our derivation is brief, because the method is essentially that explained in connection with the concept identification model. Letting $E(c_k)$ be the expected number of pairs of errors k trials apart in a single subject-item sequence, we have

$$(3.27) \qquad E(c_k) = \sum_{n=1}^{\infty} Pr(x_n = 1 \ \& \ x_{n+k} = 1)$$

$$= \sum_{n=1}^{\infty} q_n q_{n+k}$$

$$= \frac{q_1^2 \alpha^k}{1 - \alpha^2}.$$

Comparison of the Linear Model with Data and with the One-Element Model

Proceeding as we did with the one-element model, we first estimate the parameter α of the linear model from the observed mean total errors per subject-item. Then we substitute this estimate of α into the proper equations in the last section and obtain quantitative predictions for the error

Table 3.2   Comparison of One-element and Linear Models with Data

Statistic	One Element	Data	Single-Operator Linear
Var(T)	2.07	1.88	1.00
Mean number of errors before first success	0.749	0.785	0.705
Mean trial number of last error, $E(L)$	2.18	2.33	3.08
Var(L)	5.76	6.10	11.49
Total error runs, $E(R)$	0.975	0.966	1.162
Error runs of length 1	0.655	0.645	0.949
Error runs of length 2	0.215	0.221	0.144
Error runs of length 3	0.070	0.058	0.064
Error runs of length 4	0.023	0.024	0.005
Autocorrelation of errors			
one trial apart (c_1)	0.479	0.486	0.288
two trials apart (c_2)	0.310	0.292	0.195
three trials apart (c_3)	0.201	0.187	0.127
Alternations of success and failure	1.45	1.43	1.83
Probability of a success following an error	0.672	0.666	0.730

runs, variance in total errors, and "autocorrelations" of errors. Repeating Eq. 3.24,

$$E(T) = \frac{q_1}{1 - \alpha},$$

which is identical to Eq. 3.7 for $E(T)$ in the one-element model. We equate q_1 with $1 - g = 0.50$ since both denote the probability of a correct response prior to the first reinforcement. Hence c of the one-element model equals $1 - \alpha$ of the linear model, or $0.344 = 1 - \hat{\alpha}$, whence $\hat{\alpha} = 0.656$.

The predictions for Var(T), $E(R)$, and $E(c_k)$ were obtained by setting $q_1 = 0.500$ and $\alpha = 0.656$ in Eqs. 3.25, 3.26, and 3.27, respectively. Table 3.2 displays these predictions. To facilitate comparison, the corresponding values obtained from the one-element model also appear in Table 3.2. For the sake of completeness, the table also includes predictions for statistics that were not given in the preceding section (mean trial number of last error, etc.). The numerical values for these statistics were taken from Bower's article.

Table 3.2 reveals that the fit to the data is not as good for the linear model as the one-element model. The latter is closer to the data in 14 of the 15 predictions. Contrary to the linear model, the observed variance in total errors exceeds the observed mean total errors. In other words, the amount of inter-sequence variability in total errors exceeds that predicted.* Consistent with this finding is the fact that within a sequence the linear model predicts too many short runs of errors and too many alternations of successes and failures while predicting too few error pairs k trials apart ("autocorrelations" with lag k). In passing, we note then whenever $c = 1 - \alpha$, the predicted "autocorrelations" are lower for the linear model than for the one-element model, regardless of the values of α and k. A major discrepancy is that the linear model overshoots the observed mean and variance of L, the trial number of last error. Intuitively, we might explain the deviation from the observed mean trial of last error in terms of the overall failure of the linear model; namely, the model predicts too many alternations of correct responses and errors. Some of this alternation would occur after a string of correct responses, thereby postponing the trial of last error. A rough diagnosis of the failure of the linear model throughout Table 3.2 would be as follows: by postulating that the response random variables are independent of one another, the model is forced to predict too much response fluctuation within a single sequence.

In summary, then, the one-element model provides a good account of the statistical properties of these data, whereas the single-operator linear model is less adequate.

3.5 FURTHER DEVELOPMENTS

The story on models for paired-associate learning does not end here. After several impressive successes of the one-element model in fitting data, extensive experimental efforts were undertaken by a number of investigators in an attempt to devise more stringent tests of the model and to apply it to different types of paired-associate experiments. As was perhaps

---

* One might be tempted to rationalize the shortcoming of the linear model by saying that the fit suggests the subjects actually were not homogeneous, and hence data from different subjects (or items) should not have been pooled. On the other hand, the extra assumption of heterogeneity is not needed to describe the data with the one-element model.

to be expected, in very short order experiments appeared that gave results contrary to the predictions of the one-element model. Thus it soon became clear that the simple model was not valid for a wide range of paired-associate experiments. Still, some corroborating evidence continued to come in along with the negative findings. At present writing, a challenging task confronting the theorist is (1) to identify those experimental conditions where the one-element model works, and those where it does not, and (2) to construct a more general model which essentially reduces to the one-element model in the former cases but accounts for the discrepancies in the latter cases.

It is instructive to examine the kinds of discrepancies between the one-element model and recent data that are not accounted for by the model. Upon qualitative inspection, the discrepancies suggest that changes in performance may be a gradual, or incremental, or piecemeal process rather than having the strict all-or-none, "on-off" character envisaged by the one-element model. The major discrepancy, which goes directly to the core assumption of the one-element model, is that performance may improve over trials prior to the last error. Evidence to this effect has come from some experiments in which backward learning curves or Vincent curves were calculated (Suppes and Ginsberg, 1963). As noted at the end of Sec. 3.3, the one-element model predicts that for a given subject-item sequence the probability of an error should be constant over trials prior to the last error in that sequence. However, in certain experiments the observed proportion of errors decreased significantly over trials prior to the last error.

From these data we may conclude that the occurrence of an error somewhere in training does not guarantee (as the one-element model says it should) that the subject has learned nothing up to that point; an error does not have the properties of a recurrent event.* From this fundamental discrepancy (that is, lack of stationarity) a number of related flaws are implied and found. Thus, it is sometimes observed that the conditional probability of a success following an error on trial n increases with n rather than staying constant. Too, the variances of total errors and trial of last error are sometimes appreciably smaller than predicted by the one-element model.

How might one account for this lack of stationarity prior to the last error in paired-associate data? One strategy is to try retaining the basic structure of the one-element model, but to modify one or more of its

---

* An event Z is defined as recurrent if the occurrence of Z on trial n "resets" the process so that the sequence of events thereafter forms an independent replication of the sequence for trials 1 to n.

assumptions. We shall mention one modification of the response axioms which deserves some consideration. The alteration is with regard to the assumption that the subject has a constant probability g of guessing correctly when in state $\bar{C}$. Retaining the all-or-none conditioning axiom, we may tentatively assume that the probability of guessing correctly on unlearned items improves over trials. Let g_n be the average probability of a correct guess if the subject is in $\bar{C}$ on trial n. It is not difficult to conceive of several schemes that would produce increases in g_n. To take the simplest case, suppose there are 8 stimulus items paired in one-to-one correspondence to the first 8 integers as responses. We might suppose that once a given response is associated to its proper stimulus, that response is no longer given to other stimuli. Thus, as more items are learned, the subject guesses from a progressively smaller response pool, resulting in an increase in the probability of a correct guess on unlearned items. Hence, nonstationarity will result prior to the last error. Because g_n is related to the number of learned items on trial n, and the latter is directly related to the learning parameter c, an explicit expression can be derived relating g_n to n, c, and the number of responses. It is also a relatively simple matter to apply this improved-guessing scheme to cases in which there are many stimuli but few responses (for example, 16 stimuli and 4 responses), although we shall not work through the derivation here. The basic idea is the plausible assumption that the subject keeps some rough count of how many times a particular response occurs to a list of stimuli, and then uses this knowledge to strategic advantage. This simple modification would also account, at least qualitatively, for the main discrepancies from the one-element model.

An alternative proposal for accommodating nonstationarity and related phenomena is to maintain the guessing axiom of the one-element model but to postulate a more complicated conditioning process. One such possibility, which has been developed (Atkinson and Crothers, 1964), gave generally accurate fits to paired-associate learning data. Central to this model is the distinction between long- and short-term memory states. It would take us too far afield to spell out the model in greater detail here.

Our purpose in discussing these two modifications is to illustrate to the reader how theorists can revise their ideas when confronted with data disconfirming parts of a theory. Provided they are carried out with due regard to testable consequences, such modifications are an entirely justifiable and legitimate step in the theoretical enterprise. In many areas, good theories usually evolve by a series of successive approximations. To be sure, such successive approximations do not fit with the common notion that scientific creativity involves radically novel insights with vast repercussions, arrived at with attendant shouts of "Eureka." But if the truth be known, a major portion of the creative moments in science are concerned with modifying existing theories to fit new discrepant facts.

In the final section we shall examine a model from which the one-element and single-operator linear models may be derived as special cases. The fact that we terminate the chapter with this more general model is not to say that we believe it to be the last word in theories of paired-associates learning. As indicated earlier, there are a number of promising models for this area of mathematical psychology, and the jury is still out on many of them. A sampling of the range of models may be seen in the Atkinson and Crothers (1964) article. Among the versions reported there are Markov models with three states, models which combine all-or-none and linear processes, and "long-short" retention models which assume forgetting between successive presentations of the same item. This increase in the number of available models should not be cause for dismay, because although we cannot at present single out the one "best" model, the data do appear to indicate that certain versions are consistently more accurate than other seemingly plausible alternatives. Out of this collection we have selected, for the final section in this chapter, a model which is a compromise between all-or-none and linear processes. A pedagogic reason for concluding with this combination model is that it offers an opportunity for the reader to enhance his competence in handling certain novel derivational techniques.

*3.6   THE RANDOM-TRIAL INCREMENTS MODEL

We wish to examine a paired-associate model first proposed by Norman (1964 a), called the "random-trial increments" or RTI model. Discussion of this model is an appropriate ending to this chapter because, as noted above, the RTI model represents essentially a combination of the one-element and linear models discussed previously. The RTI model typifies a general model from which, by appropriate choice of two parameters, we can obtain either the one-element model, the single-operator linear model, or a quasi-mixture of the two. Since much data seems to fall in between the one-element model and the linear model, the mixture dictated by the RTI model often appears to be a good bet for fitting much of these data. Indeed, Norman (1964 a) and Atkinson and Crothers (1964), found that the RTI model did a good job of predicting data that contraindicated the one-element and linear models.

As in previous models for paired-associate learning, the RTI model is written for an individual subject-item sequence. Again, we let q_n

---

* This section treats a special topic and may be omitted at first reading.

be the error probability on trial n for a particular subject-item sequence. First, we introduce an unobservable event, called an "effective reinforcement." We introduce a corresponding random variable, y_n, which will equal one if an effective reinforcement occurs on trial n for this particular subject-item sequence, and will equal zero if trial n yields an ineffective reinforcement. We let c represent the probability that an effective reinforcement occurs on any trial n; thus

$$y_n = \begin{cases} 1, \text{ with probability } c \\ 0; \text{ with probability } 1-c. \end{cases}$$

The main axiom of the RTI model is stated in the form of a difference equation. Let α be between zero and one; then the axiom is

(3.28) $q_{n+1} = \alpha^{y_n} q_n.$

This type of difference equation is probably unfamiliar to the reader, so let us spell out its implications. Equation 3.28 is really a compact way of writing either of two possible equations. The two equations are obtained by setting the random variable y_n equal to one and zero, respectively, thus making the multiplier of q_n either α^1 or α^0. Thence Eq. 3.28 could be rewritten as follows:

$$q_{n+1} = \begin{cases} \alpha q_n, \text{ with probability } c \\ q_n, \text{ with probability } 1-c. \end{cases}$$

We see that with probability c, a decrease in the error probability occurred as specified by the linear model. However, with probability $1-c$, the nth trial was ineffective, and no learning occurred (that is, $q_{n+1} = q_n$). With these notions at hand, we are better able to understand the meaning of the phrase "effective reinforcement"—it is some event that produces learning. For example, we might conjecture that an effective reinforcement occurs in paired-associate learning every time the subject attends to an item and rehearses it or tries to construct a mnemonic code for recalling it. For the moment, however, we shall not pursue possible identifications of y_n and c.

The reason for the name "random-trial increments" model may be seen by reference to Fig. 3.8. This figure displays a graph of the changes in error probability over trials for a hypothetical subject learning according to Eq. 3.28. For this illustration, q_1 is 1.0, α is 0.6, and c is 0.33. We see that this individual's learning curve is a series of steps or successively lower plateaus. The q-values of the successive plateaus are q_1, αq_1, $\alpha^2 q_1$, and so forth, on down to $\alpha^n q_1$, approaching zero. Each step down occurs after an effective reinforcement. Between the steps, the plateaus marked 1, 2, and 3 represent trials when reinforcements were ineffective; q did not change on these trials. The length or duration of each plateau is a random variable, representing the number of trials intervening between one occasion when $y = 1$ and the next such occasion. Because the event $y = 1$ is

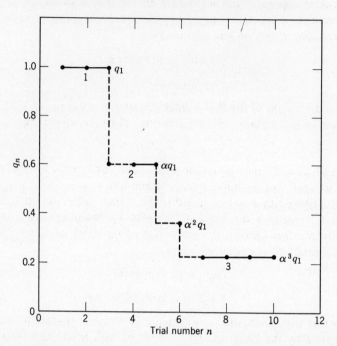

Fig. 3.8 Learning curve for a hypothetical item, computed from the RTI model with $q_1 = 1.0$, $\alpha = 0.6$, and $c = 0.33$.

assumed to have a constant probability c of occurring each trial, the length in trials of each plateau has the geometric distribution given by

$$Pr(\text{plateau } j \text{ trials long}) = c(1 - c)^{j-1}, \qquad (\text{for } j \geqslant 1).$$

This is the distribution of the number of trials separating decrements in q, or increments in $p = 1 - q$. Whence comes the name "random-trial increments" model.

The two parameters of the RTI model are c and α. Consider the case when $c = 1$ so that an effective reinforcement occurs on every trial. In this case, q_n is always transformed into αq_n to obtain q_{n+1}, yielding the single-operator linear model. Now consider the case when $c < 1$ and $\alpha = 0$. When $\alpha = 0$, the error probability is reduced to zero with the first effective reinforcement. Prior to the first effective reinforcement, performance remains stationary at the initial plateau of q_1. This one-step case, of course, is the one-element model. Thus, by appropriate choice of c and α, one obtains either the single-operator linear model, or the one-element model, or a hybrid falling between these extreme prototypes. We shall not attempt an extensive mathematical analysis of the RTI model here; interested readers should consult Norman's paper (1964 a). However, as a didactic device, we shall derive several theoretical expressions.

Distributions of Response Probabilities

Suppose we were to start off a thousand identical subjects on trial 1 with the same q_1 value and the same values of α and c and we let the process specified in Eq. 3.28 run for n trials. We ask, what values of response probability will these various individuals have on trial n? It should be clear that not all subjects will have the same q-value on trial n. They will not because for a particular subject the q-value at the beginning of trial n depends upon the number of effective reinforcements he has had on trials one through $n - 1$. The number of effective reinforcements in $n - 1$ trials is a random variable that depends on c. For convenience in the following, we define S_{n-1} to be the number of effective reinforcements prior to trial n for a particular subject-item sequence. Since $y_k = 1$ when an effective reinforcement occurs on trial k, S_{n-1} may be written as

$$S_{n-1} = \sum_{k=1}^{n-1} y_k.$$

Now y_k takes on a value of one with probability c, so the variable S_{n-1} will have the binomial distribution

$$(3.29) \qquad Pr(S_{n-1} = v) = \binom{n-1}{v} c^v (1 - c)^{n-1-v} \qquad \text{(for } v \geqslant 0).$$

For convenient reference later, the reader should note that $Pr(S_{n-1} = v)$ is the vth term in the binomial expansion of $[(1 - c) + c]^{n-1}$, where the initial term $(1 - c)^{n-1}$ corresponds to $v = 0$.

With the results on S_{n-1} in hand, let us return to our initial question: what proportions of the subjects have what q-values on trial n? The possible values of q_n are q_1, αq_1, $\alpha^2 q_1$, ..., or $\alpha^{n-1} q_1$, representing cases of 0, 1, 2, ..., or $n - 1$ effective reinforcements, respectively, in the first $n - 1$ trials prior to trial n when q_n is to be determined. Since the probability distribution of S_{n-1} has been determined in Eq. 3.29, it provides a direct way to determine the expected proportion of subjects located at any particular value of q on trial n. The relation is

$$(3.30) \qquad Pr(q\text{-value on trial } n \text{ is } \alpha^v q_1) = Pr(S_{n-1} = v).$$

Let us pause to examine some of the concepts that have been introduced. Because S_{n-1} is a random variable determining q_n, we see that q_n is also a random variable. The random variable q_n has possible values of $\alpha^v q_1$ for $v = 0, 1, \ldots, n - 1$. Whenever we wish to denote a specific one of these values we will use the symbol $q_{v,n}$. Thus, we have a *distribution of response probabilities* (q-values) on trial n; the distribution function is given by Eq. 3.30.

Moments of the q_n Distribution

Important information about a probability distribution is given by its raw moments. These occur in later derivations for the RTI model, and therefore, they must be dealt with now. We let $V_{r,n}$ denote the rth raw moment of the distribution of q-values on trial n. By definition

$$V_{r,n} = \sum_v q_{v,n}^r Pr(S_{n-1} = v).$$

That is, we take each possible value of q_n, raise it to the rth power, weight that by the probability of that particular q-value, and sum over all possible values. The first raw moment, $V_{1,n}$, represents the average q-value on trial n and is to be compared with the observed mean error probability on trial n. The higher moments, $V_{2,n}$, $V_{3,n}$, etc., occur in deriving theoretical expressions for joint response probabilities involving two trials, three trials, and so forth.

For the RTI model, it is possible to derive an explicit expression for $V_{r,n}$. This can be done by two different techniques: the first uses the distribution function of Eq. 3.30 to obtain $V_{r,n}$ directly; the second method involves solving a difference equation relating $V_{r,n}$ to $V_{r,n-1}$. This latter method is generally applicable when one either does not know the distribution of q-values or wishes to bypass them altogether (see Sec. 5.4 for an illustration).

First, we derive $V_{r,n}$ by the direct method, using the fact that q-values on trial n have the binomial distribution imposed by Eqs. 3.29 and 3.30. We begin with the definition.

(3.31) $$V_{r,n} = \sum_v q_{v,n}^r Pr(S_{n-1} = v).$$

Now we substitute $q_{v,n} = \alpha^v q_1$ and the binomial distribution values of Eq. 3.29 for $Pr(S_{n-1} = v)$, to obtain

$$V_{r,n} = \sum_{v=0}^{n-1} (\alpha^v q_1)^r \binom{n-1}{v} c^v (1 - c)^{n-1-v}.$$

This equation can be rearranged as follows:

$$V_{r,n} = q_1^r \sum_{v=0}^{n-1} \binom{n-1}{v} (\alpha^r c)^v (1 - c)^{n-1-v}.$$

Finally, we note that the terms of the sum above are those from the binomial expansion of $[(\alpha^r c) + (1 - c)]^{n-1}$. Thus,

$$(3.32) \qquad V_{r,n} = (\alpha^r c + 1 - c)^{n-1} q_1^r.$$

We defer discussion of this expression for $V_{r,n}$ until the alternative method of derivation has been illustrated.

Our alternative method begins by trying to discover a recursion or trial-by-trial transformation that takes $V_{r,n-1}$ into $V_{r,n}$. Consider that proportion of the subjects who, on trial $n - 1$, have a q-value of $q_{v,n-1}$. This proportion of subjects is denoted as $Pr(S_{n-2} = v)$. Now consider what q-values these subjects will have on trial n. A proportion $cPr(S_{n-2} = v)$ will have a q-value of $\alpha q_{v,n-1}$ on trial n, whereas a proportion $(1 - c)Pr(S_{n-2} = v)$ will have the same q-value as before, namely, $q_{v,n-1}$. Consider now the calculation of the rth moment on trial n. It may be written as follows:

$$V_{r,n} = \sum_v (\alpha q_{v,n-1})^r cPr(S_{n-2} = v) + \sum_v (q_{v,n-1})^r (1 - c)Pr(S_{n-2} = v).$$

What we have done here is to take the rth power of the possible q-values that developed from $q_{v,n-1}$ and weight these by their probability of occurrence, namely, c or $1 - c$. Finally, these are summed over all possible q-values on trial $n - 1$. The equation above can be simplified to yield

$$V_{r,n} = [\alpha^r c + (1 - c)] \sum_v q_{v,n-1}^r Pr(S_{n-2} = v).$$

Now the term in the righthand summation has already been defined; it is $V_{r,n-1}$, the rth raw moment on trial $n - 1$. Making this substitution, we arrive at the following interim result:

$$(3.33) \qquad V_{r,n} = (\alpha^r c + 1 - c)V_{r,n-1}.$$

Equation 3.33 is a linear difference equation of the same type encountered earlier in this chapter and also in Chapter 2. The successive values $V_{r,1}, V_{r,2}, V_{r,3}, \ldots,$ are generated by the simple device of multiplying the nth one by a constant $(\alpha^r c + 1 - c)$ to obtain the $(n + 1)$st one. The solution to this difference equation is

$$V_{r,n} = (\alpha^r c + 1 - c)^{n-1} V_{r,1}.$$

Now $V_{r,1}$ is the rth raw moment on trial 1. By assumption, all subjects begin on trial one at the same q-value of q_1. Hence, $V_{r,1}$ is equal to q_1^r. Thus, our final expression is

$$(3.34) \qquad V_{r,n} = (\alpha^r c + 1 - c)^{n-1} q_1^r.$$

The reader will note that this agrees with the result in Eq. 3.32 obtained by direct calculation from the distribution of q_n.

We comment briefly upon this expression for $V_{r,n}$. First, note that moments of higher order r decrease with increasing r; this simply reflects the fact that q_1^r decreases as r increases. Second, we note that for $\alpha < 1$ and $c > 0$, all moments decrease with trials to an asymptote of zero, representing eventual perfect learning for all subject-item sequences. Third, consider the first raw moment

$$(3.35) \qquad V_{1,n} = (\alpha c + 1 - c)^{n-1} q_1.$$

This is the expression for the average error probability on trial n and would be compared to the observed mean learning curve. The mean learning curve for the RTI model is thus an exponential decay function of trials. We note that if $c = 1$, then we obtain the expression for the single-operator linear model (Eq. 3.22), whereas if $\alpha = 0$, we obtain the mean learning curve for the one-element model. Finally, if $c = 0$ so that no effective reinforcements occur, then no learning occurs and the mean error probability remains at its initial value q_1.

Conditional Error Probabilities

From the RTI model we wish to derive an expression for the conditional probability of an error on trial $n + 1$, given an error on trial n. Employing our previous notation that $x_n = 1$ for an error on trial n, we may write this conditional probability as

$$(3.36) \qquad Pr(x_{n+1} = 1 \mid x_n = 1) = \frac{Pr(x_n = 1 \ \& \ x_{n+1} = 1)}{Pr(x_n = 1)}.$$

The term in the denominator is simply the probability of an error on trial n, which is $V_{1,n}$ given in Eq. 3.35. We concentrate upon deriving an expression for the numerator, the joint probability of errors on trials n and $n + 1$. To do this, we return to consideration of the distribution of q_n-values, and that proportion of the subjects who have a specific value called $q_{v,n}$. Recall that the probability that a subject has this particular value, $q_{v,n}$, has been called $Pr(S_{n-1} = v)$. Let us draw out a two-trial tree diagram to represent what happens to this branch (see Fig. 3.9). Since we are interested only in those cases where errors occur on trials n and $n + 1$, we do not bother to fill in the tree following a correct response on trial n. The branches of interest to us are the first and the third, since those are the only ones with errors on trials n and $n + 1$. The probabilities of these branches in the overall history of the experiment are

$$Pr(\text{first branch}) = Pr(S_{n-1} = v) q_{v,n} c \alpha q_{v,n}$$

$$Pr(\text{third branch}) = Pr(S_{n-1} = v) q_{v,n} (1 - c) q_{v,n}.$$

By summing these two quantities we obtain the probability that a subject has value $q_{v,n}$ on trial n and also makes an error on both trials n and $n + 1$.

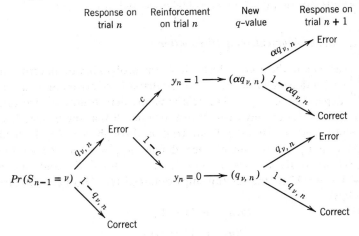

Fig. 3.9   Tree diagram for computing $Pr(x_n = 1 \,\&\, x_{n+1} = 1)$.

To find the overall probability of errors on trials n and $n + 1$, we sum over all possible values of $q_{v,n}$:

$$Pr(x_n = 1 \,\&\, x_{n+1} = 1)$$
$$= \sum_v c\alpha q_{v,n}^2 Pr(S_{n-1} = v) + \sum_v (1 - c)q_{v,n}^2 Pr(S_{n-1} = v).$$

This equation can be simplified to the form

$$(3.37) \qquad Pr(x_n = 1 \,\&\, x_{n+1} = 1) = (\alpha c + 1 - c)V_{2,n}.$$

Thus, we find that the joint probability of errors on trials n and $n + 1$ is directly related to the second moment of the q-distribution on trial n. Using this result in conjunction with Eqs. 3.34 and 3.36 yields

$$Pr(x_{n+1} = 1 \mid x_n = 1) = (\alpha c + 1 - c)\frac{V_{2,n}}{V_{1,n}}$$
$$= (\alpha c + 1 - c)\frac{(\alpha^2 c + 1 - c)^{n-1}q_1^2}{(\alpha c + 1 - c)^{n-1}q_1}$$
$$= V_{1,2}\gamma^{n-1},$$

where

$$\gamma = \frac{\alpha^2 c + 1 - c}{\alpha c + 1 - c}.$$

We note that γ is a fraction less than one (unless $\alpha = 0$ or $c = 0$), so that the conditional probability of another error decreases with trials. By taking $\alpha = 0$, γ becomes one, and the prediction of the one-element model, that $Pr(x_{n+1} = 1 \mid x_n = 1)$ is constant independent of n, is obtained. This result for the one-element model appeared in Eq. 3.17.

Use of Higher Moments of q-Distribution

As was seen in the above illustrations, the probability of an error on the single trial n depended on $V_{1,n}$. The probability of errors on trials n and $n + 1$ depended on $V_{2,n}$. The relationships here follow a nice orderly relation; the reader may easily prove for himself that the probability of j consecutive errors running from trial n through $n + j - 1$ inclusive depends on $V_{j,n}$. For convenience, define "$u_{j,n} = 1$" as the joint event "errors on trials n, $n + 1$, $n + 2$, ..., $n + j - 1$" and let $b_j = \alpha^j c + 1 - c$. Then the relationships obtained (cf. Norman, 1964 a) are as follows:

$$Pr(u_{1,n} = 1) = V_{1,n}$$
$$Pr(u_{2,n} = 1) = b_1 V_{2,n}$$
$$Pr(u_{3,n} = 1) = b_1 b_2 V_{3,n}$$
$$Pr(u_{4,n} = 1) = b_1 b_2 b_3 V_{4,n}.$$

We may write the general expression for $Pr(u_{j,n} = 1)$ as

$$(3.38) \qquad Pr(u_{j,n} = 1) = \left(\prod_{i=1}^{j-1} b_i \right) V_{j,n}.$$

As noted in Chapter 2, the symbol $\prod$ is an abbreviation for a product. In the present case, the factor in parentheses in the last equation is equivalent to $b_1 b_2 b_3 \cdots b_{j-1}$.

Suppose now we are interested in finding the mean number of times a j-tuple of errors occurs over the entire course of the experiment. We define u_j as this sum over all trials. The following manipulations suffice to calculate the expected value of u_j.

$$E(u_j) = \sum_{n=1}^{\infty} Pr(u_{j,n} = 1)$$
$$= \sum_{n=1}^{\infty} \left(\prod_{i=1}^{j-1} b_i \right) b_j^{n-1} q_1^j.$$

The second line of the derivation comes from using Eq. 3.34 and the definition of b_j to replace the $V_{j,n}$ in Eq. 3.38. Moving the product term outside the summation sign and summing:

$$(3.39) \qquad E(u_j) = \frac{q_1^j}{1 - b_j} \left(\prod_{i=1}^{j-1} b_i \right).$$

Despite the cumbersome appearance of this equation, the expected numbers of j-tuples of errors are easy to calculate once c and α have been estimated.

The result above for $Pr(u_{k,n} = 1)$ can be used to calculate the distribution of errors before the first correct response if $n = 1$. Let $J = 0, 1, 2, \ldots$ represent the errors before the first success. The following relation may be seen to obtain between various event probabilities:

$$Pr(x_1 = 1 \cdots x_k = 1) = Pr(x_1 = 1 \cdots x_k = 1 \,\&\, x_{k+1} = 1)$$
$$+ Pr(x_1 = 1 \cdots x_k = 1 \,\&\, x_{k+1} = 0),$$

or

$$Pr(u_{k,1} = 1) = Pr(u_{k+1,1} = 1) + Pr(J = k).$$

From this latter relationship, we obtain the result

$$(3.40) \qquad Pr(J = k) = q_1^k \prod_{i=1}^{k-1} b_i - q_1^{k+1} \prod_{i=1}^{k} b_i$$

$$= q_1^k \left(\prod_{i=1}^{k-1} b_i \right)(1 - q_1 b_k) \qquad \text{(for } k \geq 1\text{).}$$

For $k = 1$, the product $\prod_{i=1}^{0} b_i$ is defined to be 1. For $k = 0$, $Pr(J = 0)$ is just $1 - q_1$, the likelihood of a success on trial 1. This relationship will be used later in fitting the RTI model to data.

Parameter Estimates

We shall use $E(u_1)$ and $E(u_2)$ to estimate the parameters c and α of the RTI model. The former quantities are calculated under the assumption that subjects are run to a strict learning criterion (effectively an infinite number of trials). The starting value q_1 is presumed to be known; in applications to date, q_1 has been set equal to $\left(1 - \dfrac{1}{r}\right)$, where r is the number of response alternatives available for guessing. We note that $E(u_1)$ is just the expected total number of errors, whereas $E(u_2)$ is the mean number of pairs of errors on adjacent trials. Utilizing the general expression in Eq. 3.39, we find the theoretical expressions are

$$(3.41) \qquad \begin{aligned} E(u_1) &= \frac{q_1}{1 - b_1} = \frac{q_1}{c(1 - \alpha)} \\[2ex] E(u_2) &= \frac{q_1^2 b_1}{1 - b_2} = \frac{q_1^2(\alpha c + 1 - c)}{c(1 - \alpha^2)}. \end{aligned}$$

Now we employ the "method of moments" to estimate α and c. The idea is to choose $\hat{\alpha}$ and $\hat{c}$ so that $E(u_1)$ and $E(u_2)$ are identical to the corresponding observed quantities. That is, we assume that $E(u_1)$, the unknown first moment of the distribution of u_1, equals the observed mean total errors (call the latter $\bar{u}_1$). Likewise, we assume that the unknown first moment $E(u_2)$ is exactly equal to the observed mean number of error 2-tuples (call this $\bar{u}_2$). These assumptions allow us to replace $E(u_1)$ and $E(u_2)$ in Eqs. 3.41 by $\bar{u}_1$ and $\bar{u}_2$. After these substitutions are made and assuming a known value of q_1, we have two equations in two unknowns. Hence, there is only one value of α and one value of c such that both equations are satisfied simultaneously. This particular pair is denoted $\hat{\alpha}$, $\hat{c}$, the moments estimates from $E(u_1)$ and $E(u_2)$. Note that the estimates refer to moments of particular distributions. If we had used first moments of other distributions, say, $E(R)$ and $E(L)$, then the corresponding moments estimates $\hat{\alpha}$, $\hat{c}$ would differ numerically from those obtained with $E(u_1)$ and $E(u_2)$. By some algebraic manipulation of the two expressions in Eq. 3.41, we arrive at the following estimators:

$$\hat{\alpha} = q_1 \frac{(\bar{u}_1 - q_1)}{\bar{u}_2} - 1,$$

(3.42)

$$\hat{c} = \frac{q_1}{(1 - \hat{\alpha})\bar{u}_1}.$$

Some Further Paired-Associate Data

We shall consider another set of paired-associate data to see how well the RTI model rectifies discrepancies between the data and the one-element model and between the data and the linear model. These data are described in Norman's paper, and were taken from an unpublished experiment by Suppes and Schlag-Rey. Forty college students received 25 training trials on a list of 12 paired associates. The stimuli were nonsense syllables; the response for each was a depression of one of three keys available before the subject. Each response key was assigned as correct to a random 4 of the 12 stimuli for each subject. Following the subject's response to a stimulus, the correct answer was designated by briefly lighting a lamp above the correct key. Four seconds later, the next stimulus in the series was presented. In the following, all the $40 \times 12 = 480$ subject-item sequences are pooled for analysis. Further, since error probabilities were practically zero after trial 18, we assume that the data from the fixed 25-trial series closely approximate what would have been obtained in an infinite-trial experiment.

First, we note the types of discrepant predictions that the one-element and single-operator linear models deliver for these data. The basic learning parameter of each model, c or α, can be estimated from the mean errors per sequence, which was 3.256. We assume that $q_1 = 0.667$, since there were three response alternatives. The estimates are $c = 0.205$ for the one-element model, and $\alpha = 1 - c = 0.795$ for the linear model (cf. Eqs. 3.7 and 3.24). Both models predict the same mean learning curve, namely,

$$q_n = q_1 \alpha^{n-1} = 0.667(0.795)^{n-1},$$

and these predictions are compared to the data from the first 13 trials in Table 3.3. It may be seen that the predicted q_n values fall fairly close to the observed values, except for the point at trial 2.

Table 3.3   Comparison of Data with Mean Learning Curves Predicted by One-element, Linear, and RTI Models

Trial	Observed q_n	Predicted q_n
1	0.67	0.67
2	0.48	0.53
3	0.43	0.42
4	0.37	0.34
5	0.25	0.27
6	0.22	0.21
7	0.18	0.17
8	0.14	0.13
9	0.11	0.11
10	0.09	0.08
11	0.08	0.07
12	0.05	0.05
13	0.03	0.04

Consider now two predictions from the single-operator linear model, the variance of total errors (Eq. 3.25) and the mean number of pairs of errors on adjacent trials, called u_2 or c_1 (Eq. 3.27). With an estimate of $\alpha = 0.795$, the single-operator model predicts that $\text{Var}(T) = 2.04$. The observed value was 8.40, over four times the predicted value. Using Eq. 3.27 for c_1, the predicted mean number of consecutive pairs of errors per sequence is 0.96 whereas the observed mean was 1.48; the prediction is definitely too low. On the basis of this small sample of statistics, we can presume (correctly, as it happens) that the single-operator model will do a poor job in predicting these data.

Observe now how the one-element model fares with these data. First, with $c = 0.205$, the variance of total errors predicted by Eq. 3.14 is 9.51, which is larger than the observed variance of 8.40. The predicted number of consecutive pairs of errors is 1.73, which is also larger than the observed value of 1.48 for u_2. But the decisive fact for the one-element model is that the sequences of responses prior to the last error are not a stationary and independent series of Bernoulli observations. Rather, the probability of a correct response increases over trials before the last error, and during these trials the conditional probability of a success was significantly higher following a success than following an error. Also, the average number of errors following an error on trial n decreases with n, whereas the one-element model expects constancy in this statistic. Thus, the data clearly disconfirm the basic premise of the one-element model.

In the comparisons above, we saw that the one-element model overpredicted the data statistics u_2 and $\mathrm{Var}(T)$, whereas the single-operator model underpredicted them. Perhaps a mixture specified by the RTI model will come closer to the data. Assuming $q_1 = 0.667$, we estimate c and α for the RTI model, using mean total errors $[E(T)$ or $u_1]$, and mean pairs of errors $(u_2$ or $c_1)$. The estimators were given in Eq. 3.42. The observed values of $u_1 = 3.256$ and $u_2 = 1.481$ were inserted into Eq. 3.42 to obtain the estimates $\hat{c} = 0.245$ and $\hat{\alpha} = 0.166$.

These estimates for the RTI model are of interest because they tell us by how far the predictions of the RTI model deviate from those of the one-element model. Recall that a value of $\alpha = 0$ reduces the RTI model to the one-element model. In the present case, α is 0.166. After one effective reinforcement, the error probability is reduced to $0.667(0.166) = 0.111$; and after two reinforcements, to 0.018, which is negligibly different from zero.

We use the RTI model with the estimates $\hat{q}_1 = 0.667$, $\hat{\alpha} = 0.166$, and $\hat{c} = 0.245$ to predict a few statistics of this data. Consider first the mean learning curve, given in Table 3.3 above. The expression for the mean error probadility (Eq. 3.35) is reproduced here:

$$V_{1,n} = b_1^{n-1}q_1,$$

where $b_1 = \alpha c + 1 - c$. For our α and c estimates the value of b_1 is approximately 0.795. It will be noted that 0.795 was also the α (or $1 - c$) estimate used in predicting, from the two prototype models, the learning curve in Table 3.3. Hence, in this case the RTI model predicts the same mean curve as did the one-element and linear models in Table 3.3, and thus gives a tolerable fit to the data.

Next we predict the mean j-tuples of errors using Eq. 3.39 of the RTI model. The observed values of u_1 and u_2 have already been used for estimating α and c. So we predict u_3, u_4, u_5, and u_6. Note that since α is small in our case,

$$b_i = \alpha^i c + 1 - c$$

rapidly converges to $1 - c = 0.755$, so calculation of the b_i is simplified. The predicted values of u_3 through u_6 are given in Table 3.4 along with

Table 3.4   Comparison of Data with Mean Number of j-tuples Predicted by RTI Model

u_j	Expression	Predicted Value	Observed Value
u_3	$q_1^3 b_1 b_2/(1 - b_3)$	0.73	0.72
u_4	$q_1^4 b_1 b_2 b_3/(1 - b_4)$	0.37	0.35
u_5	$q_1^5 b_1 b_2 b_3 b_4/(1 - b_5)$	0.19	0.18
u_6	$q_1^6 b_1 \cdots b_5/(1 - b_6)$	0.09	0.10

the observed values. The predicted values follow the observed values closely.

Next we consider predictions of the distribution of J, the number of errors before the first success. We use Eq. 3.40 derived from the RTI

Table 3.5   Probability of k Errors Before the First Correct Response, Comparing Data with Predictions of the RTI Model

k	Observed	Predicted
0	0.33	0.33
1	0.33	0.31
2	0.15	0.17
3	0.08	0.09
4	0.05	0.04
5	0.02	0.02
≥ 6	0.03	0.02

model. A comparison of the predictions with the data is shown in Table 3.5. There it may be seen that the observed distribution of J is well approximated by the RTI predictions. This statistic, however, tends not to discriminate. For example, the reader can easily prove for himself that the predictions of the J distribution from the one-element model are practically the same (to two decimals) as those shown in Table 3.5 for the RTI model.

Finally, we use the RTI model to predict the variance of total errors, denoted Var(T). We let $E(T)$ be the mean total errors and $E(u_2)$ be the mean pairs of consecutive errors. The expression for Var(T) derived by Norman (1964 a) is

$$(3.43) \qquad \text{Var}(T) = E(T)\left[1 + \frac{2}{q_1} E(u_2) - E(T)\right].$$

We shall not attempt to sketch the derivation here; it is simple but lengthy. The reader may check that Eq. 3.43 is consistent with our prior expressions. Substitute for $E(T) = E(u_1)$ and $E(u_2)$ from Eq. 3.39 of the RTI model. Then setting $\alpha = 0$ yields Eq. 3.14, the Var(T) for the one-element model; setting $c = 1$ yields Eq. 3.25, the Var(T) for the single-operator model. For the present case $E(T) = 3.256$, $E(u_2) = 1.481$ and $q_1 = 0.667$; hence, the predicted Var(T) is 7.15, which is somewhat lower than the observed value of 8.40. We note, however, that Var(T) predicted by the RTI model falls in between the predictions of the one-element and single-operator models (9.51 and 2.04, respectively), as do the data.

In sum, the RTI model fits these data more adequately than do the one-element and single-operator prototypes. Necessarily, because of the nature of the RTI model, it logically could not do worse than the better of the two prototypes. In practice, of course, one would defer an evaluation of the RTI model until it had been compared to alternatives that are not special cases of it. Evidence to date from a number of studies indicates that the RTI model is one of the more promising formulations.

CHAPTER 4

CHOICE
BEHAVIOR

The notion of choice is a common theme running through psychology. The most typical experimental datum is response probability, which almost always involves, or can be conceived to involve, the choice by the subject of one out of a set of k alternatives. Because choice is an ubiquitous concept, there is some benefit in considering abstract models of choice behavior somewhat divorced from concrete experiments.

The usefulness of choice theories can be discussed from many points of view. One approach is illustrated in the behavior theory of Hull (1951) and Spence (1956). This theory pertains mainly to specifying variables that affect the strength of single responses; a choice theory is then invoked to predict the outcome of placing two or more responses into competition with one another. In actual practice, one almost never has a prior numerical estimate of the strength of a response, and the theory is used essentially as a measuring device. When we observe a particular pattern of choice probabilities among various subsets of responses, we use the theory to infer or estimate the strengths of the various responses; these strengths would, according to the theory, lead to the observed pattern of choice probabilities. According to this view, a choice theory is a testable set of ideas for measuring the strength (value, utility, attractiveness, etc.) of the various alternatives, and it is the latter values that are of principal interest.

A second point of view regards a choice theory as a device for suggesting a variety of "response-response" laws to summarize the data. These laws are expressed in terms of constraints upon the overall pattern of choice probabilities among various subsets of the k alternatives. A simple example of such a constraint is *weak stochastic transitivity*; if A is preferred to B and B is preferred to C, then there is better than an even chance that A will be preferred to C.

A third approach asks that a choice theory be a device for explaining various aspects of the subject's behavior during a single act of choice. There are several descriptors of an act of choice besides the obvious one specifying the alternative eventually chosen. These other descriptors include:

(1) vicarious trial-and-error behavior (VTE): instances of incipient starts and stops, orienting back and forth between the alternatives, etc.
(2) time to respond, or decision time
(3) the subject's expressed confidence in the correctness of his choice
(4) the difficulty he experiences in making the decision.

These terms describe various aspects of a subject's behavior either during or after a choice and are items that a useful choice theory should account for. Another descriptor that was not listed above involves a post-decision phenomenon. It is believed, for example, that following a difficult decision of importance to a person, he engages in thinking and re-evaluation that results in the chosen alternative becoming more highly valued and the unchosen alternative less highly valued than before the choice was made. This process is presumed to reduce any discomfort (dissonance) the person might have incurred in thinking he has made an unwise choice (Festinger, 1957; Brehm and Cohen, 1962). Such post-decision phenomena are beyond the scope of the choice models to be discussed here.

As indicated above, theories such as Hull's assume that each response alternative can be represented by a number denoting its strength and that the strength of a response increases when it is reinforced and decreases when it occurs and is not reinforced. Such theories require additional rules relating the hypothetical strengths of the various responses to the probability that a particular response will occur. In our discussion, the set of postulates relating the response strength variable to response probability will be called a choice theory. This chapter discusses several such theories; namely, Luce's choice axiom and a class of Markov chain models for choice behavior. These theories have been applied in the context of simple learning experiments, and they generalize readily to complex multiple choice situations.

Such choice theories are very closely related to theories of scaling (see Torgerson, 1958). The strength of a response may be called its "scale value" on some hypothetical scale; the system relating scale values to choice probabilities thus can be thought of as a measurement theory telling us how the hypothetical scale values may be estimated from a set of observed choice data. A variety of such scaling theories have been proposed (see Torgerson, 1958; Guilford, 1954; Coombs, 1964); some are relevant to a wide class of problems ranging over topics from psychophysics to attitude measurement to aesthetic judgments. We will not review these theories, since excellent accounts are available in the references cited. Rather, we restrict our account to a selected set of theories that (a) treat choice behavior as a probabilistic process, as opposed to a deterministic, algebraic process, and (b) have a natural interpretation when applied to learning situations.

Despite our emphasis on learning, it is recognized that often the simplest situation in which to test a choice theory is a static one where the underlying scale values are not changing over the series of tests used to estimate response probabilities. Thus, several of the experimental situations we use to illustrate predictions of the choice theories are presumed to be static; that is, for a fixed set of alternatives, the probability of choosing a particular one remains constant over successive trials. Also, the only situations considered here are those in which the subject is making a "preferential" choice. In experiments with humans, the subject is instructed to choose his preferred alternative (object, commodity, stimulus). With animals, preliminary training is required to teach them the outcomes (payoffs) associated with each response alternative; then his choice presumably will reflect his preference among the various payoffs.

4.1   THE PARADIGM FOR CHOICE EXPERIMENTS

The basic ingredients for a choice experiment are a set of k alternatives (stimuli, objects, commodities, responses, etc.) and a subject who chooses from the set. Suitable instructions or preliminary training is used to orient the subject's judgments with respect to the appropriate attribute of the k stimuli. In the experiment, the subject is presented repeatedly with various subsets of the k alternatives and asked to make a choice. There are $\binom{k}{2}$ subsets of two stimuli, $\binom{k}{3}$ subsets of three stimuli, etc., if the presentation order (spatial or temporal) within each subset is ignored. The experimenter prepares a particular presentation schedule, specifying which subset will be presented on each trial. Usually this schedule is determined by random selection (without replacement) from the subsets of interest. The datum recorded is, of course, the alternative selected by the subject when confronted with each presentation set. In a static choice situation, the models presume that the subject's choices over successive presentations are stochastically independent. In particular, this implies that the subject's choices are not influenced by the trial sequence in which the various presentation sets occur. Although stochastic independence is assumed, it is rarely tested by the experimenter. This brief characterization of choice experiments will suffice for our purposes here; a more complete description and classification system may be found in Bush, Galanter, and Luce (1963).

In the method of pair comparison, all possible pairs of the k alternatives are presented to the subject for his choice. There are

$$\binom{k}{2} = \frac{k(k-1)}{2}$$

such pairs. By replicating the experiment many times on a single subject, or over a population of subjects, we obtain a large enough sample to

Table 4.1   Preference Data for Car Color Combinations (Proportion of Times the Row Stimulus was chosen over the Column Stimulus)

	R	B	Y
R	—	0.71	0.89
B	0.29	—	0.73
Y	0.11	0.27	—

estimate reliably the proportion of times alternative i is chosen when the choice pair is (i, j). The data resulting from a pair-comparison experiment are summarized in an $n \times n$ matrix of choice proportions. Table 4.1 gives some illustrative data provided by W. K. Estes. One hundred and seventeen college students served in a mock consumer survey and were asked to indicate their preference for color combinations for automobiles. The color combinations compared were red-white (R), blue-gray (B), and yellow-black (Y). Each alternative was paired with the other two in single tests. The matrix in Table 4.1 gives the proportion of times the row stimulus was chosen over the column stimulus.

Two properties of a matrix of p_{ij} values should be noted. First, elements on the main diagonal are omitted since they correspond to comparing an alternative with itself. This comparison generally is not made unless one is interested in time-order or space-order errors in psychophysics (cf. Woodworth and Schlosberg, 1954 and Sec. 5.4); usually, the diagonal entries are arbitrarily set at $\frac{1}{2}$. The second feature to notice about the matrix in Table 4.1 is that complementary entries sum to one; that is,

$p_{ij} + p_{ji} = 1$. This means that all the entries below the main diagonal can be derived from the entries above the main diagonal. With k stimuli, there are $\dfrac{k(k-1)}{2}$ unordered pairs, so this quantity equals the number of independent entries, that is, the number of entries above the main diagonal.

One test of a choice theory is to see how well it predicts the p_{ij} data matrix after estimating some necessary parameters. These parameters are called scale values and correspond to the location of the stimuli or choice alternatives upon some psychologically meaningful continuum. In addition to reproducing the p_{ij} matrix, we may also ask that the theory make accurate predictions about the results of having the subject choose one of the three stimuli, or rank the three in order of preference, etc. The first theory to be discussed delivers these predictions, and they are usually quite accurate.

4.2 LUCE'S CHOICE AXIOM

The choice axiom proposed by Luce (1959*a*) is a simple but powerful assumption.* Because a substantial amount of data seems to support its

Table 4.2   Hypothetical Choice Data

Choice Proportions		Reduced Set		Normalized Proportions
a	0.50	a	0.50	$a' = 0.50/0.80 = 0.625$
b	0.30	b	0.30	$b' = 0.30/0.80 = 0.375$
c	0.20			
$a + b + c = 1.00$		$a + b = 0.80$		$a' + b' = 1.000$

predictions, the axiom is well worth investigating.

There are several equivalent versions of the axiom. Perhaps the most intuitive way to motivate it is with an example. Imagine that a subject repeatedly chooses one from among three alternatives a, b, c, and over trials his choice proportions are those given in the first column of Table 4.2. Suppose we now delete c, have the subject choose only between a and b, and we wish to predict his probability of choosing a over b. An intuitively sensible prediction scheme is as follows: delete alternative c and multiply the a and b percentages by a factor (1/0.80) which makes a' and b' add up to one. This procedure is referred to as "normalizing" the a and b scores.

---

* For pair-comparison data, Luce's model reduces to one proposed earlier by Bradley and Terry (1952).

This normalizing procedure is one version of Luce's choice axiom. The axiom refers to relationships among choice probabilities as we change the number of alternatives involved in the choice. In particular, the assumption is that the *ratio* of the likelihood of choosing *a* to the likelihood of choosing *b* is a constant irrespective of the number and composition of other alternatives in the set presented for choice. This is called the *constant ratio rule*. We can see that the example in Table 4.2 follows the constant ratio rule, since the ratio a'/b' is the same as the ratio a/b obtained when the third object *c* was present. We will now state the choice axiom more formally, so that we can study some of its consequences.

Statement and Derivation of Implications

For clarity of notation, we will let x, y, z, t, u denote alternatives, T denote the total set of alternatives, R denote some subset of T. Further, $Pr(x; R)$ will denote the probability that x is chosen when the choice is restricted to members of set R, and $Pr(x, y)$ denotes the probability that x is chosen when only x and y are presented.

The axiom may be stated as follows: let T be the set of alternatives $(x, y, z, t, u, \ldots)$ and let R be some appropriate subset of T containing alternative x, for example, $R = (x, y, z)$. Then Luce's axiom states that

(4.1) $$Pr(x; T) = Pr(R; T)Pr(x; R).$$

In words, Eq. 4.1 assumes that the probability that x is chosen from the entire set T is given by the product of (1) the likelihood that some element of R is chosen when all of T is presented, and (2) the probability of choosing x when the choice is restricted by presenting only members of the set R. It should be noted that $Pr(x; T)$ and $Pr(x; R)$ come from two different empirical observations; the former involves presentations of the whole set T, and the latter, presentations of the reduced set R. Luce's axiom makes a directly testable prediction about the relationship that should be found among these probabilities. Let us now use Eq. 4.1 to prove some of the equivalent forms of Luce's axiom.

(i) *The constant ratio rule:* Let T be a larger set containing x and y. Then

(4.2) $$\frac{Pr(x, y)}{Pr(y, x)} = \frac{Pr(x; T)}{Pr(y; T)}.$$

The proof of Eq. 4.2 follows directly from Luce's axiom by defining R to be the set $R = (x, y)$. Then, by Eq. 4.1,

$$Pr(x; T) = Pr(x, y) \cdot Pr(\{x, y\}; T)$$
$$Pr(y; T) = Pr(y, x) \cdot Pr(\{x, y\}; T).$$

By taking the ratio of lines 1 and 2, the result in Eq. 4.2 follows. Equation 4.2 tells us that the ratio of the proportion of x choices to the proportion of y choices is independent of what other elements, and how many, are in T.

(ii) *Relation of pairwise choices to choices from larger sets:* Define $Pr(x, x) = \frac{1}{2}$. Then

(4.3)
$$Pr(x; T) = \frac{1}{\sum\limits_{y} \dfrac{Pr(y, x)}{Pr(x, y)}},$$

where the sum is over all y in T. Proof of Eq. 4.3 makes use of the constant ratio result above. There we found that

$$\frac{Pr(y, x)}{Pr(x, y)} = \frac{Pr(y; T)}{Pr(x; T)}.$$

Substituting this result into Eq. 4.3 yields

$$Pr(x; T) = \frac{1}{\sum\limits_{y} \dfrac{Pr(y; T)}{Pr(x; T)}} = \frac{Pr(x; T)}{\sum\limits_{y} Pr(y; T)}.$$

The sum over all y of $Pr(y; T)$ is one; hence, we have verified Eq. 4.3. This theorem exhibits the assumption that the pairwise choices, $Pr(x, y)$, give sufficient information to account for choices from all larger sets of three or more alternatives.

(iii) *Defining the* v-*scale:* Choose any arbitrary element a of T. Then define the strength of x, denoted by $v(x)$, as

(4.4)
$$v(x) = \frac{Pr(x, a)}{Pr(a, x)} = \frac{Pr(x; T)}{Pr(a; T)}.$$

The v-values so defined turn out to have some very useful properties. The first property is stated below:

(4.5)
$$\frac{v(x)}{v(y)} = \frac{Pr(x, y)}{Pr(y, x)}.$$

We prove Eq. 4.5 by construction. By using Eq. 4.4,

$$\frac{v(x)}{v(y)} = \frac{Pr(x; T)}{Pr(a; T)} \cdot \frac{Pr(a; T)}{Pr(y; T)} = \frac{Pr(x; T)}{Pr(y; T)} = \frac{Pr(x, y)}{Pr(y, x)}.$$

Going from the second term to the third term involves cancellation; the last equality comes from the constant ratio rule. We may then use the result of Eq. 4.5 to rewrite Eq. 4.3 as follows:

$$(4.6) \qquad Pr(x; T) = \cfrac{1}{\sum\limits_{y} \cfrac{Pr(y, x)}{Pr(x, y)}} = \cfrac{1}{\sum\limits_{y} \cfrac{v(y)}{v(x)}} = \cfrac{v(x)}{\sum\limits_{y} v(y)} .$$

From Eq. 4.6 we observe the following: if a set of choice probabilities conform to the implications of Luce's axiom, then we can assign numbers $v(x)$ to the alternatives in a manner such that these numbers reflect the choice probabilities and are unique except for multiplication by a positive constant. That is, the v's form what is called a "ratio scale" of measurement.

To prove this last point regarding the uniqueness of the assigned v-values, recall that $v(x)$ was defined relative to an arbitrary element a of the set T. Suppose we were to define new scale values, $v'(x)$, with respect to a different arbitrary element b of the set T. Then we can show that $v'(x) = kv(x)$, where k is some positive constant. The proof is as follows:

$$v'(x) = \frac{Pr(x, b)}{Pr(b, x)} = \frac{Pr(x; T)}{Pr(b; T)},$$

but

$$v(x) = \frac{Pr(x, a)}{Pr(a, x)} = \frac{Pr(x; T)}{Pr(a; T)}.$$

Therefore,

$$v'(x) = \frac{Pr(a; T)}{Pr(b; T)} v(x) = kv(x).$$

This property ensures that if all scale values are multiplied by a positive constant, we preserve the original relationships of the scale values to the choice probabilities. This invariance occurs because the choice probabilities depend only upon the ratios of the v's, and in ratios of the form $v(x)/v(y)$ the scale constant k will cancel.

The reader may note that we have assumed throughout that all probabilities $Pr(x, y)$ are neither one nor zero. A second part of Luce's axiom (cf. Luce, 1959a, p. 6) takes care of cases of perfect discrimination. The gist of the idea is that if $Pr(x, y) = 0$ for some x and y, then x may be deleted or ignored whenever it occurs in any choice set containing y. The axiom in Eq. 4.1 then applies to the remaining elements among which there is imperfect discrimination. This assumes that if $Pr(x, y) = 0$, then

$$Pr(y; x, y, z, w) = Pr(y; y, z, w).$$

This seems to be a reasonable restriction and is empirically testable. If one always chooses Buicks in preference to Fords, then in choosing among a Buick, Ford, or Dodge one can immediately reduce the problem to consideration of a Buick or a Dodge. Throughout the following, we will assume that we are dealing only with cases of imperfect discrimination, in which none of the $Pr(x, y)$ values is zero.

For our purposes there are important formal, as well as empirical, criteria for evaluating a choice theory. The chief formal criterion is that the theory be amenable to generalization to nonstatic (learning) situations. Learning is interpreted as a change in scale values produced by stimulus, response, and reinforcement contingencies. Luce's theory can indeed be generalized to treat learning phenomena. The extension amounts to postulating that a trial creates a transformation on the set of response strengths. As we shall see in Sec. 6.4, one plausible transformation leads to the beta model for learning.

Some Tests of Luce's Axiom

Let us consider a testable consequence of Luce's axiom for a case in which we have pairwise choice probabilities for at least three objects x, y, and z. The theorem depends upon the fact that $v(y)$ cancels when we take the product

$$\frac{v(x)}{v(y)} \cdot \frac{v(y)}{v(z)},$$

yielding $v(x)/v(z)$. If we write the corresponding result in terms of pairwise choice probabilities, we have

(4.7)
$$\frac{Pr(x, y)}{Pr(y, x)} \cdot \frac{Pr(y, z)}{Pr(z, y)} = \frac{Pr(x, z)}{Pr(z, x)}.$$

For simplicity, we may define a ratio w_{xy} as

$$w_{xy} = \frac{Pr(x, y)}{Pr(y, x)}.$$

Then the relation in Eq. 4.7 may be written simply as

(4.8a)
$$w_{xz} = w_{xy} w_{yz}.$$

This equation is called the *product rule*. It has the virtue of being easily tested as we shall show later.

The predicted value of w_{xz} is related to the predicted value of $Pr(x, z)$ by the following reasoning:

$$\frac{Pr(x, z)}{Pr(z, x)} = \frac{Pr(x, z)}{1 - Pr(x, z)} = w_{xz};$$

or

$$Pr(x, z) = w_{xz} - w_{xz}Pr(x, z)$$

or

(4.8b) $$Pr(x, z) = \frac{w_{xz}}{1 + w_{xz}}.$$

The product rule is a probabilistic statement of transitivity. It says that if we know the probability that x is chosen over y and the probability that y is chosen over z, then we can predict the likelihood that x will be chosen over z. The rule can be extended along a "linear chain" of alternatives a, b, c, d, e, f, for which only the adjacent pairwise choice probabilities $Pr(a, b)$, $Pr(b, c)$, $Pr(c, d)$, etc., are known. By repeatedly applying Eq. 4.8, we obtain

(4.9) $$w_{af} = w_{ab}w_{bc}w_{cd}w_{de}w_{ef}.$$

From Luce's axiom, by knowing only the $k - 1$ adjacent choice probabilities, we can predict the entire array of $\dfrac{k(k - 1)}{2}$ choice probabilities in the pairwise data matrix. For example, to predict $Pr(b, d)$ we need know only the observed values of $Pr(a, b)$ and $Pr(a, d)$ in Eqs. 4.7 or 4.9. Then, by Eq. 4.7,

$$\frac{Pr(b, a)}{Pr(a, b)} \cdot \frac{Pr(a, d)}{Pr(d, a)},$$

yields an estimate of $\dfrac{Pr(b, d)}{Pr(d, b)}$. Calling this ratio w_{bd}, $Pr(b, d)$ is found to be $(w_{bd})/(1 + w_{bd})$. Clearly, all pairwise predictions could also have been obtained if we had known the choice probabilities involving some element a with every other alternative, that is, $Pr(a, b)$, $Pr(a, c)$, $Pr(a, d)$, etc. In any event, we need $k - 1$ independent proportions, involving in some way all of our k alternatives. From these $k - 1$ independent proportions, we can estimate the $k - 1$ parameters $v(x)/v(a)$ for $x = b, c, d, \ldots$. If Luce's axiom holds, then the remainder of the pairwise proportions, namely

$$\frac{k(k - 1)}{2} - (k - 1) = \frac{(k - 1)(k - 2)}{2}$$

of them, should be predictable from our $k - 1$ proportions used for estimation purposes. Thus, for each estimate, we obtain $(k - 2)/2$ predictions to test the axiom.

We now illustrate the product rule with several sets of data. Consider first the mock consumer survey on automobile colors shown in Table 4.1.

Recall that R represents the alternative red-white, B represents blue-gray, and Y represents yellow-black. The observed choice proportions were $Pr(R, B) = 0.71$, $Pr(B, Y) = 0.73$ and $Pr(R, Y) = 0.89$. Using $Pr(R, B)$ and $Pr(B, Y)$ in conjunction with the product rule, we try to predict $Pr(R, Y)$. We use $\hat{w}_{RY}$ to represent the prediction of w_{RY}.

$$w_{RB} \cdot w_{BY} = \frac{Pr(R, B)}{Pr(B, R)} \cdot \frac{Pr(B, Y)}{Pr(Y, B)}$$

$$= \frac{0.71}{0.29} \cdot \frac{0.73}{0.27} = \frac{0.5183}{0.0783} = 6.62 = \hat{w}_{RY}.$$

Therefore, by Eq. 4.8b,

$$Pr(R, Y) = \frac{\hat{w}_{RY}}{1 + \hat{w}_{RY}} = \frac{6.62}{7.62} = 0.87.$$

Thus, the predicted value of $Pr(R, Y)$ is close to the observed value of 0.89.

Consider a second example. In an experiment by Young (1947), rats' preferences for three different food substances (sugar, wheat, casein) were tested. Each animal received three series of extended preference tests; each series of tests corresponded to a choice between sugar versus wheat, or sugar versus casein, or wheat versus casein. For example, in the series of sugar versus casein tests, sugar would be in the food box to the left of the choice chamber and casein in the box to the right. After freely choosing one side, the rat was allowed five seconds in which to eat the substance chosen before being removed to run another trial. Sufficient pretraining was given to familiarize the rats with the locations of the different foods. The average choice percentages were: sugar preferred to wheat on 55 per cent of the trials, so $Pr(s, w) = 0.55$; wheat preferred to casein, $Pr(w, c) = 0.70$; and sugar preferred to casein, $Pr(s, c) = 0.74$. We use the product rule to predict $Pr(s, c)$ from the other two proportions. By the method used with the first example,

$$\hat{w}_{sc} = \frac{Pr(s, w)}{Pr(w, s)} \cdot \frac{Pr(w, c)}{Pr(c, w)}$$

$$= \frac{0.55}{0.45} \cdot \frac{0.70}{0.30} = \frac{0.385}{0.135} = 2.85.$$

Therefore,

$$Pr(s, c) = \frac{\hat{w}_{sc}}{1 + \hat{w}_{sc}} = \frac{2.85}{3.85} = 0.74.$$

In this instance, the prediction that sugar will be preferred over casein on 74 per cent of the trials corresponds exactly to the data.

Other data could be marshalled in favor of the product rule as a descriptive law regarding constancy of pairwise choice probabilities. However, our aim here is primarily didactic, so we move on to some data illustrating the constant ratio principle for choices involving two and three alternatives.

Illustrative Data on Constant Ratio Rule

In the Estes experiment mentioned earlier, the same 117 college students were asked to indicate which of several famous persons they would most

Table 4.3 Proportion of Times the Row Stimulus was Preferred to the Column Stimulus

	E	C	H	F
E	—	0.57	0.80	0.82
C	0.43	—	0.76	0.80
H	0.20	0.24	—	0.60
F	0.18	0.20	0.40	—

like to meet and talk with. The alternatives were: Dwight Eisenhower (*E*), Winston Churchill (*C*), Dag Hammarskjold (*H*), and William Faulkner (*F*).* The subjects chose among all possible pairs of persons,

Table 4.4 Proportion of Times the Row Stimulus was Chosen out of the Respective Set of Three

Set 1 (E, C, H)		Set 2 (C, H, F)	
Man	Per Cent	Man	Per Cent
E	0.51	C	0.65
C	0.36	H	0.20
H	0.13	F	0.15

yielding the choice proportions shown in Table 4.3. In addition to the pairwise choices, subjects were asked to select their most preferred out of two different sets of three, the sets being either (*E*, *C*, *H*) or (*C*, *H*, *F*). The results on the three-choice sets are given in Table 4.4.

The aim of the choice theory is to predict the three-alternative data from the pair data, or vice versa. The relevant calculations are exhibited below.

---

* These men were all living in 1960 when the experiment was conducted.

To maintain formal simplicity, we will drop the v-notation, using instead the first letter of the name to represent the scale value, that is, $v(C) = C$, $v(E) = E$, etc.

Predicting the Three-choice Data from the Pair Data.   Consider Set 1 consisting of E, C, and H. Then $Pr(E; \text{Set } 1)$ can be written as

$$Pr(E; \text{Set } 1) = \frac{E}{E + C + H} = \frac{1}{1 + \dfrac{C}{E} + \dfrac{H}{E}} .$$

Estimates of the ratios C/E and H/E may be obtained from the pair data in Table 4.3; they are

$$\frac{C}{E} = \frac{0.43}{0.57} = 0.75$$

and

$$\frac{H}{E} = \frac{0.20}{0.80} = 0.25.$$

When these values are substituted into the equation above for $Pr(E; \text{Set } 1)$, the resulting prediction is

$$Pr(E; \text{Set } 1) = \frac{1}{1 + 0.75 + 0.25} = 0.50.$$

The observed value in Table 4.4 for choice of E in Set 1 was 0.51, which agrees closely with the predicted value.

The predicted proportions of choices of the other two alternatives in Set 1 are readily obtained as follows:

$$Pr(C; \text{Set } 1) = \frac{C}{E + C + H} = \frac{\dfrac{C}{E}}{1 + \dfrac{C}{E} + \dfrac{H}{E}} = \frac{0.75}{2.00} = 0.375$$

and

$$Pr(H; \text{Set } 1) = \frac{H}{E + C + H} = \frac{\dfrac{H}{E}}{1 + \dfrac{C}{E} + \dfrac{H}{E}} = \frac{0.25}{2.00} = 0.125.$$

Referring again to Table 4.4, we note that the predictions are quite close to the observed proportions.

Turning to the results on Set 2,

$$Pr(C; \text{Set } 2) = \frac{1}{1 + \dfrac{H}{C} + \dfrac{F}{C}} .$$

From the pair data in Table 4.3 we obtain the estimates

$$\frac{H}{C} = \frac{0.24}{0.76} = 0.316$$

and

$$\frac{F}{C} = \frac{0.20}{0.80} = 0.250.$$

Substituting these estimates into prediction formulae yields

$$Pr(C;\, \text{Set } 2) = \frac{1}{1 + 0.316 + 0.250} = \frac{1}{1.566} = 0.64$$

$$Pr(H;\, \text{Set } 2) = \frac{\dfrac{H}{C}}{1 + \dfrac{H}{C} + \dfrac{F}{C}} = \frac{0.316}{1.566} = 0.20$$

$$Pr(F;\, \text{Set } 2) = \frac{\dfrac{F}{C}}{1 + \dfrac{H}{C} + \dfrac{F}{C}} = \frac{0.250}{1.566} = 0.16.$$

Putting these calculations in concise form, the observed three-choice proportions and those predicted from the two-choice data are displayed together in Table 4.5. It is clear that the predictions are quite accurate.

Table 4.5   Comparison of Observed and Predicted Choice Proportions
in Three-alternative Tests

Set 1 (E, C, H)			Set 2 (C, H, F)		
Alternative	Observed	Predicted	Alternative	Observed	Predicted
E	0.51	0.50	C	0.65	0.64
C	0.36	0.37	H	0.20	0.20
H	0.13	0.13	F	0.15	0.16

Predicting the Pairwise Choices from the Three-choice Data. An alternative (although redundant) test of the constant ratio assumption involves predicting the pairwise choice probabilities from the three-choice data. The direction of prediction is reversed from that above, but the data are the same and hence the computations are redundant. Since it adds little information, this reverse method will be illustrated only briefly here.

Consider predicting the pairwise probability $Pr(E, C)$. This can be written as follows:

$$Pr(E, C) = \frac{E}{E + C} = \frac{1}{1 + \frac{C}{E}}.$$

The ratio C/E is estimated from the three-choice data in Table 4.4:

$$\frac{C}{E} = \frac{Pr(C; \text{Set } 1)}{Pr(E; \text{Set } 1)} = \frac{0.36}{0.51} = 0.706.$$

Substituting this value for C/E into the expression above for $Pr(E, C)$ yields the prediction

$$Pr(E, C) = \frac{1}{1 + 0.706} = 0.586.$$

This prediction accords well with the observed 0.57 in Table 4.3. The remaining pairwise predictions can be derived in an analogous fashion. Of some interest is prediction of the pair $Pr(E, F)$, because E and F do not occur in the same triple in Table 4.4. The derivation is executed by comparing a common intermediary with both E and F, using the product rule. Our first and second computations employ the intermediaries C and H, respectively. The two outcomes in this case for $Pr(E, F)$ are as follows:

$$Pr(E, F) = \frac{1}{1 + \frac{F}{E}}$$

(C as middle stimulus)

$$\frac{F}{E} = \frac{F}{C} \cdot \frac{C}{E} = \frac{0.15}{0.65} \cdot \frac{0.36}{0.51} = 0.163$$

and

$$Pr(E, F) = \frac{1}{1.163} = 0.86;$$

(H as middle stimulus)

$$\frac{F}{E} = \frac{F}{H} \cdot \frac{H}{E} = \frac{0.15}{0.20} \cdot \frac{0.13}{0.51} = 0.191$$

and

$$Pr(E, F) = \frac{1}{1.191} = 0.84.$$

The average of the two predictions is 0.85 (compared with an observed value of 0.82). By continuing in this fashion, all the pairwise predictions can be

Table 4.6   Observed Pairwise Choice Proportions and Predicted
Values (in parentheses) from Three-choice Data

	C		H		F	
E	0.57	(0.59)	0.80	(0.80)	0.82	(0.85*)
C	—		0.76	(0.75*)	0.80	(0.83)
H	—		—		0.60	(0.57)
F	—		—		—	

* Average of two determinations.

found, and they are listed in parentheses in Table 4.6 juxtaposed to the
corresponding observed proportions. The pairwise predictions are fairly
accurate.

4.3   A HYPOTHESIS ABOUT STIMULUS RANKING

We may apply the foregoing choice theory to data obtained from
preference ranking experiments. In such studies, the subject is shown k
different stimuli simultaneously and is told to rank these in his order of
preference. We can conceive of several schemes by which subjects might
rank the k objects. Each suggested scheme amounts to a psychological
hypothesis about how people do in fact generate their preference rankings.
When the schemes are specified in sufficient detail, they may differ in
their predictions about rank-order data.

We will investigate a particular hypothesis about ranking proposed by
Luce (1959 a). It is assumed that when the subject is to rank k objects,
he first picks the most preferred object and gives it rank 1. He then
eliminates this one from the set, considers the remaining $k - 1$ objects
and from these chooses the most preferred object and gives it rank 2.
He continues this process of "pick the most preferred, then eliminate it"
until the k objects have been ranked. The ranking of k objects requires the
subject to make $k - 1$ successive decisions. A further addition to the
hypothesis is that choices in this series are assumed to follow Luce's
axiom; that is, each choice depends on the ratios of the scale values,
computed from the stimuli remaining in the reduced choice set.

Consider this hypothesis for the case of three objects A, B, C with
v-scale values of a, b, c. With three objects, there are 3! or six possible
rankings, namely, ABC, ACB, BAC, BCA, CAB, and CBA, reading from
most to least preferred within each triple. Given a large number of
replications of the experiment, each of these six possible rankings will
occur a certain proportion of the time. We would like a theory to predict
the probability with which each ranking will occur, and also quantities

such as the probability that A gets ranked second, that B's rank exceeds A's, and so forth.

Consider predicting $Pr(BAC)$, the likelihood of the ranking BAC. From the choice axiom, we first calculate the probability that B is chosen out of the three elements. Eliminating B from the choice set, we then calculate the probability that A is chosen over C in this two-object comparison. The joint probability of the ranking BAC is given by the product of these two probabilities; that is,

$$Pr(BAC) = \left[\frac{b}{a+b+c}\right]\left[\frac{a}{a+c}\right].$$

The predictions for the probabilities of the other possible rankings are derived in a similar manner.

There are two points to notice about this ranking rule. The first is that the likelihood that an element receives rank one is the same as the likelihood that it is chosen from the set of three when only one choice is permitted. For example, the likelihood that B receives rank one, written as $Pr(B = R1)$, is

$$(4.10) \quad Pr(B = R1) = Pr(BAC) + Pr(BCA)$$

$$= \left[\frac{b}{a+b+c}\right]\left[\frac{a}{a+c}\right] + \left[\frac{b}{a+b+c}\right]\left[\frac{c}{a+c}\right]$$

$$= \frac{b}{a+b+c}.$$

The last line above is just the likelihood that b is chosen first from the set ABC.

The second noteworthy point concerns a relationship between ranking data with three objects (or more) and pairwise choice data that could be collected in a separate experiment. If the ranking hypothesis is correct, then the likelihood that (say) A would be chosen over B in a two-choice test is equal to the sum of the probabilities of all those cases in which A receives a higher rank than B when the subject is ranking the set of objects ABC. Using $Pr(A, B)$ to denote the probability that A is chosen in the pair (A, B), then the ranking hypothesis implies the identity

$$(4.11) \qquad Pr(A, B) = Pr(ABC) + Pr(ACB) + Pr(CAB).$$

The proof of this identity is by construction. From Luce's axiom, we know that $Pr(A, B)$ is just $a/(a + b)$. We then have to show that the three right-hand terms sum to $a/(a + b)$ when we substitute for them according to the ranking hypothesis. To save space, we may cite the result in Eq. 4.10 that the first two terms sum to the probability that A receives rank one, which is $a/(a + b + c)$. We then add on the final term and simplify, as follows:

$$Pr(ABC) + Pr(ACB) + Pr(CAB) = \frac{a}{a + b + c} + \left[\frac{c}{a + b + c}\right]\left[\frac{a}{a + b}\right]$$

$$= \left[\frac{a}{a + b + c}\right]\left[1 + \frac{c}{a + b}\right]$$

$$= \frac{a}{a + b}.$$

We have thus proved the identity in Eq. 4.11 by showing that the three terms on the right side of Eq. 4.11 sum to $a/(a + b)$. It is a simple matter to extend this theorem to the ranking of more than three objects.

Let us perform one more derivation with this ranking scheme, a derivation that will be used later when we apply the scheme to the prediction of data. We wish to derive an equation for the probability that some arbitrary element (say) C receives a rank of two when the three objects ABC are to be ranked. This quantity is derived by summing the probability of all those cases in which C receives rank two, namely,

(4.12)

$$Pr(C = R2) = Pr(ACB) + Pr(BCA)$$

$$= \left[\frac{a}{a + b + c}\right]\left[\frac{c}{c + b}\right] + \left[\frac{b}{a + b + c}\right]\left[\frac{c}{a + c}\right]$$

$$= Pr(A = R1) \cdot Pr(C, B) + Pr(B = R1) \cdot Pr(C, A).$$

With the equations for the ranking hypothesis now at hand, we turn to the task of applying them to choice data. The application consists of attempting to predict ranking data of three objects from known pairwise choice probabilities. The data to be used were supplied by W. K. Estes. The situation was that described earlier in which 117 college students indicated their preference for color combinations of automobiles. Again, the color combinations compared were red-white (R), blue-gray (B), and black-yellow (Y). Each subject chose his preferred combination in each of the three possible pair comparisons, (RB), (RY), and (BY). He then ranked the three alternatives in his order of preference. The group mean data from the pair comparisons were shown in Table 4.1. The data from the ranking task are shown in Table 4.7, depicted in terms of the relative frequency with which each row stimulus received a rank of one, two, or three. The mean rank for a stimulus is obtained by multiplying the ranks (one, two, or three) by the probability that the stimulus received that rank, and then summing over the three ranks. Except for rounding errors, each column and each row of Table 4.7 sums to 1.00.

Table 4.7   Ranking Data on Car-color Combinations

Color Combination	Rank 1	Rank 2	Rank 3	Mean Rank
R	0.65	0.32	0.03	1.38
B	0.29	0.43	0.28	1.99
Y	0.06	0.24	0.70	2.64
Sum	1.00	0.99	1.01	

We wish to predict the numbers in Table 4.7 from Luce's ranking hypothesis, using the data in Table 4.1. First, consider the prediction of the probability that R receives rank one. Using the reasoning that led to Eq. 4.10, we have the following outcome:

$$(4.13) \qquad Pr(R = R1) = \frac{r}{r + b + y} = \frac{1}{1 + \dfrac{b}{r} + \dfrac{y}{r}}.$$

The ratios in the denominator may be estimated from the pairwise probabilities in Table 4.1, namely,

$$\frac{b}{r} = \frac{Pr(B, R)}{Pr(R, B)} = \frac{0.29}{0.71} = 0.409$$

$$\frac{y}{r} = \frac{Pr(Y, R)}{Pr(R, Y)} = \frac{0.11}{0.89} = 0.124.$$

Substituting these values into Eq. 4.13, we get the prediction

$$Pr(R = R1) = \frac{1}{1 + 0.409 + 0.124} = 0.652.$$

This is an accurate prediction of the 0.65 value in Table 4.7. Similarly, the likelihoods that B and Y receive rank one are readily determined:

$$Pr(B = R1) = \frac{b}{r + b + y} = \frac{\dfrac{b}{r}}{1 + \dfrac{b}{r} + \dfrac{y}{r}} = \frac{0.409}{1.533} = 0.267$$

$$Pr(Y = R1) = 1 - 0.652 - 0.267 = 0.081.$$

The last equation comes from the fact that

$$Pr(R = R1) + Pr(B = R1) + Pr(Y = R1) = 1.$$

Now let us predict the probabilities that each alternative receives a rank of two. Utilizing Eq. 4.12

$$Pr(R = R2) = Pr(B = R1) \cdot Pr(R, Y) + Pr(Y = R1) \cdot Pr(R, B)$$
$$= 0.267(0.89) + 0.081(0.71)$$
$$= 0.296.$$

We see in this instance that all necessary information is given for calculating the value of $Pr(R = R2)$. The rank-one probabilities were

Table 4.8   Comparison of Observed and Predicted Ranks

Color	Rank 1		Rank 2		Rank 3		Mean Rank	
Combination	Obs.	Pred.	Obs.	Pred.	Obs.	Pred.	Obs.	Pred.
R	0.65	0.65	0.32	0.30	0.03	0.05	1.38	1.40
B	0.29	0.27	0.43	0.50	0.28	0.23	1.99	1.96
Y	0.06	0.08	0.24	0.21	0.70	0.71	2.64	2.63

calculated above, and the pairwise choice probabilities, $Pr(R, Y)$ and $Pr(R, B)$, are read directly from the data in Table 4.1. In a similar manner, we obtain the probabilities that the other alternatives receive rank two, as follows:

$$Pr(B = R2) = Pr(R = R1)Pr(B, Y) + Pr(Y = R1)Pr(B, R)$$
$$= 0.652(0.73) + 0.081(0.29)$$
$$= 0.500$$
$$Pr(Y = R2) = 1 - 0.296 - 0.500$$
$$= 0.204.$$

To summarize, Table 4.8 presents a direct comparison of the observed and predicted ranks, each rounded to two decimal places.

Examining this table, we can see that in most cases the predicted values come close to the corresponding observed values. The mean ranks indicate that the preference order from most to least preferred color combination was as follows: red-white, blue-gray, and black-yellow. The goodness of fit in this case could be evaluated by a χ^2 test where the number of observations contributing to each row and column is 117. The reader will have noticed that although there are nine cells in the table, only four of them are independent. The loss of five degrees of freedom results from the constraints that each row and each column of proportions must sum to one. Phrasing it differently, if the entries in the four cells in the upper left of the table are given, then the entries in the remaining five cells are determined. Thus, a χ^2 test for goodness of fit would be based on four degrees of freedom.

4.4 A RANDOM WALK MODEL

The next model to be discussed attempts to account for other features of choice behavior in addition to the alternative chosen. Such features include vicarious trial-and-error (VTE) behavior that precedes the final choice, the time taken to make the choice, the subject's degree of confidence in the correctness of his choice, and how difficult he felt the decision was. These auxiliary features of choice behavior have been much investigated (for example, see Guilford, 1954, Chapter 12), and they tend to show orderly relationships to experimental variables of the choice situation. The existence of such uniformities raises a challenge to the theorist to devise a conception of the act of choice that will interrelate these various indices as well as account for the object chosen.

There have been several models of this variety proposed. The first prominent theory was that by Tolman (1939), which involved a useful qualitative analysis of vicarious trial-and-error (VTE) behavior but unfortunately never reached the stage of quantitative testing. More recent quantitative theories of choice have been reported by Bower (1959 *b*), Estes (1960 *b*), Audley (1960), Spence (1960), Atkinson (1960 *b*), and LaBerge (1962). These various authors do not propose radically different ideas, since the first five papers cited present special cases of a general class of models; the paper by LaBerge presents a model which differs in some significant details from the other class of choice theories. In mathematical parlance, these theories are represented as special kinds of Markov chains, called "random walks with absorbing barriers." More on this later.

In the following we will explicate one of these random walk models. The one devised by Bower (1959 *b*, 1962 *b*) will be illustrated because it involves simpler mathematical expressions than do the others, and it is representative of the general approach. That model was first devised to describe VTE and choice behavior of rats performing in a standard *T*-maze. That situation serves as a convenient paradigm for later extensions, so the model will be elaborated first in the context of a *T*-maze experiment.

The initial analysis involves specification of the relevant sets of stimuli and a definition of the response alternatives available in the presence of those sets. Cues in the *T*-maze can be classified into three sets: those stimuli in the stem and vicinity of the choice point, denoted as the set S_0; those stimuli likely to be sampled when the subject at the choice point orients to the right side of the maze, denoted as the set S_1; and those likely to be sampled when the subject at the choice point orients to the left side, called the set S_2. No restriction is made on the constituent elements of these complexes; anything that can serve as a cue is included. For example, the set S_1 may contain visual, auditory, olfactory, and spatial location cues as well as kinesthetic feedback involved in orienting to that side of the maze. The actual cues involved and the extent to which they must be specified or analyzed into functional elements varies with one's interest in particular experiments.

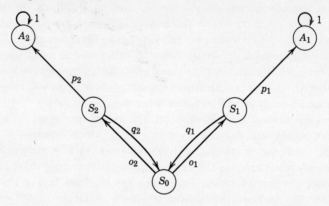

Fig. 4.1 State transition diagram of a random walk model for choice behavior (Model A).

We assume that the S_0 cues at the choice point elicit an orientation to the right or left; we let o_i represent the probability that the subject orients to S_i ($i = 1, 2$) when at the choice point, and $o_1 + o_2 = 1$. It is supposed that when the subject orients to S_i and considers it, there is probability p_i that he approaches this stimulus and terminates the trial with choice A_i, whereas with probability $q_i = 1 - p_i$, he reorients away from S_i and reverts to the neutral state S_0. The process is best seen in diagrammatic form (Fig. 4.1).

Let us examine Fig. 4.1 for a moment to bring out several important points. First, there are five different positions or "states": the states S_0, S_1, and S_2 correspond to the subject's orienting to these stimuli, and the states A_1 and A_2 correspond to the subject's having approached (chosen) stimulus 1 or stimulus 2 and thus terminated the trial. The arrows between two states represent possible transitions. Beside each arrow is written the probability that the transition occurs next when the subject is in the state at the origin of the arrow. The states A_1 and A_2 have arrows only back to themselves, with associated transition probabilities of unity. This identifies A_1 and A_2 as "absorbing" states in the sense that once the subject enters either of these states, we terminate the opportunity for any further state transitions on that experimental trial.

An experimental trial is viewed as follows: introducing the subject into the stem leading to the choice point ensures that he begins each trial in state S_0; S_0 elicits an orientation to S_1 or to S_2; from S_i he can either approach A_i or can return to S_0, in the latter case repeating the process of scanning or considering the alternatives. The sequence of orientations continues until the subject is absorbed at A_1 or A_2. The primary datum from observing the rat at the choice point may be represented as a hypothetical sequence of his state transitions before absorption. Examples of three such sequences would be $S_0S_1A_1$, $S_0S_2S_0S_2A_2$, and $S_0S_1S_0S_2S_0S_1A_1$.

By the representation in Fig. 4.1, we mean to assert that such sequences of states form a homogeneous Markov chain. To reiterate from Chapters 2 and 3, two things are involved in this Markov assumption. (1) *Independence of past:* the probability of a transition depends only upon the current state and does not depend upon the past sequence of moves that brought the subject to the current state. That is, the process is ahistorical and involves dependencies that go back only one step in the sequence. (2) *Homogeneity:* the transition probabilities o_1, p_1, p_2 remain constant for the duration of a trial.

This completes the explication of the formal machinery involved in the model. The intent is to analyze the predecisional component behaviors and to suppose that the eventual choice reflects the outcome of the interaction of these components. The reason for the "random walk" label is easily seen in Fig. 4.1. Consider the states to be aligned in a row with A_2 on the left and A_1 on the right. Then transitions can occur only between adjacent states. Starting the subject in the middle state S_0, he randomly walks or drifts from state to state like a bouncing particle until he is trapped at one of the absorbing barriers.

Mathematical Derivations

The primary data from our experiment will be sequences of the form $S_0S_1S_0S_2S_0S_2A_2$, and so forth. For convenience in notation, we will replace states S_0, S_1 and S_2 by their subscripts 0, 1, 2. Thus the sequence above will read $010202A_2$. The infinity of possible sequences of this form constitute a "sample space," since each represents a possible outcome of one trial in the maze. The rules of the model permit us to attach to each possible sequence a number representing its probability of occurrence. Thus, the sequence $01A$ has probability o_1p_1, whereas the sequence

$02010202A_2$ has probability $o_2q_2o_1q_1o_2q_2o_2p_2$. These probabilities can be generated directly from the representation in Fig. 4.1.

Given such a sample space of possible outcomes, we may define various simple or compound events and obtain the probability of an event by adding up the probabilities of all those sequences (sample points) where the designated event occurs. Three examples of such events are: (1) the sequence terminates with an A_1, (2) there is at least one occurrence of state 2 in the sequence, and (3) there are at least two occurrences of state 2 and the sequence terminates with response 1. In addition to these types of events, we shall want some general events that will describe in quantitative terms how much VTE behavior occurs. For these purposes we can construct several indices; two of these are illustrated here: (1) the "loop" index, which counts whenever the subsequence 010 or the subsequence 020 occurs, and (2) the "switch" index, which counts whenever the subsequences 201 or 102 occur. Within any particular sequence, the loop event may occur several times. Thus, we could define the compound event: "the loop event occurs k times before the sequence terminates." To handle such cases, we will define a random variable, L, which counts the number of loops before absorption. Possible values of L are the nonnegative integers $0, 1, 2, \ldots$. Then calculation of the probability of the compound event "k loops occur" is tantamount to finding the probability distribution of L, that is, $Pr(L = k)$.

Probability of Absorption at A_1

As can be seen in Fig. 4.1, unless p_1 and p_2 are both zero the subject eventually terminates the trial by absorption at (choosing) A_1 or A_2. We begin our derivations by obtaining the probability that the subject is absorbed at A_1 instead of at A_2. To enumerate all possible sequences that end with A_1 is a tedious and nonending task because in principle there is an infinite number of such chains. Instead, we will attack the problem by inspecting the general trend of the terms and then summing an infinite series. We begin by writing down some initial terms of the series to get an idea of the pattern.

a) No loops before absorption on A_1:
   sequence: $01A_1$
   probability: o_1p_1
b) One loop before absorption on A_1:
   sequences: $0101A_1$ and $0201A_1$
   probabilities: $o_1q_1o_1p_1$ and $o_2q_2o_1p_1$

c) Two loops before absorption on A_1:

  sequences: $010101A_1$, $010201A_1$, $020101A_1$, and $020201A_1$

  probabilities: $o_1q_1o_1q_1o_1p_1$, $o_1q_1o_2q_2o_1p_1$, $o_2q_2o_1q_1o_1p_1$,

  and $o_2q_2o_2q_2o_1p_1$

Let us pause to examine the trend of our calculated strings of probabilities. First, notice that each sequence ends with the three states $01A_1$ and hence the corresponding final terms in the probability expressions are o_1p_1. Second, the probability of the loop 010 is o_1q_1 and of the loop 020 is o_2q_2. Thus, the sum of the probabilities of getting absorbed at A_1 after one loop is $(o_1q_1 + o_2q_2)o_1p_1$. The probability of absorption at A_1 after two loops involves the sum of four terms, $(o_1q_1)^2$, $(o_1q_1o_2q_2)$, $(o_2q_2o_1q_1)$, and $(o_2q_2)^2$, each multiplied by the common final terms o_1p_1. These four terms are identical to what we would obtain by the expansion of $(o_1q_1 + o_2q_2)^2$. By writing out the terms for absorption at A_1 after three loops (there are eight such terms), we see that the termwise coefficients of o_1p_1 correspond to the expansion of $(o_1q_1 + o_2q_2)^3$.

These considerations suggest that the general term for n loops preceding absorption at A_1 will be $(o_1q_1 + o_2q_2)^n o_1p_1$. Thus, the total probability of ultimate absorption at A_1 may be written as the infinite sum

$$(4.14) \qquad Pr(A_1) = \sum_{n=0}^{\infty} Pr(\text{absorption at } A_1 \text{ following } n \text{ loops})$$

$$= \sum_{n=0}^{\infty} o_1p_1(o_1q_1 + o_2q_2)^n.$$

In this case we must evaluate the sum of a geometric series with ratio $(o_1q_1 + o_2q_2)$. By customary techniques,

$$(4.15) \qquad Pr(A_1) = \frac{o_1p_1}{1 - (o_1q_1 + o_2q_2)}$$

$$= \frac{o_1p_1}{o_1p_1 + o_2p_2}.$$

The substitution in the denominator of the last line is legitimate because $(o_1q_1 + o_2q_2) + (o_1p_1 + o_2p_2) = 1$.

By using the same method we could have derived directly the probability of eventual absorption at A_2 simply by replacing o_1p_1 with the terms o_2p_2 in Eq. 4.14. The result would be

$$Pr(A_2) = \sum_{n=0}^{\infty} Pr(A_2 \text{ after } n \text{ loops})$$

$$= \sum_{n=0}^{\infty} o_2p_2(o_1q_1 + o_2q_2)^n$$

$$= \frac{o_2p_2}{o_1p_1 + o_2p_2}.$$

Of course, we could have obtained $Pr(A_2)$ from the fact that

$$Pr(A_1) + Pr(A_2) = 1.$$

From this point, it is also a simple matter to derive the probability distribution of the number of loops, L. It is

$$Pr(L = n) = Pr(A_1 \text{ after } n \text{ loops}) + Pr(A_2 \text{ after } n \text{ loops})$$
$$= o_1 p_1 (o_1 q_1 + o_2 q_2)^n + o_2 p_2 (o_1 q_1 + o_2 q_2)^n$$
$$= (o_1 p_1 + o_2 p_2)(o_1 q_1 + o_2 q_2)^n.$$

We may set $J = o_1 p_1 + o_2 p_2$ and rewrite the distribution more simply as

(4.16) $$Pr(L = n) = J(1 - J)^n \qquad \text{(for } n \geqslant 0).$$

Equation 4.16 tells us that, if the model is correct, then the number of loops in the data protocols will be geometrically distributed. The mean and variance of L will be:

$$E(L) = \sum_{n=0}^{\infty} nJ(1 - J)^n = \frac{1 - J}{J}$$

$$\text{Var}(L) = \sum_{n=0}^{\infty} [n - E(L)]^2 J(1 - J)^n = \frac{1 - J}{J^2}.$$

We will now illustrate the geometric distribution of L by predicting some data. Figure 4.2 shows the predicted and obtained distributions of L from two groups of 15 rats learning a T-maze problem. These data were collected during the middle course of learning and the parameter J was

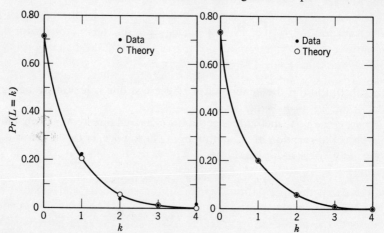

Fig. 4.2 Observed and predicted distributions of L, the number of loops before absorption.

estimated from the initial point of the empirical distributions. It is clear from Fig. 4.2 that the model adequately predicts the VTE distributions obtained in these experiments. The model has performed this well in a number of similar experiments.

We now have enough equations at hand to examine their implications. First consider the expression for $Pr(A_1)$, which is

$$Pr(A_1) = \frac{o_1 p_1}{o_1 p_1 + o_2 p_2} = \frac{o_1 p_1}{o_1 p_1 + (1 - o_1) p_2} .$$

It is seen that $Pr(A_1)$ will be unity either if $o_1 = 1$ or if $p_2 = 0$. In general, p_1 and p_2 will differ, but in case $p_1 = p_2$, then the p's cancel out and $Pr(A_1) = o_1$ so that the choice is determined by the orienting probabilities. Finally, in case the orientation probabilities are random ($o_1 = 1 - o_1 = \frac{1}{2}$), then the o_i's cancel and the expression reduces to

$$Pr(A_1) = \frac{p_1}{p_1 + p_2} = \frac{1}{1 + \left(\dfrac{p_2}{p_1}\right)} .$$

In this case, choice probability depends upon the ratio p_2/p_1 of the approach probabilities. Assuming that p_i reflects the strength or attractiveness of stimulus S_i, the form of the probability rule is identical to Luce's ratio rule. That is, if we assign the numbers p_1, p_2, and v_1, v_2 such that $p_1/p_2 = v_1/v_2$, then the choice probabilities are identical to those arising from Luce's axiom. We shall see later how the argument extends to choices from sets of three or more alternatives.

Next consider Eq. 4.16 for the distribution of L, the number of loops before absorption. The fact that L has a geometric distribution means that the most probable value (mode) of L is at zero, the next most probable value at one, and so on. The probability at $L = 0$ is $J = o_1 p_1 + (1 - o_1)p_2$, which is unity if either $o_1 p_1 = 1$ or $(1 - o_1)p_2 = 1$. The mean value of L is

$$E(L) = \frac{1 - J}{J}$$

$$= \frac{1}{o_1 p_1 + (1 - o_1)p_2} - 1.$$

Suppose that the orientation probabilities are random and equal to $\frac{1}{2}$; then $E(L)$ is simply a reciprocal function of the sum $p_1 + p_2$, which represents the combined "attractiveness" of the two alternatives. This means that when the two stimuli are of low attractiveness (or alternately, the responses A_1 and A_2 are of low strength), then there will be a large amount of VTE behavior preceding the choice; when the stimuli are highly attractive, then the choice will occur quickly with only a small amount of hesitation prior to the choice. Later we shall attempt an explicit model to handle choice reaction times.

Another statistic of interest is the distribution of loops or VTE's prior to the choice of a particular response, say A_1. Let L_1 represent this conditional random variable. The distribution of L_1 is easily obtained from our previous results in Eq. 4.14:

$$(4.17) \qquad Pr(L_1 = n) = \frac{Pr(A_1 \text{ after } n \text{ loops})}{Pr(\text{absorption on } A_1)}$$

$$= \frac{(o_1 q_1 + o_2 q_2)^n o_1 p_1}{\left[\dfrac{o_1 p_1}{o_1 p_1 + o_2 p_2}\right]}$$

$$= (o_1 p_1 + o_2 p_2)(o_1 q_1 + o_2 q_2)^n$$

$$= J(1 - J)^n.$$

The result in this case is another geometric distribution. In fact, the distribution of L_1 is identical to that for L in Eq. 4.16. What this means is that according to this model the average amount of hesitation, oscillation, or VTE-ing should be the same regardless of whether the subject terminates the trial by choosing A_1 or by choosing A_2. Thus, in a learning situation for example, we would not expect the mean number of VTE's to differ before correct versus incorrect responses.

Application to Pair Comparisons in Preferential Judgments

The foregoing model was developed to describe the behavior of animals in a T-maze, and initial tests in that context were fairly successful. Suppose we try now to extend it to pair comparison experiments using human subjects. In abstract terms, such experiments are characterized by presenting the subject with two stimuli (objects, commodity bundles, wagers, etc.) and allowing him to choose between them. We shall assume that we are dealing with situations in which the spatial or temporal order of presentation of the two stimuli is of no importance. To represent this notion in terms of our model, we shall assume that the subject randomly orients to (or considers) the two objects indifferently, so that $o_i = \frac{1}{2}$. The "approach probability," p_i, reflects the net attraction of stimulus S_i when the subject orients to it. We shall assume that a random walk process (considering an alternative, reorienting, etc.) operates in this instance just as it does with the animal wiggling his head at the choice point of the *T*-maze. The important difference between these two experiments is that in the human one this activity may be covert rather than observable. However, we may still use the model to try to predict interrelations among choice probabilities and to analyze decision times. Additionally, in the human experiment we can collect and analyze confidence ratings, which is not possible with animal subjects (at least, no one has tried it). We may use a suggestion by Audley (1960) and simply hypothesize that confidence ratings (*C*) are inversely proportional to the number of vacillations (*L*) or VTE's prior to the choice, that is, $C = h/(L + 1)$ where *h* is a constant of proportionality. Thus, quick choices are made with confidence; very slow choices, preceded by much vacillation, will be given low confidence ratings. This is clearly an *ad hoc* assumption with no justification other than that it seems to capture our common sense meaning of high or low confidence.

To return to the pair comparison situation, with *k* stimuli $S_1, S_2, \ldots, S_k$, the model identifies *k* approach probabilities $p_1, p_2, \ldots, p_k$. The parameter p_i, representing the strength of attraction or value assigned to S_i, is presumed to be stable and not dependent upon what other alternatives may be involved in a particular choice. By the assumption of random orientation, the probability of choosing S_i given a pairwise choice between S_i and S_j is

$$Pr(i, j) = \frac{p_i}{p_i + p_j}.$$

Because the form of this expression is the same as Luce's ratio rule, all the same implications hold as discussed in the initial section of this chapter. Thus the "product rule" will follow relating $Pr(i, l)$ to $Pr(i, j)$ and $Pr(j, l)$. As in Luce's system, the description of pair comparison data for *k* alternatives requires evaluation of $k - 1$ parameters, representing the ratios of the p_i's to some standard referent such as p_1.

Choices from *k* Alternatives

We want to ascertain whether Luce's constant ratio rule will be implied by the random walk model. To investigate this question, we must first derive an expression for choice probability of S_i when *k* different alternatives are simultaneously presented for choice. The *k*-choice situation would be represented by *k* orientation probabilities $o_1, o_2, \ldots, o_k$, which sum to one and by *k* approach probabilities $p_1, p_2, \ldots, p_k$. The state-to-state transition diagram for this general case is just an obvious extension of the diagram for the two-choice situation in Fig. 4.1. The probability of direct absorption at A_i without any loops is $o_i p_i$. Further the likelihood of a single loop (that is, 010, 020, etc.) is simply

$$o_1 q_1 + o_2 q_2 + \cdots + o_k q_k;$$

similarly, the likelihood of two loops is

$$(o_1 q_1 + o_2 q_2 + \cdots + o_k q_k)^2,$$

and so forth. Thus the likelihood of x loops and then absorption on A_i is

$$(o_1 q_1 + o_2 q_2 + \cdots + o_k q_k)^x o_i p_i.$$

Thus, by an argument analogous to the derivation of Eq. 4.14, the probability that A_i is chosen when there are k alternatives is

$$(4.18) \quad Pr(i; 1, 2, \ldots, k) = \sum_{x=0}^{\infty} o_i p_i (o_1 q_1 + o_2 q_2 + \cdots + o_k q_k)^x$$

$$= \frac{o_i p_i}{1 - (o_1 q_1 + o_2 q_2 + \cdots + o_k q_k)}$$

$$= \frac{o_i p_i}{o_1 p_1 + o_2 p_2 + \cdots + o_k p_k}.$$

The form of the above expression resembles that obtained in the two-choice case. If the orientation probabilities are random and equal to $1/k$, then the o_i's cancel and the resulting expression is a function only of the ratio of the p_i values.

Suppose in this latter case we take the ratio of the probability of first choosing S_i to the probability of first choosing S_j when the entire set of k stimuli is presented. The resultant ratio, which we will call w_{ij}, is

$$w_{ij} = \frac{Pr(i; 1, 2, \ldots, k)}{Pr(j; 1, 2, \ldots, k)} = \frac{p_i}{p_j}.$$

The sum of the p_i values in the denominator of each probability expression cancels, and we are left with the ratio of p_i to p_j. If only S_i and S_j had been presented for a pairwise choice, the ratio of $Pr(i, j)$ to $Pr(j, i)$ would have been exactly the same ratio, p_i/p_j. The significance of this observation is that the ratio of i to j choices is a constant that does not depend upon the number of other alternatives that may be available for choice. In other words, Luce's constant ratio rule follows from the random walk model under the restriction that the orientation probabilities are random and equal to $1/k$, where k is the number of objects among which any given choice is to be made.

If we reflect on this result for a moment, however, we can detect the source from which the random walk model gets the ingredients to derive the constant ratio rule. In fact, the constant ratio rule was introduced with the innocent-sounding assumption that the orientation probabilities are random. This means, of course, that o_i changes when we change the size of the choice set. The assumption that o_i will equal $1/k$ amounts to postulating that the constant ratio rule holds for calculating the o_i as we change the size of the choice set. Thus, a fairer statement of the result for the random walk model would be as follows: if the orientation probabilities follow the constant ratio rule, then so do the choice probabilities.

Learning Assumptions

In applying this model to learning situations, we would assume that the basic approach and orienting probabilities increase with reinforcement and decrease with nonreinforcement. Bower (1959 b, 1962 b) works out some of the predictions that follow from assuming that the probabilities change according to linear operators. Using the full system, linear changes in the values of $o_i(n)$ and $p_i(n)$ produce nonlinear changes in the observable choice probabilities. Consequently, only a few results have been obtained for the full system.

Various special cases may be considered. If all the approach probabilities are equal, then the A_i choice probability reduces to $o_i(n)$, the probability of orienting to alternative i. With differential approach tendencies out of the way, the system reduces to a "one-habit" model; then linear operators acting on $o_i(n)$ produce linear changes on the choice probabilities. Alternatively, if the orienting probabilities are assumed equal, then the choice probabilities are a function of the basic approach probabilities. If the learning operators are such that they leave the sum of the approach probabilities constant from trial to trial, then linear operators are implied on the choice probabilities.

An approach toward simplification of the full system is illustrated in Atkinson (1960 b), Myers and Atkinson (1964), and Suppes and Atkinson (1960, p. 247). The basic notions of orienting to stimuli and approaching the stimulus observed is kept, but the learning on each component of the system is assumed to be an all-or-none process. This effects a major simplification in the total number of states in the Markov representation of learning. The papers cited should be consulted for further details.

*4.5   CHOICE TIMES

We wish to relate the random walk model of choice behavior to data regarding decision times. Assume that a clock starts when the subject

---

* This section involves some techniques from the calculus and may be skipped by readers unfamiliar with this area of mathematics.

enters state S_0 and continues to run until the subject enters one of the absorbing states, at which time the clock is stopped. We wish to predict the probability distribution of clock readings obtained in such a manner. We call these readings "choice times."

One source of variability in the choice times is the amount of looping (or VTE-ing) the subject does before absorption. A simple initial hypothesis is that each step (transition) in the process takes a fixed small period of time, h seconds, and that the total time to absorption is just h times the number of steps. To obtain the probability distribution of choice times, we need only obtain the distribution of steps to absorption. This is easy because the number of steps equals two plus twice the number of loops (each loop is two steps). Defining S as the number of steps, then

$$S = 2L + 2.$$

The possible values of L are $0, 1, 2, \ldots$, so the possible values of S are the even integers $2, 4, 6, \ldots$. The probability distribution of S is

$$Pr(S = k) = Pr\left(L = \frac{k - 2}{2}\right)$$

$$= J(1 - J)^{k-2/2} \qquad \text{(for } k = 2, 4, 6, \ldots)$$

by Eq. 4.16.

Returning to our choice time derivations, we let T be the total choice time. Because of the assumption $T = hS$, the possible values of T are $2h, 4h, 6h$, etc. The probability that T takes on the value $k \cdot h$ is just $Pr(S = k)$. The expected value of S is

$$(4.19a) \qquad E(S) = 2E(L) + 2 = \frac{2(1 - J)}{J} + 2 = \frac{2}{J}.$$

Thus, the mean value of T will be

$$(4.19b) \qquad E(T) = hE(S) = \frac{2h}{J}$$

The variance of T will be

$$(4.20) \qquad \text{Var}(T) = h^2\text{Var}(S) = h^2\text{Var}(2L + 2)$$

$$= h^2 2^2 \text{Var}(L) = 4h^2\left(\frac{1 - J}{J^2}\right).$$

There are several problems with this simple model when we consider its empirical accuracy. First, the model quantizes time into units of length h and thus permits only choice time values of $2h, 4h, 6h, \ldots$. In fact, of course, time is a continuous variable and any positive real number may result in a choice experiment. A second problem is that the predicted distribution of choice times is geometric just as are the distributions of S and L. Empirical choice time distributions simply do not have this geometric shape if the time-class intervals are taken small enough. Rather, they tend more to resemble the hump-shaped distribution function shown in Fig. 4.3. A third problem with this choice-time model is that it predicts no variance if $J = 1$, which is a reasonable value of J when subjects are at asymptote in a learning task. When $J = 1$, there are no loops, T is always equal to $2h$ (see Eq. 4.19), and the variance

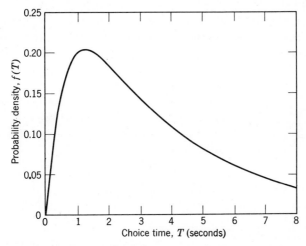

Fig. 4.3   Choice time distribution for $J = 0.5$, $b = 1.00$.

is zero (see Eq. 4.20). This prediction is, of course, contrary to fact; many experimental situations may involve 100 per cent choice of one stimulus, yet response will still display some variability.

Continuous Response Times

As it happens, there is a direct way to modify this simple theory so as to circumvent the three problems mentioned. The modification consists of the simple expedient of letting the time per step be a continuous time variable rather than a fixed constant h. We postulate that the time per step is a random variable with an exponential distribution, that is,

$$f(t) = be^{-bt}, \qquad \text{(for } t \geqslant 0, \text{ and } b > 0).$$

To establish that $f(t)$ is in fact a probability density function note that $f(t) \geqslant 0$ for permissible values of t and also that the integral from $t = 0$ to ∞ equals one; that is,

$$\int_0^\infty be^{-bt}\, dt = 1.$$

This exponential probability density has mean and variance equal to

$$E(t) = \int_0^\infty tbe^{-bt}\,dt = \frac{1}{b}$$

$$\text{Var}(t) = \int_0^\infty \left(t - \frac{1}{b}\right)^2 be^{-bt}\,dt = \frac{1}{b^2}.$$

Our problem is to derive the probability density function for the total time T. The total time T will be composed of the (random) times taken to complete the S steps before absorption. But the number of steps S is itself a random variable. Thus, T is the sum of a randomly determined number of exponential random variables. To discover properties of T will require some more mathematical machinery.

We will first change the S notation and talk in terms of "two-steps." Let X represent the number of two-steps before absorption. Then, because $S = 2L + 2$, we have $X = L + 1$, and the distribution of X will be

$$Pr(X = n) = J(1 - J)^{n-1} \quad \text{(for } n = 1, 2, 3, \ldots).$$

The justification for this equation is that $Pr(X = n) = Pr(S = 2n)$, by definition of a two-step. And $Pr(S = 2n)$ is found by setting $k = 2n$ in the earlier equation $Pr(S = k) = J(1 - J)^{k-2/2}$. The mean and variance of the X distribution are

$$E(X) = \frac{1}{J}$$

$$\text{Var}(X) = \frac{1 - J}{J^2}.$$

The mathematical concept that needs to be introduced is the notion of a moment generating function. We will let $M_t(\theta)$ represent the moment generating function (abbreviated mgf) of the random variable t which has probability density $f(t)$. Formally, $M_t(\theta)$ is defined as the expected value of $e^{\theta t}$, where t is the random variable and θ is a dummy variable whose usefulness will be illustrated soon. Writing out the definition of $M_t(\theta)$, we then expand $e^{\theta t}$ into its power series form:

$$(4.21) \quad M_t(\theta) = E(e^{\theta t}) = \int e^{\theta t} f(t)\,dt$$

$$= \int \left[1 + \frac{\theta t}{1} + \frac{(\theta t)^2}{2!} + \frac{(\theta t)^3}{3!} + \cdots\right] f(t)\,dt.$$

Recall that the rth raw moment, μ_r, of a probability density $f(t)$ is defined as

$$\mu_r = \int t^r f(t)\,dt.$$

Using this definition, we see that the series expansion in Eq. 4.21 can be rewritten as

$$(4.22) \qquad M_t(\theta) = 1 + \theta\mu_1 + \frac{\theta^2}{2!}\mu_2 + \frac{\theta^3}{3!}\mu_3 + \frac{\theta^4}{4!}\mu_4 + \cdots .$$

Thus, $M_t(\theta)$ is the sum of the raw moments of $f(t)$, where the coefficient of μ_r is $\theta^r/r!$. Suppose now that we wished to find the first moment of $f(t)$ using $M_t(\theta)$. A simple way to do so is to take the first derivative of $M_t(\theta)$ with respect to θ, namely,

$$\frac{dM_t(\theta)}{d\theta} = \mu_1 + \frac{2\theta}{2!}\mu_2 + \frac{3\theta^2}{3!}\mu_3 + \frac{4\theta^3}{4!}\mu_4 + \cdots .$$

If we now evaluate this expression at $\theta = 0$, we see that all terms vanish except μ_1, which was what we wanted to find. If we wished to know the second raw moment, we would take the second derivative of $M_t(\theta)$ with respect to θ, which is

$$\frac{d^2M_t(\theta)}{d\theta^2} = \mu_2 + \frac{3 \cdot 2 \cdot \theta}{3!}\mu_3 + \frac{4 \cdot 3 \cdot \theta^2}{4!}\mu_4 + \cdots .$$

When this second derivative is evaluated at $\theta = 0$, we obtain the second raw moment. The general result is that the rth raw moment of $f(t)$ can be obtained by evaluating the rth derivative of $M_t(\theta)$ at $\theta = 0$. This property gives rise to the term "moment generating function."

For our present purposes the importance of the mgf is not that it can be used to generate moments but rather that the mgf gives a complete description of its associated density function $f(t)$. That is, there is a unique relationship between $f(t)$ and its mgf, although it is sometimes difficult to discover what is the $f(t)$ corresponding to a known mgf. A second fact of importance here is the following: if $f(t)$ and $g(z)$ are two density functions with mgf's of $M_t(\theta)$ and $M_z(\theta)$, then the sum $t + z$ has a density function whose mgf is $M_t(\theta) \cdot M_z(\theta)$ provided that t and z are independent. Thus, the mgf of a sum of independent random variables is equal to the product of their separate mgf's. It is this feature of mgf's that we will use below in finding the mgf of the sum of a number of exponentially distributed random variables.

With these notions at hand, we return to our primary task of deriving the distribution of T. We begin by obtaining the mgf of the exponential random variable:

$$(4.23) \qquad M_t(\theta) = \int_0^\infty e^{\theta t} b e^{-bt}\, dt = b\int_0^\infty e^{-(b-\theta)t}\, dt$$

$$= \frac{b}{b - \theta}$$

$$= \left(1 - \frac{\theta}{b}\right)^{-1} .$$

Next we find the mgf for a two-step. The time for a two-step is the sum of two values of t, each $f(t)$ having a mgf given by Eq. 4.23. Thus the mgf of the time to complete a two-step is the product of the two mgf's, namely,

$$(4.24) \qquad M_{t_2}(\theta) = \left(1 - \frac{\theta}{b}\right)^{-2}.$$

Now consider the case where there are n two-steps that occur before absorption. Each two-step has the mgf given by Eq. 4.24. The sum of n two-steps will have an mgf given by the product of n terms, each $(1 - \theta/b)^{-2}$. Let t_{2n} be this summated time variable. Its mgf is

$$(4.25) \qquad M_{t_{2n}}(\theta) = \left(1 - \frac{\theta}{b}\right)^{-2n}.$$

This expression is known to be the mgf of the gamma distribution (cf. McGill, 1963), which has the density function

$$(4.26) \qquad f(t_{2n}) = \frac{b^{2n}}{(2n - 1)!}\, t^{2n-1} e^{-bt}.$$

The gamma distribution in this equation has a mean of $2n/b$ and variance of $2n/b^2$. Now the number of two-steps, n, is a random variable whose probability distribution we have already calculated; namely,

$$Pr(X = n) = J(1 - J)^{n-1}.$$

To obtain the mgf of the total time T, we must take the $M_{t_{2n}}(\theta)$ expression in Eq. 4.25 and weight it by the probability that there are n two-steps before absorption. Summing over all possible values of $X = n$ gives the expected mgf for T. We let $M_T(\theta)$ represent the mgf for the total time. The expression for $M_T(\theta)$ is

$$
\begin{aligned}
M_T(\theta) &= \sum_{n=1}^{\infty} Pr(X = n) M_{t_{2n}}(\theta) \\
&= \sum_{n=1}^{\infty} J(1 - J)^{n-1} \left(1 - \frac{\theta}{b}\right)^{-2n} \\
&= J\left[1 - \frac{\theta}{b}\right]^{-2} \sum_{n=1}^{\infty} \left[(1 - J)\left(1 - \frac{\theta}{b}\right)^{-2}\right]^{n-1} \\
&= \frac{J\left(1 - \dfrac{\theta}{b}\right)^{-2}}{1 - (1 - J)\left(1 - \dfrac{\theta}{b}\right)^{-2}},
\end{aligned}
$$

or

$$(4.27) \qquad M_T(\theta) = \frac{J}{\left(1 - \dfrac{\theta}{b}\right)^2 - (1 - J)}.$$

By direct methods we may obtain the first and second raw moments from $M_T(\theta)$. They are

(4.28)

$$\mu_1 = E(T) = \left.\frac{dM_T(\theta)}{d\theta}\right|_{\theta=0} = \frac{2}{bJ}$$

$$\mu_2 = \left.\frac{d^2M_T(\theta)}{d\theta^2}\right|_{\theta=0} = \frac{2(4-J)}{(bJ)^2} .$$

The variance of T is the second moment minus the square of the mean, or

(4.29)
$$\mathrm{Var}(T) = \mu_2 - [E(T)]^2 = \frac{2(2-J)}{(bJ)^2} .$$

Now let us comment upon these results for the mean and variance of T. We recall (Eq. 4.19a) that the expected number of steps S is $2/J$ and the expected time per step is $1/b$. Thus the result for mean total time is just the mean steps multiplied by the mean time per step, or $2/Jb$, which is an intuitively sensible relation. In regard to the variance of T, we note that the variance of the number of two-steps before absorption is $\mathrm{Var}(X) = (1-J)/J^2$. From the mgf in Eq. 4.24, we may see that the variance of the times taken to complete a two-step [that is, $\mathrm{Var}(t_2)$] is $2/b^2$. Thus, the result in Eq. 4.29 for the variance of T can be restated as follows:

$$\mathrm{Var}(T) = \frac{2 + 2(1-J)}{(bJ)^2} = \frac{2}{(bJ)^2} + \mathrm{Var}(X) \cdot \mathrm{Var}(t_2).$$

Note that even when there is no variability in the steps to absorption [that is, $\mathrm{Var}(X) = 0$], we still expect a fair amount of variance in the choice times. Thus, we have solved one of the difficulties encountered by the former model that had fixed time h per step.

We wish to know the probability density function of the total time T, which we will call $f(T)$. The derivation of $f(T)$ is achieved by taking the density functions $f(t_{2n})$ in Eq. 4.26 and multiplying them by the likelihood that n two-steps occur before absorption.

$$f(T) = \sum_{n=1}^{\infty} Pr(X = n)f(t_{2n})$$

$$= \sum_{n=1}^{\infty} [J(1-J)^{n-1}]\left[\frac{b^{2n}t^{2n-1}e^{-bt}}{(2n-1)!}\right].$$

To perform this summation, we manipulate terms involving the exponent n until each term appears with an exponent of $2n-1$, and then bring the constant terms outside the summation. This operation yields

$$f(T) = \frac{Jbe^{-bt}}{\sqrt{1-J}} \sum_{n=1}^{\infty} \frac{[bt\sqrt{1-J}]^{2n-1}}{(2n-1)!} .$$

Let $\alpha = bt\sqrt{1-J}$. Then the summation above may be written as

$$\sum_{n=1}^{\infty} \frac{\alpha^{2n-1}}{(2n-1)!} = \alpha + \frac{\alpha^3}{3!} + \frac{\alpha^5}{5!} = \frac{\alpha^7}{7!} + \cdots.$$

We see that this progression contains only the odd terms of the series expansion of e^{α}. Therefore, we know that the series sum converges to a limit and, furthermore, that this sum is less than e^{α}. In fact, one may show that the limiting sum is one-half the difference between e^{α} and $e^{-\alpha}$, namely,

$$\sum_{n=1}^{\infty} \frac{\alpha^{2n-1}}{(2n-1)!} = \frac{1}{2}\left[1 + \alpha + \frac{\alpha^2}{2!} + \frac{\alpha^3}{3!} + \cdots\right]$$

$$- \frac{1}{2}\left[1 - \alpha + \frac{\alpha^2}{2!} - \frac{\alpha^3}{3!} + \cdots\right]$$

$$= \tfrac{1}{2}[e^{\alpha} - e^{-\alpha}].$$

Substituting the right hand side of this equation for the summation in the expression for $f(T)$ yields

$$f(T) = \frac{Jbe^{-bT}}{\sqrt{1-J}} \tfrac{1}{2}[e^{\alpha} - e^{-\alpha}].$$

We rewrite this in terms of T by the substitution $\alpha = bTa$ and $a = \sqrt{1-J}$. The final result is

(4.30) $$f(T) = \frac{Jb}{2a}[e^{-b(1-a)T} - e^{-b(1+a)T}].$$

As a check on our derivation of this equation, we may prove that the mgf of this $f(T)$ is the same as was obtained in Eq. 4.27 by the indirect method, namely

$$M_T(\theta) = \int_0^{\infty} e^{\theta T} f(T)\, dT$$

$$= \frac{Jb}{2a}\left[\int_0^{\infty} e^{-b\left(1-a-\frac{\theta}{b}\right)T}\, dT - \int_0^{\infty} e^{-b\left(1+a-\frac{\theta}{b}\right)T}\, dT\right]$$

$$= \frac{Jb}{2a}\left[\frac{-1}{b\left(1+a-\frac{\theta}{b}\right)} + \frac{1}{b\left(1-a-\frac{\theta}{b}\right)}\right]$$

$$= \frac{J}{\left(1+a-\frac{\theta}{b}\right)\left(1-a-\frac{\theta}{b}\right)}$$

$$= \frac{J}{\left(1-\frac{\theta}{b}\right)^2 - (1-J)}.$$

In the last line we have substituted the identity $a^2 = 1 - J$. Because there is a one-to-one relationship between a density function and its mgf, the fact that the result here coincides with the mgf calculated by the other method in Eq. 4.27 means that the $f(T)$ in Eq. 4.30 is indeed the correct one for our problem.

Note that in case $J = 1$, then $a = 0$ and the expression in Eq. 4.30 reduces to the indeterminate form of $0/0$. However, when $J = 1$, we know there is only one two-step before absorption. Therefore, the total time distribution will be given by Eq. 4.26 with $n = 1$, namely,

$$f(t_2) = b^2 t e^{-bt},$$

which has a mean of $2/b$ and a variance of $2/b^2$.

Let us study the general density function $f(T)$ in Eq. 4.30 to see how well it solves the problems that arose in the simple discrete-time model with a constant h seconds per step. First, the new model does allow for continuous time variations. Second, the form of the distribution is not an exponential decay but instead rises to a peak before tapering off. A graph of $f(T)$ is shown in Fig. 4.3 for the parameter values $J = 0.50$ and $b = 1$. With $J = 0.50$, there will be an appreciable amount of VTE-ing, so the choice time density function will reflect these instances of prolonged hesitation before choice. The location of the mode (maximal value) of the density function may be found by standard methods; we solve for T in the equation resulting from setting $df(T)/dT$ equal to zero. In this fashion, the mode of $f(T)$ is found to be located at

$$\text{Mode } f(T) = \frac{1}{2ab} \log_e \left[\frac{1 + a}{1 - a} \right].$$

For our illustrative values of $b = 1$ and $a = \sqrt{1 - J} = 0.71$, the mode is at $T = 1.25$, where $f(T)$ takes on the value 0.204. As expected from the equation for $\text{Var}(T)$, when $J = 1$ and there is no variability in VTE's, there still remains substantial variability in the choice times. Finally, we note that the decision times before choices of response A_1 and A_2 should be identically distributed, according to this model. This accords with our earlier result that the frequency distribution of loops was independent of which response was chosen eventually.

A model of this kind accounts for many of the qualitative aspects known about choice times; however, it is not known at present how well it would fit quantitative details of the observed frequency distributions. An ideal testing situation would somehow arrange for observation and recording of orientations and VTE's as well as choices. In such cases, the parameter J could be estimated from the VTE data, leaving b as the only free parameter available for fitting the choice time distributions.

When VTE data are recorded, a strict test of the model would be provided by considering time distributions conditional upon the occurrence of exactly n steps before absorption. For fixed values of n steps, the times should have the gamma distribution given by Eq. 4.26; moreover, the value of b should be the same for time distributions obtained after two steps, four steps, six steps, etc. These constitute very strict tests of the model.

In practice, such attempts at testing the model require that the experimental situation be so contrived as to approximate the idealized assumptions of the model. A critical feature in this regard is that the steps between any two adjacent states take approximately the same time on the average; for example, the time for going from orienting state S_0 to S_1 should be about the same as the time taken to "approach" A_1 from S_1, and this the same time as reorienting from S_1 to S_0, and so forth. Another problem that often arises with empirical applications of gamma-type latency models is the likely existence of an irreducible deadtime or minimum value below which the choice time cannot go. The exponential step-time idea supposes that the subject "waits" t seconds before initiating the response (of stepping to the next state), but once initiated that response goes through to completion in an instant. According to such notions, it is possible for subjects to make some very fast responses. For example, in Fig. 4.3, with the reasonable values of $J = 0.5$ and $b = 1.0$, a significant proportion of the choice times are expected to be 0.25 seconds or less, which is known to be less than the minimal reaction time for a rat. This particular problem can be solved in several different ways. One way is simply to estimate a constant deadtime t_0 below the minimum value of the raw data time scores, transform all time scores to $T - t_0$, and predict the latter scores from the model. An alternative is to suppose that each transition between states consists of an exponentially variable waiting time t plus a fixed constant h for actually executing the response. Thus when there are n steps before absorption, the total time would be nh plus the sum of n exponential waiting-time variables. A third method is to let the duration h of the response-step component be itself another random variable with its minimal value being some positive number h'.

In closing this section, we wish to point out that a variety of mathematical models have been proposed to deal with simple and disjunctive reaction times. It was not our intent to review these here, but rather to show how predictions about reaction times can follow from a particular representation of the response process. For further relevant material and alternative models, the reader can consult Christie and Luce (1956), Stone (1960), or McGill (1962). An excellent article reviewing developments in this field is that by McGill (1963).

4.6 OTHER RANDOM WALK MODELS
FOR CHOICE BEHAVIOR

Once the general idea of representing the individual act of choice as a random walk is grasped, it becomes clear that the model in Fig. 4.1 is by no means the only possible representation. In this section we briefly review the salient features of a few alternative formulations for the purpose of contrasting them with the model depicted in Fig. 4.1, which for convenience we will call Model A.

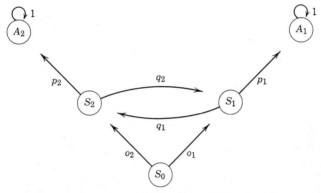

Fig. 4.4 Alternative representation of the random walk involved in an act of choice (Model B).

A simple variant of Model A is obtained by supposing that the subject orients back and forth between states S_1 and S_2 without, in a psychological sense, returning to the neutral state S_0. The initial state S_0 is used only to start the subject on his first orientation to S_1 or S_2. This representation, which we will call Model B, is displayed pictorially in Fig. 4.4. For Model B, the probability that the process is eventually absorbed in state A_1 is

$$Pr(A_1) = \frac{p_1[o_1 + (1 - o_1)(1 - p_2)]}{p_1 + p_2 - p_1 p_2}.$$

In order to note an interesting feature about this model, let $o_1 = \frac{1}{2}$, and rearrange $Pr(A_1)$ as follows:

$$Pr(A_1) = \frac{p_1\left[1 - \dfrac{p_2}{2}\right]}{p_1\left[1 - \dfrac{p_2}{2}\right] + p_2\left[1 - \dfrac{p_1}{2}\right]}.$$

Dividing through by $\left(1 - \dfrac{p_1}{2}\right)\left(1 - \dfrac{p_2}{2}\right)$ yields

$$Pr(A_1) = \cfrac{\cfrac{p_1}{1 - \cfrac{p_1}{2}}}{\cfrac{p_1}{1 - \cfrac{p_1}{2}} + \cfrac{p_2}{1 - \cfrac{p_2}{2}}}.$$

We define a number $v_k(i)$ as

(4.31a) $$v_k(i) = \cfrac{p_i}{1 - \cfrac{p_i}{k}}.$$

With $k = 2$, it may be seen that $Pr(A_1)$ can be expressed as

(4.31b) $$Pr(1, 2) = \frac{v_2(1)}{v_2(1) + v_2(2)}.$$

We thus arrive at the formula relating pairwise choice probability to the ratio of two "strength" parameters, much as in Luce's theory and in Model A. Thus, Model B implies the product rule (cf. Eq. 4.7) for relations among pairwise choice probabilities.

Consider the generalization of Model B to the case of choice from among k alternatives, and let us retain the assumption that orientations are random. This means, first, that $o_i = \dfrac{1}{k}$ for all i. Second, if the subject is in orienting state S_i, but does not approach A_i and instead reorients away from S_i, then he has probability $\dfrac{1}{k - 1}$ of orienting to any one of the other $k - 1$ alternatives. Under these general circumstances, the expression for probability of absorption at A_1 can be shown (see Estes, 1960b) to be

$$Pr(A_1; k) = \frac{v_k(1)}{\sum v_k(j)},$$

where the sum is over all j. This expression again preserves the ratio form of Luce's choice rule. However, because the number k is involved in the v-values here, the constant ratio rule is not implied by Model B. To prove this statement, consider the ratio of the probability that (for a k-choice problem) the A_1 response is chosen to the probability that A_2 is chosen. The sum of $v_k(j)$ terms cancels out of the denominators, and the ratio is

$$\frac{Pr(A_1; k)}{Pr(A_2; k)} = \frac{v_k(1)}{v_k(2)} = \frac{p_1}{p_2}\left(\frac{k - p_2}{k - p_1}\right).$$

This ratio is a decreasing function of k if $p_1 > p_2$ and an increasing function of k if $p_2 > p_1$. On the contrary, for Luce's choice theory and for Model A, this ratio is expected to be constant and independent of the number of alternatives involved in the choice. In practice, however, it may prove difficult to obtain data that sharply discriminate between a constant ratio and Model B's prediction that the choice ratio should vary with the set size k. Depending upon the estimated p_i values for Model B, the change in the ratio going from a k of 2 to 3 or 4 may be quite small relative to the variability in empirical estimates of the ratios of choice probabilities. At the moment, there has been no sharp experimental test to discriminate between these two models; hence both are logical contenders.

To continue our review of random walk models of choice behavior, a paper by Spence (1960) should be mentioned. Working independently, he proposed a choice model whose formal representation is identical to that of Model B. In addition to formulating this choice theory, Spence concerned himself with deriving the transition probabilities o_1, p_1, and p_2 from Hullian learning theory. Another example of a similar model is seen in a paper by Audley (1960). Audley considers that prior to choosing between alternatives A_1 and A_2, the individual generates covert or implicit behaviors resembling responses A_1 or A_2. These covert responses we may label as a_1 or a_2. The time rate of occurrence of implicit responses of type a_1 is α and of implicit responses of type a_2 is β. These two rate parameters α and β determine the probability that the next implicit response will be an a_1. Let p represent this probability that the next implicit response is of type a_1. Then it may be shown that $p = \alpha/(\alpha + \beta)$. The choice rule Audley proposes is as follows: when the subject generates some number K of *consecutive* covert responses of one type, this generation elicits the overt response which corresponds to that covert response. The case investigated in detail in Audley's paper was for $K = 2$.

It is easy to show that for $K = 2$ this model is a special case of Model B formulated in Fig. 4.4. We make the following state identifications: S_0 is the state prior to the first covert response; S_1 is the state entered after generation of a covert a_1 response, S_2 is entered after a covert a_2 response, A_1 is entered after two consecutive covert a_1 responses and A_2 is entered after two consecutive covert a_2 responses. Audley lets p be the probability of a covert a_1 response and $q = 1 - p$ be the probability that the next covert response is of type a_2. In terms of the transition parameters of Model B, this means that $o_1 = p_1 = p$ and $o_2 = p_2 = q$. Given these identifications, then Model B is equivalent to Audley's model. Audley supposes that the rate parameters α and β remain invariant as the choice set is changed. By following out the implications of this assumption, it is seen that the model does not imply the product rule for pairwise choices, nor does it imply anything resembling the constant ratio rule as the choice set is increased in size. The reason for this is that the probability that the next covert response is of type a_1 is not constant, but rather changes as one manipulates the number and nature of the alternative responses in competition with A_1.

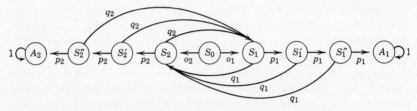

Fig. 4.5   State transition diagram for approach gradient model.

Estes (1960b) has proposed a generalization of Model B which is similar to Audley's proposal that the overt choice be made to depend upon K consecutive covert responses of one type. Estes' extension is displayed in Fig. 4.5. The path between orienting to S_i and approaching A_i is segmented into a number m of states along a gradient of "approach to A_i." The analogy is to the behavior of a rat in a T-maze taking successive steps along the path leading to a particular terminal stimulus. A two-choice illustration for $m = 3$ is shown in Fig. 4.5, where the appropriate transition probabilities have been indicated beside each arrow.

The intermediate states of orienting and moving progressively nearer to A_i have been labeled S_i, S_i', and S_i'', and each move to a state farther along the line has probability p_i. However, with probability q_i the subject may reorient completely to the beginning of the path pointing towards the other alternative. Model B in Fig. 4.4 is seen to be the special case where $m = 1$ of the general model represented in Fig. 4.5.

For purposes of computing choice probabilities, the chain of m steps leading from the initial orienting state S_i to the absorption state A_i may be replaced by a "single step" having probability p_i^m; with probability $1 - p_i^m$ an orientation to S_i is not followed by absorption but rather by eventual reorientation to the opposite stimulus. Following this line of reasoning, the expression for probability of eventual absorption on A_1 may be derived to be

$$Pr(A_1) = \frac{p_1^m[o_1 + (1 - o_1)(1 - p_2^m)]}{p_1^m + p_2^m - p_1^m p_2^m}.$$

When $m = 1$, this expression is identical to that obtained previously for Model B. Again, for random orientation, we may define strength parameters, $s_n(i)$,

$$s_n(i) = \frac{p_i^m}{1 - \frac{p_i^m}{n}}$$

and prove that the probability of choosing A_1 from among n alternatives is

$$Pr(A_1; n) = \frac{s_n(1)}{\sum_j s_n(j)}.$$

If $m = 1$ in the two above equations, the results correspond to Model B's Eq. 4.31.

From a quantitative point of view, the main effect of m is to amplify the effect on $Pr(A_1)$ of small differences between p_1 and p_2. To illustrate, suppose $p_1 = 0.7$ and $p_2 = 0.5$; then the $Pr(A_1)$ values for $m = 1, 3$, and 6 are 0.66, 0.76, and 0.89, respectively. In this manner experimental variables that theoretically have only small effects on the basic parameters p_1 and p_2 can still exert rather large effects on observable choices. It should be clear that this requirement of m consecutive approach responses to enter the absorption state could also be tacked onto Model A depicted in Fig. 4.1. Expressions for absorption probabilities would be modified merely by replacing p_i by p_i^m. However, deriving the distribution of the number of steps and time before absorption would present some mathematical complexities.

One possible line of application of these general m-step models is to the scaling of psychological distances between stimuli using data obtained by the method of triads (cf. Torgerson, 1958). In the method of triads, the human subject is shown a standard stimulus S_i and two comparison stimuli S_j and S_k and is asked to choose that comparison stimulus which is "more like" or "more similar to" the standard S_i. Over successive trials, the standard and comparison stimuli are interchanged and combined with other stimuli until judgments have been collected many times on all possible triples that can be formed from a set of n stimuli. A choice or scaling theory is then expected to predict choice probabilities for all such triples once the basic parameters of the system have been estimated. Several models for such "multidimensional" scaling problems have been proposed (cf. Torgerson, 1958, Chapter 11). Each involves the idea that stimuli are to be represented as points in a psychological space and that the intuitive notion of similarity between two stimuli is to be represented by the metric distance between the two points in the space.

To apply the generalized version of Model A to such data, we consider the triad consisting of S_i as standard and S_j and S_k as comparison stimuli. The subject begins by orienting to S_i and is at the point S_i in the corresponding psychological space. From S_i to S_j, we will suppose that there are m_{ij} steps before absorption (choosing S_j). We assume for simplicity that the probability of approaching closer toward a stimulus is p, whereas $q = 1 - p$ is the likelihood of reorienting and considering the alternative comparison stimulus. Let $Pr(j \mid ijk)$ represent the probability that S_j is chosen as more similar when S_i is the standard and S_j and S_k are the comparison stimuli. Then the expanded version of Model A gives the following expression:

$$Pr(j \mid ijk) = \frac{p^{m_{ij}}}{p^{m_{ij}} + p^{m_{ik}}}$$

$$= \frac{1}{1 + p^{m_{ik} - m_{ij}}}.$$

Thus, $Pr(j \mid ijk)$ is given by a logistic function of the difference between the distances m_{ik} and m_{ij} that are being compared. If the distances are equal, then the choice probability is 0.50. If the distance m_{ik} is very much larger than the distance m_{ij}, then the p-term in the denominator is reduced close to zero, so that the probability of the subject selecting S_j as more similar to S_i is brought close to one. An estimate of the difference between the distances may be obtained by the following transformation:

$$\log \frac{Pr(j \mid ijk)}{Pr(k \mid ijk)} = (m_{ij} - m_{ik}) \log p.$$

By this equation one obtains estimates of the distance differences scaled to the common unit of $\log p$. Given such estimates, there are standard procedures (cf. Torgerson, 1958, pp. 254–259) for determining (1) whether the m_{ij} show sufficient internal consistency to be represented as distances between points in a Euclidean metric space, and if so, (2) to determine the number of orthogonal dimensions in the spatial representation, and (3) the projections of each stimulus "point" upon the axes corresponding to the dimensions of the space. We will not continue this development further; the idea has been elaborated sufficiently to give the reader some notion of how the choice model can be used as a distance-scaling device for locating stimuli in a psychological space.

4.7   A RANDOM WALK MODEL WITH MEMORY

We conclude our review of random walk models by considering a theory of choice behavior proposed by LaBerge (1962). This model is most relevant to situations involving presentation of a single stimulus, to which the subject is to respond with one of two or more available responses. A disjunctive reaction time experiment is an example: if a red light appears, the subject should quickly depress the left key; if a green light appears, the subject should quickly depress the right key. Of course, there are a large number of choice situations that can be characterized in this manner, so the model has a potentially wide range of applicability. LaBerge represents the stimulus as a large population of many small details or aspects and uses the label "stimulus elements" to refer to such aspects. This representation of the stimulus is frequently adopted in stimulus sampling theory (cf. Chapter 8). Suppose there are two responses, A_1 and A_2, of interest to the experimenter, and a trial continues until the subject chooses one of these. LaBerge assumes that the population of stimulus elements acting at any one time may be partitioned into three sets of elements: a proportion p_1 that is connected (or conditioned) to response A_1, a proportion p_2 that is connected to response A_2, and the remaining proportion p_0 that is connected neither to A_1 nor to A_2.

The model supposes that when a stimulus is presented, the subject begins sampling stimulus elements from the stimulus population, one element at a time, in a random sequence. Depending upon the conditioning of the element, it will be called an a_1, an a_2, or an a_0 element. As the subject samples sequentially from the stimulus population, he keeps a running total of how many a_1 and how many a_2 elements he has sampled up to this point in the trial. If the count on the a_1 counter ever reaches a threshold value of r_1, then the subject makes overt response A_1. If the count on the a_2 counter ever reaches its threshold value of r_2, then the subject makes overt response A_2. Sampled elements of type a_0 are not registered by either counter, and they simply add deadtime to the response evocation process. In metaphorical terms, choice is thought of as a race between the two counters, the response being determined by whichever counter reaches its finish line first (threshold value, r_i). At the end of the trial, after the overt choice, the counters are reset to zero for the start of the next trial.

This "sequential inspection" idea of LaBerge's, which he calls a "recruitment" model, bears an interesting contrast to the random walk models of Audley and Estes. In the Audley and Estes models, choice depends upon the occurrence of K (or m) *consecutive* covert responses of the same type; effectively, their a_1 counter was reset to zero every time an a_2 element

intervened, and vice versa. In the recruitment model, there is no requirement that the r_i elements occur in consecutive order; here the a_1 counter
does not reset when an a_2 element intervenes, but rather the system remem-
bers and accumulates the number of a_1 and a_2 counts over time within the
trial. Thus, the recruitment model is a random walk with a memory for
how far it has come.

For purposes of exposition, the recruitment model can be represented as
a two-dimensional random walk. The states of the Markov chain are
the possible integer pairs (i, j), where i is the current count on the a_1
counter and j is the current count on the a_2 counter. The possible values
of the a_1 counter are $0, 1, \ldots, r_1$, and of the a_2 counter are $0, 1, \ldots, r_2$.
In total, there are $(r_1 + 1)(r_2 + 1)$ possible state pairs. The states (r_1, j)
for $j < r_2$ and (i, r_2) for $i < r_1$ are absorbing. Each time an element is
sampled, the process takes a step. The transition probabilities for the
steps from state (i, j) are as follows: to $(i + 1, j)$ with probability p_1;
to $(i, j + 1)$ with probability p_2; and remain at (i, j) with probability
p_0 when an a_0 element is sampled.

Let us derive the expression for the probability of choosing A_1. The a_0
elements affect choice times but have nothing to do with which response
is finally chosen. Thus, for this derivation, we will assume that $p_0 = 0$
and that p_1 and p_2 add to unity. The probability of drawing an a_1 element
is p_1, and of drawing an a_2 element is $p_2 = 1 - p_1$. The probability that
A_1 occurs is the likelihood that r_1 elements of type a_1 are drawn before r_2
elements of type a_2 are drawn. Imagine that the r_1th a_1-element is obtained
on the mth draw, where $m \geq r_1$ and $m - r_1 < r_2$. The probability of the
event "r_1 of type a_1 and $m - r_1$ of type a_2" is the negative binomial
probability given by

$$Pr(r_1 \text{ in } m \text{ draws}) = \binom{m - 1}{r_1 - 1} p_1^{r_1} p_2^{m-r_1}.$$

The binomial coefficient here results from enumerating all possible
sequences in which $r_1 - 1$ of the first $m - 1$ elements can be of type a_1.
The mth element drawn is the r_1th of type a_1, by assumption. What has
to be done now is to sum these probabilities over all permissible values of
m from $m = r_1$ up to $m = r_1 + r_2 - 1$. Thus, $Pr(A_1)$ is

$$Pr(A_1) = \sum_{m=r_1}^{r_1+r_2-1} \binom{m - 1}{r_1 - 1} p_1^{r_1} p_2^{m-r_1}.$$

An alternate way of writing the expressions is to let $x = m - r_1$ be the
number of a_2 elements drawn and to sum the probabilities over x values
from 0 to $r_2 - 1$, yielding

$$Pr(A_1) = \sum_{x=0}^{r_2-1} \binom{r_1 + x - 1}{r_1 - 1} p_1^{r_1} p_2^{x}.$$

This expression can not be simplified any further. However, it is a function well known to mathematicians, and has been extensively tabled. It is called the incomplete beta ratio, and tables for the function have been published by Pearson (1932).

To investigate the nature of the $Pr(A_1)$ function, let us study the special case where $r_1 = r_2 = r$. Figure 4.6 shows a graph taken from LaBerge's

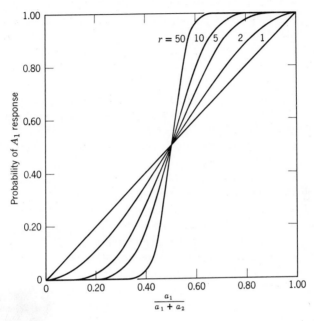

Fig. 4.6   Response probability as a function of the ratio of conditioned elements.

paper (1962) depicting the relationship between p_1 and $Pr(A_1)$. The recruitment factor, r, is the parameter varying from one curve to another. We see that when $r = 1$, the response is completely determined by the first element sampled, so $Pr(A_1) = p_1$, and the straight line in Fig. 4.6 results. As r is increased, $Pr(A_1)$ deviates more toward one for p_1 values above 0.50 and deviates more toward zero for p_1 values below 0.50. For very large values of r, $Pr(A_1)$ approximates a step-function, jumping from zero up to one as p_1 increases from slightly below to slightly above 0.50. As with the parameters K and m in the Audley and Estes models, the effect of r is to amplify the effect of small changes in p_1, thereby creating a large change in $Pr(A_1)$.

LaBerge goes on in his paper to derive implications about choice-time distributions, the relationship between choice times and response probabilities, and so forth. For our purposes, however, this brief review of the recruitment model suffices to describe the essential ideas of the approach.

4.8 CONCLUDING COMMENTS

In concluding this chapter, we wish to point out that we have only scratched the surface of the vast area known as choice theory and/or scaling. The research area has expanded in many directions, and most topics can not be covered in a short chapter. The theories presented in this chapter represent a selection bias on the authors' part; we have covered only probabilistic theories of choice with which we have been directly concerned in our own research on learning. For more detailed coverage of choice theories related to the stimulus-scaling problem, we recommend books by Torgerson (1958) and Coombs (1964). For coverage of developments in algebraic theories of decision making (utility theory), we refer the reader to articles by Edwards (1961a) and Luce and Suppes (1965). In closing, we will cite two criticisms of the choice theories reviewed—one of a general nature regarding interpretation, the other of a specific nature regarding data collection for testing the theories.

The general criticism is that most of the choice theories are lacking in what might be called a "representation" theory. In brief, the best method of representing a given choice situation in terms of the constructs of the theory is not always clear. This criticism applies with particular force to the random walk models, and less so to Luce's theory, which has been widely applied. Ideally, one would like to have an associated set of statements that would tell us how to make the appropriate identifications in specific experiments. At present, the process of applying the models to specific cases involves a mixture of intuition, experience with the situation, and pure chance in hitting upon a useful representation.

The problem occurs because choice is a ubiquitous notion. Many different kinds of stimuli can be presented to a subject for choice; similarly, we can ask him to perform a large number of operations upon the set of stimuli presented. To illustrate the diversity: in presenting the subject with n stimuli, we can ask him to pick one by any number of criteria, to select the best (or worst) k of the n stimuli, to rank all n stimuli, to sort them into different categories on the basis of some criterion, to assign qualitative ratings or quantitative estimates to each stimulus according to the degree to which it possesses some attribute, to segregate pairs of stimuli into classes representing equal-similarity pairs, to rank-order the distances between each pair of stimuli, and so on. The book by Coombs (1964) gives an excellent review and systematic classification of such methods of data collection. These operations and many more can be carried out on a set of stimuli by a suitably instructed subject, and there will usually be a certain lawfulness and consistency to how he performs. The problem is that the choice theories do not have sufficient conceptual richness to suggest how these various operations by the subject are to be uniquely represented in the model. The ambiguity is not restricted to complex operations required of the subjects; it could be illustrated as well in a simple psychophysical experiment in which the subject is judging which of two tones is louder (for example, there are at least three different representations of this task in terms of the random walk models). Each choice theory was originally constructed with a limited range of situations in mind, so perhaps we should not be surprised that it is unsure in its identifications for other types of choice operations.

Our second criticism is that data for the testing of choice theories is often difficult to collect. The theories as written describe the act of choice by a single individual. To obtain choice percentages, we must repeatedly offer the same pair of alternatives to the subject for his choice. Except for cases involving imperfect discrimination, it is highly likely that the subject's successive choices from a given pair will not be statistically independent. The problem is that the subject will remember his most recent choice from the presentation set, and is likely to make his present choice consistent with that one. If we were to ask a subject once whether he prefers Fords or Chevrolets, he would give us a reasonable answer; if we were to put the same question to him a hundred times, he would begin to doubt our sanity. Thus with a small set of discriminable stimuli, it is generally difficult to construct a data-collection procedure yielding reliable estimates of $Pr(i, j)$ from single subjects.

A frequently proposed solution to this problem is the use of a large group of subjects, each of whom makes only one choice from each presentation set. Then the theoretical probability, $Pr(i, j)$, is estimated by the proportion of subjects who choose i when presented with the set i, j. This group procedure was employed in the initial part of this chapter. The theory is then tested by seeing whether the group proportions satisfy constraints like the product rule or the constant ratio rule. Careful analysis of the choice theories (in particular, those discussed in this chapter) shows that the group average results may be of questionable status. Considering Luce's axiom, for example, it is not difficult to demonstrate that although subjects with differing v-values conform to the axiom, the group average will not in general.

To illustrate, suppose that three objects for choice are A, B, and C and suppose that of N subjects, the ith person has scale values a_i, b_i, and c_i for the three objects. According to the theory, the group average proportion of choices of A over B in the pair comparison will be

$$\overline{Pr(A, B)} = \frac{1}{N} \sum_i \frac{a_i}{a_i + b_i} .$$

We consider now the ratio of choosing A over B when the set is (A, B) and when it is (A, B, C). The group average results are

(4.32)
$$\frac{\overline{Pr(A, B)}}{\overline{Pr(B, A)}} = \frac{\sum_i \dfrac{a_i}{a_i + b_i}}{\sum_i \dfrac{b_i}{a_i + b_i}}$$

and

(4.33)
$$\frac{\overline{Pr(A; ABC)}}{\overline{Pr(B; ABC)}} = \frac{\sum_i \dfrac{a_i}{a_i + b_i + c_i}}{\sum_i \dfrac{b_i}{a_i + b_i + c_i}} .$$

Clearly, these two expressions will not be equal in general unless all subjects have the same scale values. The assumption that group averages may be used for testing the constant ratio rule reduces to the assertion that approximations of the form

$$\sum_i \frac{a_i}{a_i + b_i + c_i} \approx \frac{\sum a_i}{\sum (a_i + b_i + c_i)}$$

are adequate. If approximations of this sort are used throughout, then the values in Eq. 4.32 and Eq. 4.33 are equal and the constant ratio rule holds for the group averages. The approximation essentially replaces the mean value of a ratio by the ratio of the two mean values.

The result of this approximation is to put some slippage between the theory and tests of it using group data (which, after all, are the easiest to collect). If the theory's predictions regarding the product rule, constant ratio rule, and so forth, are slightly in error when tested against group data, then the approximation may be questioned. Contrariwise, if the group predictions are accurate, then we are uncertain about the contribution of the approximation in making these accurate predictions. Although this problem of averaging group data has been illustrated for Luce's choice theory, it applies with equal force to the other theories considered in this chapter.

CHAPTER 5

SIGNAL DETECTION AND PROBABILITY LEARNING

Although the focus of this book is mathematical developments in learning theory, it is not always feasible to draw a sharp line of demarcation between the various fields of psychology. Lines become blurred particularly when one looks at the areas of learning and psychophysics. A great deal of research in learning, especially on topics like discrimination and generalization, is closely allied to work in psychophysics; similarly, problems in psychophysics, such as recognition and scaling, are of central relevance to learning theory. Introductory textbooks in psychology generally organize the field so that a clear distinction is made between psychophysics and learning; and if one is principally concerned with a description of behavioral phenomena, the categorization is useful. However, when one turns to the task of theory construction in either of these fields, the analysis frequently leads to a model that incorporates both a perceptual-sensory process and a learning mechanism.

The theoretical work to be described in this chapter represents a development that straddles the fence between learning and psychophysics. The model is formulated so that with one set of correspondence rules it provides an account of signal detection, and with another set of rules an account of probability learning. Thus, for this model it is appropriate to discuss a problem in psychophysics and one in learning at the same time.

An exact characterization of signal detection and probability learning will be given later. For now it suffices to say that both experimental procedures usually involve a long series of discrete trials. On each trial the subject is required to make a choice from an experimenter-defined set of alternative responses, and then receives an information event (reinforcement) indicating whether or not his response was correct.

Signal detection and probability learning are distinguished by the nature of the stimulus that initiates the trial. For the detection task the stimulus is a weak signal embedded in a noise background, and the subject is required to indicate where he thinks the signal occurred by making an appropriate response. For the probability learning task, the stimulus is the onset of a warning light that is identical from trial to trial; here the stimulus does not provide any new information, and the subject must make a response on the basis of the past pattern of reinforcing events. The early work in signal detection was designed to measure the limits of the sensory system, whereas probability learning was originally devised as a verbal analogue to Pavlovian conditioning (Humphreys, 1939).

In order to simplify the discussion of these two topics, it is helpful at the outset to treat each somewhat separately. We will begin with a description of the signal detection task and will develop the model and related methods of data analysis within this framework. Then we will turn to probability learning, indicating how the same model can be applied to this situation, and considering some of the model's predictions that are unique to the learning task. At the end of the chapter, an experiment will be described that permits us to investigate simultaneously signal detection and probability learning. Throughout the chapter, only the two-alternative case for both signal detection and probability learning will be considered. There are no new mathematical or conceptual problems introduced by generalizing the analysis to the case of multiple alternatives, but the notation and development are more cumbersome. The reader will have no difficulty formulating the multiple-alternative case for himself, once he understands the two-alternative model.

5.1 TWO-ALTERNATIVE FORCED-CHOICE DETECTION TASK

One of the simplest types of signal detection experiments involves the two-alternative, forced-choice design. On each trial two temporal intervals are defined; in one interval noise plus a signal is presented, while in the other interval only the noise is presented. Thus the two presentations are the temporally ordered pairs $\langle s, \bar{s} \rangle$ and $\langle \bar{s}, s \rangle$ where s denotes signal plus noise and $\bar{s}$ denotes noise alone. After the stimulus presentation the subject responds "1" or "2" to indicate which interval he believes is more likely to have contained the signal.

To make matters concrete we will describe the procedure used in an acoustic experiment involving the two-interval forced-choice design; data from this experiment will be presented later. Band-limited Gaussian noise* was presented binaurally in the subject's headphones throughout a test session and the signal was a 1000 cycles per second (cps) sinusoidal tone; the tone was presented for 100 milliseconds, including equal fall and rise times of 20 milliseconds. The subject was seated before a stimulus display board. On each trial three lights flashed on briefly in succession: a red light, an amber light, and another amber light. Each light was on for 100 milliseconds with a 500 millisecond delay between each successive on period. The red light was simply a warning light, while the amber lights defined two observation periods. The onset of the 1000 cps signal occurred simultaneously with the onset of one of the amber lights. After the second amber light went off, the subject had 2.5 seconds to indicate his response by pressing a push button located under the appropriate amber light. At the conclusion of the response period, a green light flashed on for 700 milliseconds above the correct response button. There was a 1.5 second intertrial period, thus each trial lasted for 6 seconds. A typical experimental session ran for 300 to 500 trials (thirty to fifty minutes).

In studies of this type the experimenter may manipulate any of the following independent variables:

1. Physical parameters of the experimental situation
2. Presentation schedule of signals
3. Information feedback
4. Outcome structure.

The *presentation schedule* refers to the scheme used to generate the sequence of stimuli. In general, experimenters have adopted a simple probabilistic schedule; namely, letting the events $\langle s, \bar{s} \rangle$ and $\langle \bar{s}, s \rangle$ form a binomial sequence with fixed parameter γ. However, more complex stimulus schedules have been used; that is, the stimulus presentation on trial n can depend on the stimulus on trial $n - k$, the response on trial $n - k'$, or both (Friedman and Carterette, 1964). Generally, an analysis of the simpler schedule is sufficient for most purposes. Manipulation of the *physical parameters* refers to any change in the physical aspects of the experimental situation, but in particular to changes in the level of the background noise and/or the level of the signal. The nature of the *information feedback* may also be manipulated. In the experiment described above, the subject was always given information regarding the correctness of his response, but one can delete such information or even give false information. The remaining variable deals with the *outcome*

---

* Gaussian noise is a hissing sound compounded of all frequencies of vibration in equal amounts. Because all frequencies within the band limits are present, it is analogous to certain kinds of white light and so it is sometimes called white noise. The spectrum of such a noise is simply a horizontal line.

structure of the experiment. In general, the outcome structure of a psychophysical experiment is specified by giving the subject a payoff function; that is, a list of prizes and penalties that he receives depending on what he does under the various stimulus conditions. For example, he might be shown the matrix

Response

		1	2
Stimulus	$\langle s, \bar{s} \rangle$	$+10$	-3
	$\langle \bar{s}, s \rangle$	-1	$+2$

and be told that if the signal is presented in the first interval, he will win 10 points for a correct response and lose 3 points for an incorrect response, whereas if the signal is presented in the second interval, he will win 2 points for a correct response and lose one point for an incorrect response.

In the course of this chapter we shall refer to experimental manipulations that involve all four of these variables, but by and large our analyses will be concerned with a very special case of the two-response, forced-choice design. The presentation schedule will be a binomial sequence with parameter γ, and the outcome structure will involve no payoffs. The subject will simply be instructed to do the best he can in detecting the signals. Further, on each trial the subject will be given information regarding the correctness of his response.

With this experimental procedure in mind, let us now introduce some notation. The presentation of a signal plus noise in the first interval and noise alone in the second interval on trial n will be denoted as $S_{1,n}$, and the presentation of noise in the first observation interval followed by signal plus noise in the second observation interval on trial n as $S_{2,n}$; that is,

$$S_{1,n} = \langle s, \bar{s} \rangle \text{ on trial } n$$
$$S_{2,n} = \langle \bar{s}, s \rangle \text{ on trial } n.$$

Furthermore, the subject's responses will be labeled $A_{1,n}$ and $A_{2,n}$ to indicate which interval he reported contained the signal on trial n. Finally, $E_{1,n}$ and $E_{2,n}$ will denote the occurrence of an information event at the end of trial n that informs the subject that stimulus S_1 or S_2, respectively, was presented. Thus

$S_{i,n} =$ the presentation of stimulus S_i on trial n,

$A_{j,n} =$ the occurrence of response A_j on trial n,

$E_{k,n} =$ the occurrence of an information event at the end of trial n indicating that stimulus S_k was presented.

Each of the indices i, j, and k can take on the values 1 or 2.

The basic dependent variable is the probability of an A_j response on trial n, given that stimulus S_i occurred. The four outcomes are represented by the matrix

$$(5.1) \qquad \mathbf{P}_n = \begin{array}{c} \\ S_{1,n} \\ S_{2,n} \end{array} \begin{array}{c} A_{1,n} \qquad\qquad A_{2,n} \\ \begin{bmatrix} Pr(A_{1,n} \mid S_{1,n}) & Pr(A_{2,n} \mid S_{1,n}) \\ Pr(A_{1,n} \mid S_{2,n}) & Pr(A_{2,n} \mid S_{2,n}) \end{bmatrix} \end{array}.$$

Henceforth, this matrix will be called the *performance matrix*. Note that each row of the matrix sums to one, for on every trial the subject makes either an A_1 or A_2 response. Thus, if one entry in a row is known, so also is the other. Typically the performance matrix is specified by giving the entries in the first column; namely $Pr(A_{1,n} \mid S_{1,n})$ and $Pr(A_{1,n} \mid S_{2,n})$. In the literature the occurrence of an A_1 response to an S_1 stimulus is called a *hit*, and the occurrence of an A_1 response to an S_2 stimulus is called a *false alarm*. We shall frequently refer to hits and false alarms, denoting them as H_n and F_n, respectively, that is,

$$(5.2a) \qquad\qquad Pr(H_n) = Pr(A_{1,n} \mid S_{1,n})$$

$$(5.2b) \qquad\qquad Pr(F_n) = Pr(A_{1,n} \mid S_{2,n}).$$

Fixing $Pr(H_n)$ and $Pr(F_n)$, then, completely specifies the performance matrix. It is important to realize that $Pr(H_n)$ and $Pr(F_n)$ are independent quantities, and that knowing one in no way determines the other.

The above definition of hits and false alarms is not very compelling in the context of a forced-choice design, because of the symmetry between the S_1 and S_2 events. Nevertheless, we use these terms because they have a natural counterpart in another type of detection experiment frequently compared with the forced-choice design. The terminology derives from signal detection experiments that employ the Yes-No design. In a Yes-No experiment there is only one observation interval on each trial, and the interval either does or does not contain a signal. The subject's task is to answer "yes" or "no" on each trial, depending on whether he thinks a signal did or did not occur. For this design it is appropriate to define a hit as saying "yes" when a signal actually occurred, and a false alarm as saying "yes" when no signal occurred.

Other quantities of interest can be defined in terms of the hit and false-alarm probabilities. Frequently in analyzing an experiment, we wish to know the probability of an A_1 response on trial n independent of which stimulus event occurred; namely,

$$(5.3) \quad Pr(A_{1,n}) = Pr(A_{1,n} \mid S_{1,n})Pr(S_{1,n}) + Pr(A_{1,n} \mid S_{2,n})Pr(S_{2,n}).$$

Also, we shall be interested in the probability of a correct response on trial n (which in this chapter is denoted as C_n); namely,

$$(5.4) \qquad Pr(C_n) = Pr(A_{1,n} \mid S_{1,n})Pr(S_{1,n}) + Pr(A_{2,n} \mid S_{2,n})Pr(S_{2,n}).$$

5.2 THEORY

There are several theories of signal detection in the literature of psychology. Some of the theories are quite specific concerning the mechanisms by which the sensory system processes the stimulus input, but are less detailed concerning the mechanisms that generate the subject's response. Other theories take a very simple view of the sensory phase of the process and tend to stress the mechanisms that control the response. Also, signal detection theories can be characterized in terms of the type of mechanisms that are postulated: some are highly physiological and have definite implications concerning the neurology of the input-output system, whereas others are hypothetical in character and do not have clear implications for neurophysiological research. It is not our purpose in this chapter to review these theories and the empirical research that favors one or the other. Rather, the aim is to select one such model and discuss both its conceptual base and its mathematical structure. It is reasonable to suppose that a reader who understands the developments in this chapter will then be able to explore much of the literature on his own.

The model to be considered postulates that the observable stimulus-response relations are a product of two processes: an activation process and a decision process. The *activation process* specifies the relation between the external stimulus event and hypothesized sensory states of the subject. The *decision process* specifies the subject's response in terms of his sensory state and of information that he has acquired during the course of a given experiment. Roughly speaking, the stimulus is fed into the activation process, which converts external energy changes into sensory information (sensory state); the decision process then operates on the sensory information to determine the response.

The sensory states are theoretical constructs to which certain properties are assigned. Although it is sometimes convenient and suggestive to speak in such terms, we should not assume that the sensory states are to be identified with any simple neurophysiological mechanism. At the present stage of theory construction, we mean only to assume that certain properties of the model represent certain properties of the process of stimulation. If these assumptions prove to be adequately substantiated when the model is tested against a wide range of behavioral data, then the next order of business will be to look for neurophysiological variables that might underlie the correspondence.

We shall assume that one and only one sensory state can occur on each trial of the experiment. The sensory states will be denoted as s_0, s_1, s_2, s_3, ... Thus in the signal detection experiment, the signal event S_i gives rise to a sensory state s_j which in turn elicits an A_k response as illustrated below.

$$S_i \rightarrow \boxed{\begin{array}{c} \text{Activation} \\ \text{Process} \end{array}} \rightarrow s_j \rightarrow \boxed{\begin{array}{c} \text{Decision} \\ \text{Process} \end{array}} \rightarrow A_k$$

Stimulus	Sensory	Response
Input	State	Output.

It will not be assumed that the same sensory state necessarily occurs whenever a given stimulus is presented, but rather that the state is determined by a probabilistic process. Thus the activation process on trial n of an experiment can be represented by the stochastic matrix

$$\mathbf{A}_n = \begin{array}{c} \\ S_1 \\ S_2 \end{array} \overset{\begin{array}{ccc} s_0 & s_1 & s_2 \quad \cdots \end{array}}{\begin{bmatrix} a_{10}^{(n)} & a_{11}^{(n)} & a_{12}^{(n)} & \cdots \\ a_{20}^{(n)} & a_{21}^{(n)} & a_{22}^{(n)} & \cdots \end{bmatrix}},$$

where $a_{ij}^{(n)}$ denotes the probability of eliciting sensory state s_j on trial n given stimulus S_i on that trial. Similarly, the decision process can be represented by the matrix

$$\mathbf{D}_n = \begin{array}{c} \\ s_0 \\ s_1 \\ s_2 \\ \cdot \\ \cdot \\ \cdot \end{array} \overset{\begin{array}{cc} A_1 & A_2 \end{array}}{\begin{bmatrix} d_{01}^{(n)} & d_{02}^{(n)} \\ d_{11}^{(n)} & d_{12}^{(n)} \\ d_{21}^{(n)} & d_{22}^{(n)} \\ \cdot & \cdot \\ \cdot & \cdot \\ \cdot & \cdot \end{bmatrix}},$$

where $d_{ij}^{(n)}$ is the probability of eliciting response A_j on trial n given sensory state s_i. Then to obtain the performance matrix specified by Eq. 5.1 we need only take the product of the activation matrix and the decision matrix; that is,

(5.5) $\mathbf{P}_n = \mathbf{A}_n \mathbf{D}_n.$

In the literature of signal detection, some theories have assumed a continuum of sensory states (Swets, Tanner and Birdsall, 1961), others a discrete but large number of states (McGill, 1965; Norman, 1964; Békésy, 1962), and yet others a set of two or three sensory states (Luce, 1963a; Fechner, 1860; Atkinson, 1963a; Blackwell, 1953). Further, some theories have proposed that the activation process is static over trials, whereas others have suggested that it varies within certain limits from trial to trial as a function of preceding events. One point of agreement among almost all theories is that the decision process is dynamic and that it may change over time as information accrues to the subject.

The model to be considered here postulates exactly three sensory states for the two-interval, forced-choice task:

$$s_0 = \text{no detection}$$
$$s_1 = \text{detection in observation interval 1}$$
$$s_2 = \text{detection in observation interval 2.}$$

The activation process and the decision process are defined by the following matrices:

(5.6)
$$\mathbf{A}_n = \begin{array}{c} \\ S_1 \\ S_2 \end{array} \begin{array}{c} \overset{s_0 \quad\quad s_1 \quad s_2}{\left[\begin{array}{ccc} 1-\sigma & \sigma & 0 \\ 1-\sigma & 0 & \sigma \end{array}\right]} \end{array}$$

(5.7)
$$\mathbf{D}_n = \begin{array}{c} \\ s_0 \\ s_1 \\ s_2 \end{array} \begin{array}{c} \overset{A_1 \quad\quad A_2}{\left[\begin{array}{cc} p_n & 1-p_n \\ 1 & 0 \\ 0 & 1 \end{array}\right]} \end{array}.$$

There are several points to note about these matrices. First, the entries in matrix $\mathbf{A}_n$ are constants independent of the trial number; thus the activation process is fixed over all trials of the experiment. In contrast, the decision process may vary as a function of the trial number, and this dependence is indicated by affixing the trial index n to p. Also note that s_1 can occur only if S_1 is presented, and s_2 can occur only if S_2 is presented. Thus, these sensory states have an unambiguous relation to the stimulus, for the signal event can be inferred with probability 1 when s_1 or s_2 occur. However sensory state s_0 is ambiguous, for it can occur following either signal event. The parameter σ characterizes this stimulus ambiguity in the output of the sensory system. When $\sigma = 1$, there is no ambiguity; when it is zero, there is complete ambiguity. Both loss of stimulus information due to external noise and loss due to limitations on the resolving power of the sensory system are summarized in the parameter σ. Therefore, σ may be interpreted as a measure both of the physical stimulus and of the subject's sensitivity; for this reason σ will be referred to as the *sensitivity parameter*.

The decision matrix $\mathbf{D}_n$ reflects the relative ambiguity of the sensory states. If the subject's instructions are to make an A_i response given an

S_i stimulus, then his response is completely determined when an s_1 or s_2 sensory state occurs. However, the subject faces a dilemma when he is required to make a response on the basis of s_0; either of the stimuli could have evoked s_0, so he needs some tactic by which he can resolve the ambiguity and select a response. The quantity p_n is a measure of the subject's tendency to resolve the ambiguity by making an A_1 response rather than an A_2; p_n will be referred to as the *response bias*.

From the activation matrix and the decision matrix of Eqs. 5.6 and 5.7 the performance matrix can be computed; namely,

$$(5.8) \qquad \mathbf{P}_n = \mathbf{A}_n \mathbf{D}_n = \begin{bmatrix} (1 - \sigma)p_n + \sigma & (1 - \sigma)(1 - p_n) \\ (1 - \sigma)p_n & (1 - \sigma)(1 - p_n) + \sigma \end{bmatrix}.$$

As indicated earlier, the parameter σ represents the subject's sensitivity to the signal and p_n is a response bias more or less under the control of the subject. Of the experimental variables discussed earlier, we assume that the presentation schedule, information feedback, and the outcome structure influence p_n but do not affect σ. Also, we assume that the sensitivity parameter for a given subject is determined solely by the physical aspects of the experimental situation. It is of course necessary to show experimentally that these interpretations are correct and to examine how σ and p_n are related to the objective features of a given experimental situation.

In order to see how σ and p_n interact, let us consider the relation between hits and false alarms as one or the other of these parameters is manipulated. From the matrix in Eq. 5.8 we obtain

$$(5.9a) \qquad\qquad Pr(H_n) = (1 - \sigma)p_n + \sigma$$

$$(5.9b) \qquad\qquad Pr(F_n) = (1 - \sigma)p_n.$$

If the sensitivity parameter σ is held constant and p_n is manipulated, then performance varies in a linear fashion. Specifically, as p_n changes the hit and false alarm rates are constrained by Eq. 5.9; that is, an exchange relation is established between $Pr(H_n)$ and $Pr(F_n)$ so that if one probability is changed the other is also and in a predictable way. To find the equation of this relation, we subtract Eq. 5.9b from Eq. 5.9a to obtain

$$(5.10) \qquad\qquad Pr(H_n) = \sigma + Pr(F_n).$$

Thus, if σ is held constant (fixed signal and noise levels) and p_n is varied (manipulations in the presentation schedule, outcome structure, etc.), then the relation between hits and false alarms should be linear with slope one. Plots of the relation between $Pr(H_n)$ and $Pr(F_n)$ under experimental conditions where the signal to noise ratio is held fixed and other variables are allowed to vary are often referred to as response-operating-characteristic curves, or more simply as ROC curves. Generally $Pr(F_n)$ is plotted along the abscissa and $Pr(H_n)$ along the ordinate as shown in Fig. 5.1. The theoretical ROC curve intersects the ordinate at a point whose value is σ; as p_n goes from zero to one, a straight line is traced from the point

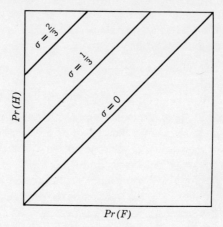

Fig. 5.1   ROC curves for various values of σ.

$(0, \sigma)$ to the point $(1 - \sigma, 1)$.* The psychological significance of the ROC curve will be discussed later.

If p_n is held constant and the sensitivity parameter changed, then again there is a linear relation between hits and false alarms. Specifically, from Eq. 5.9a we obtain

$$1 - Pr(H_n) = 1 - [\sigma + (1 - \sigma)p_n]$$
$$= (1 - \sigma)(1 - p_n).$$

But from Eq. 5.9b

$$\frac{Pr(F_n)}{p_n} = 1 - \sigma.$$

Hence

$$1 - Pr(H_n) = \frac{Pr(F_n)}{p_n}(1 - p_n)$$

or

(5.11)
$$Pr(H_n) = 1 - Pr(F_n)\left[\frac{1 - p_n}{p_n}\right].$$

---

* Throughout this chapter a point in 2-space will be denoted as an ordered pair (x, y), where the first member denotes the value of the abscissa, and the second the ordinate.

Plots of the relation between $Pr(H_n)$ and $Pr(F_n)$ when p_n is constant and σ is varied are called *iso-bias* curves. Several iso-bias curves are plotted in Fig. 5.2; each is associated with a fixed value of p_n. We note that the iso-bias curves are straight lines with a negative slope. As σ goes from zero to one, a straight line is traced out that moves from the point (p_n, p_n) to the point $(0, 1)$.

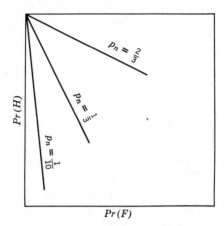

Fig. 5.2   Iso-bias curves for various values of p_n.

In summary then, changes in performance along an iso-bias curve (constant p_n, varying σ) are interpreted as changes in sensitivity, whereas changes along an ROC curve (constant σ, varying p_n) are regarded as changes in response bias. If σ and p_n are varied simultaneously, then hits and false alarms are related by an appropriately weighted combination of the iso-bias curve and the ROC curve.

Bias Process

So far no definite statements have been made about changes in p_n except to indicate that they are influenced by the presentation schedule, information feedback, and outcome structure. We now develop a model to describe changes in p_n as a function of the presentation schedule for experiments where the subject is given feedback on every trial regarding the correctness of his response. Later the analysis will be extended to account for other types of information feedback and manipulations of outcome structure.

We can postulate several mechanisms to describe changes in p_n, but one of the simplest is the assumption of a linear process of the type introduced in Sec. 3.4. That is, we will treat the bias probability on trial

$n + 1$ as a linear transformation of its value on trial n. Many readers may think that the use of linear transformations on response probabilities is a strong restriction. It is, but we should note that the linear model represents a limiting condition of several special cases of stimulus sampling theory (Estes and Suppes, 1959b; Atkinson and Estes, 1963) and thus can be derived from more fundamental psychological considerations. Further, even in those cases where the linear assumption proves empirically to be too restrictive, it nevertheless often can be used as an approximation to a more general formulation.

Granted that one is willing to assume linear changes in p_n, there is still the problem of specifying the precise form of the change. If some event that increases p_n occurs on trial n, then we shall let the increase be described by the equation

$$p_{n+1} = (1 - \theta)p_n + \theta.$$

The reader should recognize that, except for a change in the dummy parameters, the above linear equation is identical to the recursion for the single-operator model of paired-associate learning treated in Sec. 3.4. In Chapter 6 we shall again encounter linear models. Hence the generality of the immediately following treatment transcends the present chapter. Rewriting the equation above yields

$$p_{n+1} = p_n + \theta(1 - p_n)$$

or, in words, the new value of p_n is the old value plus a proportion θ of the total increase that is possible. Similarly, when we want to decrease p_n, the equation will be

$$p_{n+1} = (1 - \theta')p_n.$$

Rewriting this expression yields

$$p_{n+1} = p_n - \theta'p_n.$$

That is, the new value is simply the old value minus a proportion θ' of the total decrease that is possible. Thus both of these equations represent change in response probability as some proportion of the maximum increase or decrease that is possible.

Given that the form of the change in p_n has been specified, we must next determine when an increase or decrease is to occur. The assumption we consider is that p_n changes only on trials when the s_0 sensory event occurs. Specifically, if s_0 occurs and is followed by E_1 (that is, the experimenter informs the subject that the signal was in the first interval), then p_n will increase. If s_0 occurs and is followed by information event E_2, then p_n will decrease. For all other contingencies it will be assumed that no change occurs in p_n. These statements can be summarized as follows:

(5.12) $$p_{n+1} = \begin{cases} (1 - \theta)p_n + \theta, & \text{if } s_{0,n} \ \& \ E_{1,n} \\ (1 - \theta')p_n, & \text{if } s_{0,n} \ \& \ E_{2,n} \\ p_n, & \text{otherwise} \end{cases}$$

where $0 < \theta, \theta' \le 1$. Justification for this equation is postponed until later.

Related Models

The model described in this section is very similar to one originally proposed by Luce (1963a). His article presents a theory of signal detection that is applicable to a wide range of experimental procedures including both yes-no and the forced-choice designs. When the theory is applied to the two-alternative forced-choice experiment, a model is obtained that has four sensory states. There are four such states, because it is assumed that in each observation interval a hypothetical event D or $\bar{D}$ will occur; hence, for a two-interval problem, the sensory states are the ordered pairs $\langle DD \rangle$, $\langle D\bar{D} \rangle$, $\langle \bar{D}D \rangle$, and $\langle \bar{D}\bar{D} \rangle$. A D event will occur with probability q when a signal is presented, and with probability q' when the signal is not presented. Furthermore, the subject always makes the A_1 response when $\langle D\bar{D} \rangle$ occurs, never when $\langle \bar{D}D \rangle$ occurs, with probability v_n when $\langle DD \rangle$ occurs, and another probability w_n when $\langle \bar{D}\bar{D} \rangle$ occurs. These assumptions can be represented in matrix form as follows:

$$\mathbf{A} = \begin{array}{c} \\ S_1 \\ S_2 \end{array} \begin{array}{cccc} \langle DD \rangle & \langle D\bar{D} \rangle & \langle \bar{D}D \rangle & \langle \bar{D}\bar{D} \rangle \\ \left[\begin{array}{cccc} qq' & q(1-q') & (1-q)q' & (1-q)(1-q') \\ q'q & q'(1-q) & (1-q')q & (1-q')(1-q) \end{array} \right] \end{array}$$

$$\mathbf{D}_n = \begin{array}{c} \\ \langle DD \rangle \\ \langle D\bar{D} \rangle \\ \langle \bar{D}D \rangle \\ \langle \bar{D}\bar{D} \rangle \end{array} \begin{array}{cc} A_1 & A_2 \\ \left[\begin{array}{cc} v_n & 1 - v_n \\ 1 & 0 \\ 0 & 1 \\ w_n & 1 - w_n \end{array} \right] \end{array}.$$

Luce also postulates that the bias parameters v_n and w_n undergo trial-by-trial changes of the form specified by Eq. 5.12.

When $q' = 0$, the event D will never occur in the absence of a signal, and then the matrices above reduce to those presented in Eqs. 5.6 and 5.7 with $p_n = w_n$ and $\sigma = q$. Under these conditions Luce's model is precisely the same as the one presented in this section. Although we shall not do so here, it can be shown that the fit of the model cannot be significantly improved for the data treated in this chapter by letting q' be nonzero.

The model proposed in this section is also similar to a special case of a theory proposed by Atkinson (1963a) and Atkinson, Carterette and Kinchla (1962). The difference is that their bias process was formulated in terms of the multi-element pattern model of stimulus sampling theory (see Chapter 8). However, the two models make identical predictions for all of the statistics analyzed in this chapter and differ only on certain predictions such as sequential statistics that depend on previous responses. It should be pointed out that although both Luce's theory and Atkinson's reduce to essentially the same model in the two-alternative, forced-choice case, they make markedly different predictions for the yes-no design and for forced-choice designs with more than two intervals.

5.3 MATHEMATICAL DERIVATIONS

Mathematical Operators

In this section expressions will be derived for $Pr(H_n)$ and $Pr(F_n)$ as a function of the presentation schedule and the signal level. In order to make these derivations (and others that appear later in this chapter and in Chapter 6), it will be helpful to introduce the concept of a *mathematical operator*. In Sec. 3.4 reference was made to operators, but there the derivations were very simple, and it was not necessary to use operators in a formal way. Here, however, their use greatly simplifies the derivations.

All mathematical operations on a variable can be defined in terms of operators. For example, a familiar operator is the logarithmic operator; the quantity $\log x$ is broken into an operator log and an operand x. For each value of x, the operator log defines a new quantity $\log x$. In general an operator Q when applied to an operand x defines a new quantity Qx. Hence Q represents a transformation of all values of x. The notation Qx does not mean Q multiplied by x, but Q operating on x to yield the new quantity Qx.

In Eq. 5.12 three linear transformations were defined, and we now represent these changes in terms of mathematical operators. In particular, we define the operator Q_1 operating on the operand p_n to be

$$Q_1 p_n = (1 - \theta)p_n + \theta.$$

Similarly, we define the Q_2 operator operating on the operand p_n as

$$Q_2 p_n = (1 - \theta')p_n.$$

Finally, we define the operator Q_0 by the equation

$$Q_0 p_n = p_n.$$

The Q_0 operator is called the *identity operator*, for it leaves every operand unchanged.

We need to become familiar with the use of the operators Q_1, Q_2 and Q_0, so let us examine a few special examples. Consider what happens when we apply both operators Q_1 and Q_2 to the operand p_n. For example, if we apply operator Q_1 first to yield the result $Q_1 p_n$, and then apply operator Q_2 to the new operand $Q_1 p_n$, we write this operator sequence as follows

$$Q_2 Q_1 p_n = Q_2(Q_1 p_n).$$

But Q_1 operating on p_n yields $(1 - \theta)p_n + \theta$, hence

$$\begin{aligned} Q_2 Q_1 p_n &= Q_2[(1 - \theta)p_n + \theta] \\ &= (1 - \theta')(1 - \theta)p_n + (1 - \theta')\theta. \end{aligned}$$

Thus, if Q_1 were applied on trial n and Q_2 on trial $n + 1$, then the value of the bias parameter at the start of trial $n + 2$ would be $Q_2 Q_1 p_n$ which is given above.

It is essential to note that the order of application of the operators is from right to left. For example, $Q_1 Q_2 p_n$ means that we first apply operator Q_2 to operand p_n and then apply Q_1 to the new operand $Q_2 p_n$; that is,

$$\begin{aligned} Q_1 Q_2 p_n &= Q_1[(1 - \theta')p_n] \\ &= (1 - \theta)(1 - \theta')p_n + \theta. \end{aligned}$$

Note that $Q_2 Q_1 p_n \neq Q_1 Q_2 p_n$. By virtue of this inequality, the two operators Q_1 and Q_2 are *noncommutative*. If the order of application of a pair of operators can be reversed without affecting the result, then the pair of operators are said to commute. A discussion of commuting operator models in relation to avoidance learning appears in Chapter 6.

Consider next what happens when operator Q_2 is applied m successive times to operand p_n; the symbol $Q_2^m p_n$ will be used to denote this result. First note that

$$Q_2 p_n = (1 - \theta')p_n.$$

Applying Q_2 a second time to the new operand $Q_2 p_n$ yields

$$Q_2^2 p_n = (1 - \theta')^2 p_n$$

and in general

(5.13) $$Q_2^m p_n = (1 - \theta')^m p_n.$$

A similar result can be readily obtained for $Q_1^m p_n$; applying the operator m times to the operand p_n yields

(5.14) $$Q_1^m p_n = 1 - (1 - p_n)(1 - \theta)^m.$$

Expected Value of p_n

If we know p_1 and know on each trial which of the three operators Q_1, Q_2, or Q_0 was applied, then it is obvious that p_n is completely specified for all values of n. We would simply apply the operators one by one in

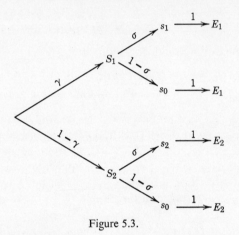

Figure 5.3.

the appropriate order to obtain the successive values of p_n. But for the present problem matters are not so simple, because we are never certain which operator is to be applied on a particular trial. In the theory Q_1 is applied if the event s_0 & E_1 occurs, Q_2 if s_0 & E_2 occurs, and Q_0 otherwise. However, the events s_0 & E_1 and s_0 & E_2 are determined probabilistically. Specifically, on any given trial the probability of events s_0 & E_1 and s_0 & E_2 are

(5.15)
$$Pr(s_{0,n}\ \&\ E_{1,n}) = \gamma(1 - \sigma)$$
$$Pr(s_{0,n}\ \&\ E_{2,n}) = (1 - \gamma)(1 - \sigma).$$

Recall that γ is the probability that the signal is in the first interval. The joint probabilities in the equation above are represented by the branches on the tree in Fig. 5.3. For example, consider the second branch: the $S_{1,n}$ event occurs with probability γ; and if S_1 occurred, sensory state s_0 is activated with probability $1 - \sigma$. The information event E_1 is always given on an S_1 trial (and E_2 on an S_2 trial), and therefore, the probability of event $s_{0,n}$ & $E_{1,n}$ is simply the product of γ and $1 - \sigma$, which verifies the first line of Eq. 5.15.

Since it is not possible to specify which operator is to be applied on each trial, we cannot calculate the exact value of p_n. However, its expected value can be calculated. For example, if p_n is known, then the expected value on trial $n + 1$ would be a simple weighting of each of the possible outcomes by its respective probability of occurrence. Specifically, the expected value of the bias on trial $n + 1$ given p_n would be

$$E(p_{n+1}) = \gamma(1 - \sigma)Q_1 p_n + (1 - \gamma)(1 - \sigma)Q_2 p_n + \sigma Q_0 p_n.$$

That is, with probability $\gamma(1 - \sigma)$ operator Q_1 would be applied, with probability $(1 - \gamma)(1 - \sigma)$ operator Q_2, and with probability σ operator Q_0. Carrying out the appropriate operations yields

$$E(p_{n+1}) = \gamma(1 - \sigma)[(1 - \theta)p_n + \theta] + (1 - \gamma)(1 - \sigma)(1 - \theta')p_n + \sigma p_n$$
$$= p_n[1 - \theta\gamma(1 - \sigma) - \theta'(1 - \gamma)(1 - \sigma)] + \theta\gamma(1 - \sigma).$$

So although the exact value of p_{n+1} cannot be computed, we can determine its expectation. We now generalize this scheme to a sequence of trials; say trials 1 to 3 of an experiment. Let us assume that p_1 has some fixed value at the start of trial 1. Then the possible sequences of operators that can occur over the three trials can be represented by the tree given in Fig. 5.4. To clarify the tree consider the uppermost branch. It tells us that operator Q_1 was applied on both trials 1 and 2 to generate the bias parameter $Q_1 Q_1 p_1$ on trial 3; furthermore, the probability of applying the Q_1 operator on both trials is simply the product of the probabilities represented on the uppermost branch, namely $[\gamma(1 - \sigma)]^2$. Similarly, the other branches on the tree represent other possible sequences of operators, and their probabilities of occurrence can be obtained by multiplying the probabilities on the appropriate branch of the tree.

By inspection of the left half of the tree in Fig. 5.4, we can immediately write

$$E(p_2) = \gamma(1 - \sigma)Q_1 p_1 + (1 - \gamma)(1 - \sigma)Q_2 p_1 + \sigma Q_0 p_1$$
$$= [1 - \theta\gamma(1 - \sigma) - \theta'(1 - \gamma)(1 - \sigma)]p_1 + \theta\gamma(1 - \sigma).$$

Similarly, by inspection of the entire tree we can write

$$E(p_3) = \gamma^2(1 - \sigma)^2 Q_1 Q_1 p_1 + \gamma(1 - \sigma)^2(1 - \gamma)Q_2 Q_1 p_1$$
$$+ \gamma(1 - \sigma)\sigma Q_0 Q_1 p_1 + \cdots + \sigma^2 Q_0 Q_0 p_1,$$

where each term in the above expression corresponds to a single branch of the tree. If we apply the operators as indicated in the expression above

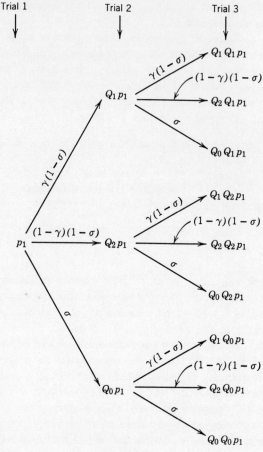

Figure 5.4.

and carry out the appropriate algebraic simplifications making use of the previous expression for $E(p_2)$, then

$$E(p_3) = [1 - \theta\gamma(1 - \sigma) - \theta'(1 - \gamma)(1 - \sigma)]E(p_2) + \theta\gamma(1 - \sigma).$$

That is, the expected value of the response bias on trial 3 is a linear function of its expected value on trial 2. The form of this equation is the same as that just derived relating $E(p_2)$ to p_1. From this observation one might conjecture that

(5.16)

$$E(p_{n+1}) = [1 - \theta\gamma(1 - \sigma) - \theta'(1 - \gamma)(1 - \sigma)]E(p_n) + \theta\gamma(1 - \sigma)$$

for all n. To prove this conjecture some additional notation will be needed, which we now develop.

If the tree in Fig. 5.4 were expanded to include trials 1 through n, then there would be 3^{n-1} branches. Associated with each branch would be (1) a particular history giving the sequence of operators applied, (2) the value of p_n given the particular history, and (3) the probability that this particular branch would occur. The following notation will be used to describe these features of the tree:

$h_{v,n}$ = history specifying the sequence of operators applied on branch v of the tree

$p_{v,n}$ = value of the bias given history $h_{v,n}$

$Pr(h_{v,n})$ = probability that history $h_{v,n}$ will occur.

To illustrate the notation consider Fig. 5.4 and let us number the branches in order from top to bottom. Then for the second branch ($v = 2$) the history is

$$h_{2,3} = \{Q_2 Q_1\}.$$

That is, branch 2 denotes the case where Q_1 was applied on trial 1 and Q_2 on trial 2. The value of the bias parameter given history $h_{2,3}$ is

$$p_{2,3} = Q_2 Q_1 p_1 = (1 - \theta')(1 - \theta)p_1 + \theta(1 - \theta').$$

Finally, the probability measure associated with history $h_{2,3}$ would be the product of the probabilities on branch 2 of the tree; namely,

$$Pr(h_{2,3}) = \gamma(1 - \sigma)^2(1 - \gamma).$$

Using this notation we can write the expected value of p_n as follows:

(5.17)
$$E(p_n) = \sum_{v=1}^{3^{n-1}} p_{v,n} Pr(h_{v,n}).$$

In words, the expected value on trial n is the weighted average of $p_{v,n}$ over the 3^{n-1} possible branches. The weighting coefficients are the probabilities, $Pr(h_{v,n})$, of the particular operator sequences.

With this notation in hand, let us now return to a proof of the conjecture in Eq. 5.16. Consider the vth branch of the tree describing the possible operator sequences up through trial n; that is, there will be 3^{n-1} such branches and we are to look at the vth branch. It is characterized by a history $h_{v,n}$ and, a bias $p_{v,n}$. Now, what happens to this branch on trial $n + 1$? It will split into three parts as indicated in Fig. 5.5. So, from the vth branch of the tree on trial n, we generate three branches; associated with each of these branches is a new value of the bias parameter and a

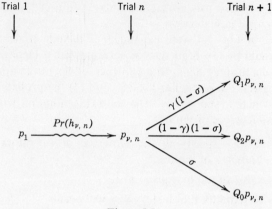

Figure 5.5.

probability measure for the branch. They are as follows:

New value of bias   New Probability Measure

$Q_1 p_{v,n} = (1 - \theta)p_{v,n} + \theta$ $Pr(h_{v,n})\gamma(1 - \sigma)$

$Q_2 p_{v,n} = (1 - \theta')p_{v,n}$ $Pr(h_{v,n})(1 - \gamma)(1 - \sigma)$

$Q_0 p_{v,n} = p_{v,n}$ $Pr(h_{v,n})\sigma$

Thus, to compute the expected value of the bias on trial $n + 1$, we can simply sum over the 3^{n-1} branches associated with trial n, taking into account that each branch splits into three parts in going from trial n to $n + 1$. That is,

$$E(p_{n+1}) = \sum_{v=1}^{3^{n-1}} [\gamma(1 - \sigma)Pr(h_{v,n})\{Q_1 p_{v,n}\} + (1 - \gamma)(1 - \sigma)Pr(h_{v,n})\{Q_2 p_{v,n}\}$$

$$+ \sigma Pr(h_{v,n})\{Q_0 p_{v,n}\}]$$

$$= [1 - \gamma(1 - \sigma)\theta - (1 - \gamma)(1 - \sigma)\theta'] \sum_{v=1}^{3^{n-1}} p_{v,n} Pr(h_{v,n})$$

$$+ \theta(1 - \sigma)\gamma \sum_{v=1}^{3^{n-1}} Pr(h_{v,n}).$$

But, as indicated in Eq. 5.17,

$$\sum_{v=1}^{3^{n-1}} p_{v,n} Pr(h_{v,n}) = E(p_n)$$

and, of course,

$$\sum_{v=1}^{3^{n-1}} Pr(h_{v,n}) = 1.$$

Hence

$$E(p_{n+1}) = [1 - \gamma(1 - \sigma)\theta - (1 - \gamma)(1 - \sigma)\theta']E(p_n) + \theta(1 - \sigma)\gamma,$$

which completes the proof of the conjecture given in Eq. 5.16.

Linear First-Order Difference Equations

The expression in Eq. 5.16 is a linear first-order difference equation*
of the form

(5.18) $y_{n+1} = A + Gy_n.$

Note that this is not the first time we have encountered a difference
equation of this type; in Sec. 2.7 and again in Sec. 3.2 we required a
solution to the special case where $A = 0$.

A solution to the equation above can be readily obtained. Suppose
that y_1 is known. Setting $n = 1$ yields

$$y_2 = A + Gy_1.$$

Now, with $n = 2$, we obtain from Eq. 5.18

$$y_3 = A + Gy_2.$$

Substituting $A + Gy_1$ for y_2 in this expression yields

$$y_3 = A + G(A + Gy_1)$$
$$= A + AG + G^2y_1.$$

---

* As indicated in Chapter 2, an equation that expresses a relation between the nonnegative integers n and successive values of a dependent variable y_n is called a difference
equation. If besides y_n the equation involves y_{n+m} but no y with a greater index than
$n + m$, the equation is said to be of order m. Thus

$$y_{n+1} - 3y_n = n + 3$$

is a first-order difference equation, whereas

$$y_{n+3} + 2y_{n+2} + 6y_n = n^2$$

is of order three. If a difference equation can be written in the form

$$f_0(n)y_{n+m} + f_1(n)y_{n+m-1} + \cdots + f_{m-1}(n)y_{n+1} + f_m(n)y_n = g(n)$$

where $f_0, f_1, \cdots f_m$ and g may be functions of n, but not y_n, then it is said to be linear.
Thus

$$y_{n+2} - (1 - n)y_n = 3n$$

is a linear difference equation, whereas

$$y_{n+3} - 3y_{n+2}y_n + y_n^2 = 1$$

is not linear since y_{n+2} and y_n appear together in a product. For a discussion of difference
equations and their solutions, see Goldberg (1958).

We now use our knowledge of y_3 to find y_4. Letting $n = 3$ in the original difference equation gives

$$y_4 = A + Gy_3$$
$$= A + G[A + AG + G^2y_1].$$

Simplification produces

$$y_4 = y_1G^3 + A[1 + G + G^2].$$

If we continue in this fashion, it will be obvious that

$$y_n = y_1G^{n-1} + A[1 + G + G^2 + \cdots + G^{n-2}].$$

The quantity in parentheses is the sum of the first $n - 1$ terms of a geometric progression with first term one and common ratio G. Therefore,

$$y_n = \begin{cases} y_1G^{n-1} + A\dfrac{1 - G^{n-1}}{1 - G}, & \text{(if } G \neq 1) \\[2ex] y_1G^{n-1} + A(n - 1), & \text{(if } G = 1). \end{cases}$$

In our case $0 < G < 1$, and therefore the top line in the equation above is appropriate. Rearranging terms in this expression yields

(5.19)
$$y_n = \frac{A}{1 - G} - \left[\frac{A}{1 - G} - y_1\right]G^{n-1}.$$

With $0 < G < 1$, the quantity G^{n-1} approaches 0 as n becomes large; hence

$$\lim_{n \to \infty} y_n = \frac{A}{1 - G}.$$

As noted above, the expression for $E(p_{n+1})$ given in Eq. 5.16 is a linear first-order difference equation. Setting

$$y_n = E(p_n)$$
$$A = \theta(1 - \sigma)\gamma$$
$$G = 1 - \gamma(1 - \sigma)\theta - (1 - \gamma)(1 - \sigma)\theta',$$

and substituting in Eq. 5.19 yields the solution equation

(5.20)
$$E(p_n) = p_\infty - [p_\infty - p_1]G^{n-1}.$$

In this case $\lim_{n \to \infty} E(p_n)$ is given by

$$p_\infty = \frac{\theta(1 - \sigma)\gamma}{\theta(1 - \sigma)\gamma + \theta'(1 - \sigma)(1 - \gamma)}.$$

Note that the expression for p_∞ can be simplified by dividing the numerator and denominator by $\theta(1 - \sigma)$, yielding

(5.21)
$$p_\infty = \frac{\gamma}{\gamma + (1 - \gamma)\varphi}$$

where $\varphi = \theta'/\theta$. Thus we have the notable result that p_∞ does not depend on the absolute values of θ' and θ but only upon their ratio.

Theoretical Expressions for Hits and False Alarms

Combining the results in Eqs. 5.9 and 5.20 yields

(5.22a) $Pr(H_n) = \sigma + (1 - \sigma)[p_\infty - (p_\infty - p_1)G^{n-1}]$

(5.22b) $Pr(F_n) = (1 - \sigma)[p_\infty - (p_\infty - p_1)G^{n-1}]$.

From these equations we see that the hit and false alarm rates will depend on p_1 at the start of an experimental session; however, over trials the subject's performance will change at a rate controlled by the quantity G and at asymptote $Pr(H_n)$ and $Pr(F_n)$ will be determined by σ and the limiting bias p_∞.

In experimental applications we are frequently interested in the number of hits and false alarms for a series of K trials. Theoretical expressions for these quantities can be obtained directly from Eq. 5.22; that is, the number of hits over trials 1 to K is simply

$$\sum_{n=1}^{K} Pr(H_n) = \sum_{n=1}^{K} \{\sigma + (1 - \sigma)[p_\infty - (p_\infty - p_1)G^{n-1}]\}$$

$$= K[\sigma + (1 - \sigma)p_\infty] - \frac{(1 - \sigma)(p_\infty - p_1)}{1 - G}(1 - G^K).$$

Also of importance in experimental applications are functions that specify the proportion of hits and false alarms in successive K-trial blocks. For example, we may be interested in determining whether performance is changing over the course of an experimental session and consequently plot the proportion of hits and false alarms in successive K-trial blocks. The theoretical expression for these functions can be obtained by an extension of the methods used to derive the above equations. Let x be the ordinal number of a K-trial block running from trial $[K(x - 1) + 1]$ to Kx where $x = 1, 2, 3, \ldots$ and define $P_x(H)$ as the proportion of hits in block x. Then

$$P_x(H) = \frac{1}{K}\left[\sum_{n=1}^{Kx} Pr(H_n) - \sum_{n=1}^{K(x-1)} Pr(H_n)\right].$$

That is, the expected number of hits in block x is the expected number for trials 1 to Kx minus the number for trials 1 to $K(x - 1)$. To obtain the proportion, we then divide by K. Carrying out the summation in the equation above yields

$$P_x(H) = [\sigma + (1 - \sigma)p_\infty] - \frac{(1 - \sigma)(p_\infty - p_1)}{K(1 - G)} G^{K(x-1)}(1 - G^K).$$

Often in experimental applications of this equation, we do not know p_1. Under these conditions p_1 can be eliminated in favor of the observed proportion of hits in the first block. This can be done in the following way. Note that from the above equation with $x = 1$,

$$P_1(H) = [\sigma + (1 - \sigma)p_\infty] - \frac{(1 - \sigma)(p_\infty - p_1)}{K(1 - G)} (1 - G^K)$$

or

$$\frac{(1 - \sigma)(p_\infty - p_1)}{K(1 - G)} (1 - G^K) = \sigma + (1 - \sigma)p_\infty - P_1(H).$$

Substituting the right-hand side of the result above into the preceding equation yields

(5.23a) $\quad P_x(H) = [\sigma + (1 - \sigma)p_\infty] - \{[\sigma + (1 - \sigma)p_\infty] - P_1(H)\}G^{K(x-1)}.$

Similarly, for false alarms

(5.23b) $\quad P_x(F) = (1 - \sigma)p_\infty - \{(1 - \sigma)p_\infty - P_1(F)\}G^{K(x-1)}.$

The change in performance predicted by Eq. 5.23 over early blocks of trials is a well-known experimental phenomenon. Generally, however, most research workers have tended to ignore the changes that occur at the beginning of an experimental session and have instead concentrated on an analysis of data after performance has settled down to some stable (asymptotic) level. For the data analyzed in this chapter, we shall adopt this policy; to do so makes matters simpler because estimates of initial values are not needed.

Since asymptotic performance will be stressed in subsequent discussions, the following notation will be useful

(5.24a) $\qquad Pr(H) = \lim_{n \to \infty} Pr(H_n) = \lim_{x \to \infty} P_x(H)$

(5.24b) $\qquad Pr(F) = \lim_{n \to \infty} Pr(F_n) = \lim_{x \to \infty} P_x(F).$

That is, asymptotic proportions will be indicated by deleting the subscript denoting the block number. Making the appropriate substitutions in

Eq. 5.22 and taking the limit yields

$$(5.25) \qquad Pr(H) = \sigma + \frac{(1 - \sigma)\gamma}{\gamma + (1 - \gamma)\varphi}$$

$$(5.26) \qquad Pr(F) = \frac{(1 - \sigma)\gamma}{\gamma + (1 - \gamma)\varphi},$$

where p_∞ has been replaced by Eq. 5.21. Similarly, for the asymptotic proportion of correct responses (see Eq. 5.4)

$$(5.27) \qquad Pr(C) = \sigma + (1 - \gamma)(1 - \sigma) + \frac{(1 - \sigma)\gamma(2\gamma - 1)}{\gamma + (1 - \gamma)\varphi}.$$

And, for the asymptotic proportion of A_1 responses (see Eq. 5.3)

$$(5.28) \qquad Pr(A_1) = \gamma\sigma + \frac{\gamma(1 - \sigma)}{\gamma + (1 - \gamma)\varphi}.$$

5.4 ANALYSIS OF SIGNAL DETECTION DATA

We now examine data collected from eight subjects in the two-alternative, forced-choice acoustic experiment described earlier.* In this study the signal and noise levels were held constant throughout the experiment, and the subject was always given information at the end of each trial regarding the correctness of his response. The only experimental manipulation involved the use of three different presentation schedules. The probability γ of an S_1 event took on the following values:

Schedule A: $\gamma = 0.25$

Schedule B: $\gamma = 0.50$

Schedule C: $\gamma = 0.75$.

Test sessions of 350 trials each were run on consecutive days. Each day a subject ran on one of the three presentation schedules for the entire session. In successive 3-day blocks a subject ran one day on each of the three schedules; within each 3-day block, the order was randomly determined. The experiment involved 15 sessions, and therefore each presentation schedule was run on five separate days.

Table 5.1 presents the proportion of A_1 responses on both S_1 and S_2 trials over the last 250 trials of replications two through five of each presentation schedule; each estimate is based on $250 \times 4 = 1000$ trials. Table 5.2 presents the corresponding results for the overall proportion of A_1 responses and correct responses. We have deleted the first replication

---

* This study is reported in Atkinson and Kinchla (1965).

Table 5.1 Predicted and Observed Proportions of Hits and False Alarms
(The observed proportions are in parentheses.)

Subject	Schedule A		Schedule B		Schedule C	
	$Pr(H)$	$Pr(F)$	$Pr(H)$	$Pr(F)$	$Pr(H)$	$Pr(F)$
1	0.601	0.154	0.744	0.297	0.877	0.430
	(0.622)	(0.163)	(0.714)	(0.260)	(0.890)	(0.462)
2	0.543	0.125	0.680	0.262	0.832	0.414
	(0.529)	(0.136)	(0.654)	(0.249)	(0.854)	(0.397)
3	0.597	0.106	0.716	0.225	0.849	0.358
	(0.626)	(0.107)	(0.707)	(0.210)	(0.842)	(0.384)
4	0.529	0.127	0.669	0.267	0.825	0.424
	(0.517)	(0.122)	(0.649)	(0.242)	(0.857)	(0.454)
5	0.520	0.120	0.658	0.258	0.816	0.416
	(0.546)	(0.142)	(0.650)	(0.240)	(0.799)	(0.413)
6	0.542	0.141	0.689	0.287	0.841	0.440
	(0.547)	(0.139)	(0.680)	(0.279)	(0.847)	(0.451)
7	0.618	0.125	0.744	0.252	0.872	0.379
	(0.627)	(0.136)	(0.742)	(0.251)	(0.864)	(0.369)
8	0.570	0.125	0.704	0.258	0.847	0.401
	(0.552)	(0.108)	(0.687)	(0.244)	(0.887)	(0.438)
Average	0.565	0.128	0.700	0.263	0.845	0.408
	(0.571)	(0.132)	(0.685)	(0.247)	(0.855)	(0.421)

of each presentation schedule because we view the subject as adapting
to the task on early days of the experiment and prefer to treat his data
only after he clearly understands the experimental routine and is well
experienced. Also, the first 100 trials of each of the subsequent experimental sessions were deleted because, as noted earlier, we will be primarily
concerned with asymptotic performance.

ROC Curves

For this experiment the signal and noise levels were constant over all
sessions, and only the presentation schedule varied. Therefore, σ should
be the same throughout the experiment, but p_∞ should vary with changes
in γ. It has already been shown (see Eq. 5.10) that when σ is fixed, the
theory predicts that $Pr(H)$ and $Pr(F)$ will fall on the linear function

$$Pr(H) = \sigma + Pr(F).$$

Table 5.2   Predicted and Observed Proportions of Correct Responses and A_1 Responses (Observed values given in parentheses.)

Subject	Schedule A		Schedule B		Schedule C	
	$Pr(C)$	$Pr(A_1)$	$Pr(C)$	$Pr(A_1)$	$Pr(C)$	$Pr(A_1)$
1	0.785	0.266	0.724	0.521	0.800	0.765
	(0.783)	(0.278)	(0.727)	(0.487)	(0.802)	(0.783)
2	0.792	0.229	0.709	0.471	0.771	0.727
	(0.780)	(0.234)	(0.702)	(0.451)	(0.791)	(0.740)
3	0.820	0.229	0.746	0.470	0.797	0.726
	(0.826)	(0.237)	(0.748)	(0.459)	(0.786)	(0.728)
4	0.787	0.227	0.701	0.468	0.763	0.725
	(0.788)	(0.221)	(0.703)	(0.446)	(0.779)	(0.756)
5	0.790	0.220	0.700	0.458	0.758	0.716
	(0.780)	(0.243)	(0.705)	(0.445)	(0.746)	(0.703)
6	0.780	0.241	0.701	0.488	0.771	0.741
	(0.783)	(0.241)	(0.701)	(0.479)	(0.772)	(0.748)
7	0.810	0.249	0.746	0.498	0.809	0.749
	(0.805)	(0.259)	(0.746)	(0.496)	(0.806)	(0.740)
8	0.799	0.236	0.723	0.481	0.785	0.735
	(0.807)	(0.219)	(0.722)	(0.465)	(0.806)	(0.775)
Average	0.795	0.237	0.719	0.482	0.782	0.735
	(0.794)	(0.241)	(0.719)	(0.466)	(0.786)	(0.746)

To test this prediction, we now fit this linear function to the three data points (schedules A, B, and C) for each subject. Figure 5.6 presents plots of $Pr(H)$ and $Pr(F)$ for each subject. It is clear for all subjects that as γ goes from 0.25 to 0.50 to 0.75, the values of $Pr(H)$ and $Pr(F)$ show corresponding increases; that is, for all graphs the points are arrayed such that A is to the bottom left, C is to the top right, and B falls somewhere intermediate.

To fit a straight line to the three points, we use the *method of least squares*. Suppose that the data consists of the n pairs

$$(X_1, Y_1), \ldots, (X_n, Y_n),$$

where

X_i = estimate of the proportion of false alarms on schedule i
Y_i = estimate of the proportion of hits on schedule i

Then we seek a value of σ such that the linear relation

$$Y' = \sigma + X$$

will "best fit" the observed data. From this equation we obtain, corresponding to the observed values $X_1, \ldots, X_n$, the following predicted

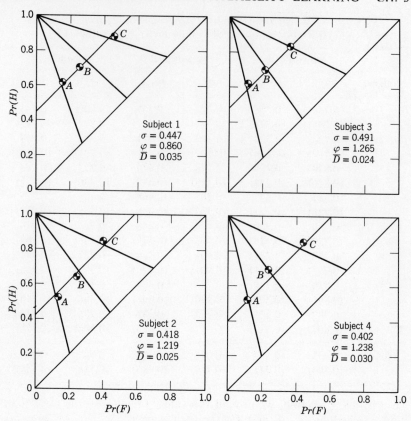

Figure 5.6.

values of Y': $\sigma + X_1, \ldots, \sigma + X_n$. The difference

$$Y_i - Y_i' = Y_i - (\sigma + X_i)$$

is the deviation of the observed value of Y_i from the predicted value Y_i'. It is reasonable that we should try to make the deviations $Y_i - Y_i'$ collectively as small as possible. The principle of least squares specifies that a desirable approach to this problem is to select the value of σ so that it minimizes the sum of the squared deviations between predicted and observed values of Y. Thus we define

$$S(\sigma) = \sum_{i=1}^{n} (Y_i - Y_i')^2$$

$$= \sum_{i=1}^{n} (Y_i - \sigma - X_i)^2$$

and find the value of σ that minimizes this function. To accomplish this,

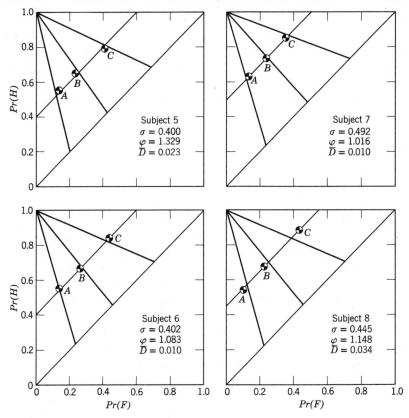

Figure 5.6 (*continued*).

we take the derivative of $S(\sigma)$ with respect to σ and then set it equal to zero.

$$\frac{\partial S(\sigma)}{\partial \sigma} = -2 \sum_{i=1}^{n} (Y_i - \sigma - X_i) = 0.$$

Solving this equation yields the least squares estimate of

(5.29)
$$\sigma = \frac{1}{n}\left[\sum_{i=1}^{n} Y_i - \sum_{i=1}^{n} X_i\right].$$

Applying the least squares method to the three data points for each subject (see Table 5.1) yields the estimates of σ that are given in Fig. 5.6; for example, for subject 1

$$\sigma = \tfrac{1}{3}[(0.622 + 0.714 + 0.890) - (0.163 + 0.260 + 0.462)]$$
$$= 0.447.$$

These estimates were used to generate the ROC curves shown in Fig. 5.6.

By inspecting the figure, we can see that there is rather good agreement between the observed data points and the predicted ROC curves. Recall that the signal and noise levels were set at the same values for all subjects; consequently, variations in σ represent inter-subject variations in sensitivity level. The maximum sensitivity level is displayed by subject 7, with $\sigma = 0.492$; whereas the minimum sensitivity level is displayed by subject 5, with $\sigma = 0.400$.

Bias Process

We now evaluate the bias process with regard to the data in Tables 5.1 and 5.2. First, however, let us make the following observation. If γ and σ are fixed in Eqs. 5.25 and 5.26 and if we let $\varphi = \theta'/\theta$ go from 0 to ∞, then the point $[Pr(F), Pr(H)]$ moves along the ROC curve and approaches the lower-left point $(0, \sigma)$ as $\varphi \to \infty$ and the upper-right point $(1 - \sigma, 1)$ as $\varphi \to 0$. Stated differently, no matter where the observed point may fall on the ROC curve for a given value of γ, there is a potential value of φ. Hence, if the three observed points in our experiment fall on a straight line with slope 1, then perfect fits of the data can be obtained by estimating separate values of φ for each presentation schedule.

Performing separate estimates of φ, however, would violate our original intentions. In formulating Eq. 5.12, we assumed that the parameters θ and θ' characterize a subject's trial-to-trial adjustments to the information events E_1 and E_2 and did not depend on the overall presentation schedule. The values of θ and θ' may vary from subject to subject reflecting the fact that individuals differ in their reaction to information feedback; however, for a given subject θ and θ' are assumed to be fixed and invariant with regard to the presentation schedule and the signal intensity. Earlier, we required that σ be independent of the presentation schedule, and now we place the same constraint on φ. Thus a single estimate of φ will be made which then can be used to make predictions for all three presentation schedules. Checks on the invariance of behavioral parameters across several experimental conditions represent an extremely strong test of a model. The history of mathematical psychology is replete with models that have proved quite satisfactory in accounting for data collected in a particular experimental condition but have failed totally when confronted with the task of accounting for results over an array of experimental conditions.

To obtain an estimate of φ we shall use the observed proportion of A_1 responses given in Table 5.2. From Eq. 5.28

$$Pr(A_1) = \gamma\sigma + \frac{\gamma(1 - \sigma)}{\gamma + (1 - \gamma)\varphi} \, ;$$

solving for φ yields

(5.30)
$$\varphi = \frac{\gamma(1 - \sigma)}{[Pr(A_1) - \sigma\gamma](1 - \gamma)} - \frac{\gamma}{1 - \gamma}.$$

For each presentation schedule we have substituted the estimated value of σ and the observed value of $Pr(A_1)$ in the equation above to obtain an

Table 5.3   Estimates of φ

Subject	$\hat{\varphi}$	$\hat{\varphi}_A$	$\hat{\varphi}_B$	$\hat{\varphi}_C$
1	0.860	0.777	1.099	0.705
2	1.219	1.162	1.400	1.096
3	1.265	1.155	1.390	1.251
4	1.238	1.324	1.446	0.945
5	1.329	1.065	1.449	1.472
6	1.083	1.085	1.147	1.018
7	1.016	0.914	1.028	1.105
8	1.148	1.384	1.284	0.775
Average	1.145	1.108	1.280	1.046

estimate of φ. For example, for subject 1, $\sigma = 0.447$, $Pr(A_1) = 0.278$, and $\gamma = 0.25$ on schedule A; hence substituting in the above equation yields

$$\hat{\varphi}_A = \frac{0.25(0.553)}{[0.278 - (0.25)(0.447)](0.75)} - \frac{0.25}{0.75}$$
$$= 0.777.$$

Similarly $\hat{\varphi}_B$ and $\hat{\varphi}_C$ can be computed using the appropriate values of γ and $Pr(A_1)$. To obtain an overall estimate of φ for each subject we have taken the average of the three $\hat{\varphi}$ values; namely,

$$\hat{\varphi} = \tfrac{1}{3}[\hat{\varphi}_A + \hat{\varphi}_B + \hat{\varphi}_C].$$

The various estimates of $\hat{\varphi}$ are presented in Table 5.3. Note that $\hat{\varphi}$ averaged over subjects is somewhat greater than one, indicating that $\theta' > \theta$. The interpretation of this result is that the E_2 event has a slightly greater effect on increasing the probability of an A_2 response than the E_1 event has on increasing the probability of an A_1 response; we return to this point later.

Given estimates of σ and φ, predictions can now be generated for $Pr(H)$, $Pr(F)$, $Pr(C)$, and $Pr(A_1)$ using Eqs. 5.25 to 5.28. These predicted values and the corresponding observed quantities are presented in Tables

5.1 and 5.2. Figure 5.6 also presents the predicted and observed values of $Pr(H)$ and $Pr(F)$; in this figure the predicted point for each presentation schedule is at the intersection of the appropriate iso-bias curve and the ROC curve. To give some measure of the correspondence between predicted and observed points, we have computed the average distance between the three predicted and observed points in the ROC space; this quantity, denoted as $\bar{D}$, is also presented in Fig. 5.6.* In terms of the $\bar{D}$ measure subjects 6 and 7 display the best fits, whereas subject 1 is the poorest.

By and large, the correspondence between predicted and observed values is remarkably good. Only subject 8 shows a systematic discrepancy between predicted and observed quantities. For this subject $\hat{\varphi} = 1.148$, and hence $Pr(A_1)$ should be about 0.236 for schedule A and about 0.735 for schedule C. However, what happened was that $Pr(A_1)$ overshot its predicted value for schedule C and went below its predicted value for schedule A. To some degree, this subject's performance deviated from the predicted values in the direction of optimizing the probability of a correct response. Specifically, consider the probability of a correct response:

$$Pr(C) = \sigma + (1 - \sigma)[\gamma p + (1 - \gamma)(1 - p)].$$

To maximize this function (for fixed σ), the subject should set the response bias as follows:

$$p = \begin{cases} 1, & \text{if } \gamma > \tfrac{1}{2} \\ 0, & \text{if } \gamma < \tfrac{1}{2}. \end{cases}$$

When $\gamma = \tfrac{1}{2}$ any value of p yields a maximum. If a subject adopted the strategy specified by the equation above, then the ROC curve would reduce to three points; one at $(0, \sigma)$ for presentation schedules where $\gamma < \tfrac{1}{2}$, another at $(1 - \sigma, 0)$ for $\gamma > \tfrac{1}{2}$, and a third point for $\gamma = \tfrac{1}{2}$. The behavior of subject 8 tends to move away from the theoretical predictions in the direction of maximization, but of course to nowhere near the extent indicated by the above equation. We contend that if monetary payoffs for correct responses and penalties for incorrect responses were

---

* The distance between two points (x_1, y_1) and (x_2, y_2) is

$$D = \sqrt{(x_2 - x_1)^2 + (y_2 - y_1)^2}.$$

Here we have computed D for each of the three pairs of points and then presented their average. One method for jointly estimating φ and σ would have been to define $\bar{D}$ as a function of these parameters. Then the values of φ and σ that minimize the function $\bar{D}(\varphi, \sigma)$ would be the appropriate estimates.

introduced into the experimental situation, then more subjects would tend to deviate from the theoretical values, the deviation being in the direction of optimization. Under these conditions the model would have to be generalized to account for such effects. We shall return to a discussion of this point later.

Time-order Effect

For many perceptual tasks a phenomenon which has been labeled the *time-order* effect is frequently observed.* In the forced-choice signal detection problem this terminology refers to the fact that subjects generally are more accurate in detecting signals embedded in the second observation interval than in the first interval. For example, on schedule B (which has S_1 and S_2 events occurring equally often), every subject had a higher probability of being correct when the signal was in the second interval than in the first; that is, $Pr(A_1 \mid S_1) < Pr(A_2 \mid S_2)$ for all subjects. In terms of the present analysis there are two possible explanations for this time-order effect. One is that p_n tends to favor the A_2 response. Hence when sensory state s_0 is activated, the subject makes the A_2 response more frequently, insuring that he will have a higher probability of being correct on the S_2 stimulus than on the S_1 stimulus. Another possibility is that the time-order effect occurs because the sensitivity level varies from one observation interval to the next; specifically, that there are two sensitivity parameters σ_1 and σ_2 associated with the two intervals and that $\sigma_2 > \sigma_1$.

Thus a time-order effect can be accounted for by postulating a bias process that tends to favor the A_2 response or by postulating a sensory mechanism that is more sensitive to stimuli presented in the second observation interval. The first proposal explains the time-order effect in terms of the decision process, whereas the second accounts for the effect in terms of the perceptual process. Both of these explanations are tenable, and one would like to have a rationale for selecting between them. Fortunately, the theory makes different predictions depending on which process is used to account for the time-order effect. If the explanation is in terms of the bias function (as was the case in our analysis), then the ROC curve has slope one and the time-order effect is simply due to the fact that $\varphi > 1$. If, however, the time-order effect is explained in terms of different sensitivity levels, then

$$Pr(H) = \sigma_1 + (1 - \sigma_1)p$$
$$Pr(F) = (1 - \sigma_2)p.$$

---

* For a review of research related to the time-order effect see Guilford (1954).

Under these conditions the ROC curve is the linear function

$$Pr(H) = \frac{1 - \sigma_1}{1 - \sigma_2} Pr(F) + \sigma_1.$$

If we assume that $\sigma_2 > \sigma_1$, then the slope of the ROC curve is greater than one. Consequently, to decide whether the time-order effect can be explained without introducing the concept of variation in sensitivity, we must ask whether the ROC curve has slope greater than one. One can see by inspection of Fig. 5.6 that for these subjects there is no reason (except possibly for subject 2) to believe that the observed points would be better fit by a line with slope greater than one. Thus, for this experiment, the conclusion is that the time-order effect is due to the bias process, and need not be explained by changes in sensitivity over the two observation intervals.

5.5 SEQUENTIAL PHENOMENA*

Derivation of Sequential Predictions

So far, we have restricted our attention to fairly gross aspects of the response data. However, the model provides a richer analysis of the experiment than the foregoing results indicate. From the model one can predict not only hit and false alarm rates, but also the detailed sequential properties of the subject's response protocol. In terms of the assumptions, sequential effects in the observable response events are produced by trial-to-trial fluctuations in p_n. Such fluctuations, of course, can take place on any trial and are not restricted to pre-asymptotic data. For example, even at asymptote the likelihood of making a correct response to an S_1 stimulus depends in a very definite way on whether an S_1 or an S_2 occurred on the preceding trial.

To indicate the type of sequential predictions obtainable from the model, consider the probability of an A_1 response to an S_1 stimulus, given that an S_1 stimulus occurred on the preceding trial; namely,

$$Pr(A_{1,n+1} \mid S_{1,n+1}S_{1,n}).$$

To derive an expression for this quantity, note that by the definition of conditional probabilities,

(5.31) $$Pr(A_{1,n+1} \mid S_{1,n+1}S_{1,n}) = \frac{Pr(A_{1,n+1}S_{1,n+1}S_{1,n})}{Pr(S_{1,n+1}S_{1,n})}.$$

---

* This section treats a special topic and may be omitted on first reading.

But, for our presentation schedule the stimulus events are generated independently, and therefore,

$$Pr(S_{1,n+1}S_{1,n}) = Pr(S_{1,n+1} \mid S_{1,n})Pr(S_{1,n}) = \gamma^2.$$

Hence, to compute the conditional probability on the left-hand side of Eq. 5.31, we can simply compute the joint probability in the numerator on the right-hand side and then divide by γ^2.

Proceeding in this manner, note first that we can express

$$Pr(A_{1,n+1}S_{1,n+1}S_{1,n})$$

in terms of the histories $h_{v,n}$ defined in Sec. 5.3;* that is,

(5.32) $$Pr(A_{1,n+1}S_{1,n+1}S_{1,n}) = \sum_{v=1}^{3^{n-1}} Pr(A_{1,n+1}S_{1,n+1}S_{1,n}h_{v,n})$$

where v is summed over all possible histories through trial n. Now let us consider a single term in the sum on the right-hand side of the equation above. It may be expressed in terms of conditional probabilities as follows:**

$$Pr(A_{1,n+1}S_{1,n+1}S_{1,n}h_{v,n})$$
$$= Pr(A_{1,n+1} \mid S_{1,n+1}S_{1,n}h_{v,n})Pr(S_{1,n+1} \mid S_{1,n}h_{v,n})Pr(S_{1,n} \mid h_{v,n})Pr(h_{v,n}).$$

But the probability of presenting an S_1 stimulus is determined solely by the parameter γ and is independent of all other events; hence

$$Pr(S_{1,n+1} \mid S_{1,n}h_{v,n}) = \gamma$$
$$Pr(S_{1,n} \mid h_{v,n}) = \gamma.$$

Therefore, Eq. 5.32 can be rewritten as

(5.33) $$Pr(A_{1,n+1}S_{1,n+1}S_{1,n}) = \gamma^2 \sum_{v=1}^{3^{n-1}} Pr(A_{1,n+1} \mid S_{1,n+1}S_{1,n}h_{v,n})Pr(h_{v,n}).$$

Next we derive an expression for the term

$$Pr(A_{1,n+1} \mid S_{1,n+1}S_{1,n}h_{v,n}).$$

---

* If $h_1, h_2, \ldots, h_m$ are a set of mutually exclusive events, one of which necessarily occurs, then any event A can occur only in conjunction with some h_j. Since A and h_j are mutually exclusive, their probabilities add. Hence

$$Pr(A) = \sum_{j=1}^{m} Pr(A \ \& \ h_j).$$

** Generalizing the so-called theorem on compound probabilities to four events A, B, C and D, we can easily show that

$$Pr(ABCD) = Pr(A \mid BCD)Pr(B \mid CD)Pr(C \mid D)Pr(D).$$

Given a history $h_{v,n}$, we know that the bias parameter associated with the history at the start of trial n is $p_{v,n}$. Now look at Fig. 5.7. If S_1 occurs on trial n then

(1) with probability σ, the s_1 sensory state is activated, which means that $p_{v,n}$ will be operated on by Q_0, or

(2) with probability $1 - \sigma$, the s_0 sensory state will be activated, which means that $p_{v,n}$ will be operated on by Q_1.

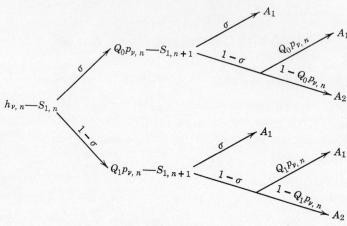

Figure 5.7.

Given history $h_{v,n}$ and the fact that S_1 occurs on trial n, there are two possible values for the bias parameter on trial $n + 1$: either $Q_1 p_{v,n}$ with probability $1 - \sigma$ or $Q_0 p_{v,n}$ with probability σ. Now, S_1 occurs again on trial $n + 1$, and the subject makes the A_1 response (1) with probability $\sigma + (1 - \sigma)Q_1 p_{v,n}$ if operator Q_1 was applied on trial n or (2) with probability $\sigma + (1 - \sigma)Q_0 p_{v,n}$ if operator Q_0 was applied. Thus, the probability $Pr(A_{1,n+1} \mid S_{1,n+1}S_{1,n}h_{v,n})$ is simply the sum of the probabilities associated with the branches in the tree of Fig. 5.7 that lead to an A_1 response. Namely,

$$Pr(A_{1,n+1} \mid S_{1,n+1}S_{1,n}h_{v,n})$$
$$= \sigma[\sigma + (1 - \sigma)Q_0 p_{v,n}] + (1 - \sigma)[\sigma + (1 - \sigma)Q_1 p_{v,n}]$$
$$= \sigma + \sigma(1 - \sigma)Q_0 p_{v,n} + (1 - \sigma)^2 Q_1 p_{v,n}.$$

Applying the operators as indicated yields

$$Pr(A_{1,n+1} \mid S_{1,n+1}S_{1,n}h_{v,n})$$
$$= \sigma + \sigma(1 - \sigma)p_{v,n} + (1 - \sigma)^2[(1 - \theta)p_{v,n} + \theta]$$
$$= \sigma + \theta(1 - \sigma)^2 + (1 - \sigma)(1 - \theta + \theta\sigma)p_{v,n}.$$

Substituting the above expression for $Pr(A_{1,n+1} \mid S_{1,n+1}S_{1,n}h_{v,n})$ in Eq. 5.33 yields

(5.34) $Pr(A_{1,n+1}S_{1,n}S_{1,n})$

$$= \gamma^2 \sum_{v=1}^{3^{n-1}} [\sigma + \theta(1 - \sigma)^2 + (1 - \sigma)(1 - \theta + \theta\sigma)p_{v,n}]Pr(h_{v,n}).$$

But as indicated earlier

$$\sum_{v=1}^{3^{n-1}} p_{v,n}Pr(h_{v,n}) = E(p_n), \quad \text{and} \quad \sum_{v=1}^{3^{n-1}} Pr(h_{v,n}) = 1.$$

Hence, carrying out the summation in Eq. 5.34 yields

(5.35)

$$Pr(A_{1,n+1}S_{1,n+1}S_{1,n}) = \gamma^2[\sigma + \theta(1 - \sigma)^2 + (1 - \sigma)(1 - \theta + \theta\sigma)E(p_n)].$$

In order to obtain an expression for the conditional probability, we divide the result in Eq. 5.35 by γ^2 as indicated in Eq. 5.31, whence

(5.36a)

$$Pr(A_{1,n+1} \mid S_{1,n+1}S_{1,n}) = [\sigma + (1 - \sigma)E(p_n)] + \theta(1 - \sigma)^2[1 - E(p_n)].$$

But we have already derived expressions for $E(p_n)$; therefore, the probability of an A_1 response to an S_1 stimulus, given that on the preceding trial an S_1 stimulus also occurred, is completely specified in terms of γ and the parameters σ, θ, and θ'.

By similar techniques expressions can be derived for the other sequential probabilities; namely,

(5.36b) $Pr(A_{1,n+1} \mid S_{1,n+1}S_{2,n}) = [\sigma + (1 - \sigma)E(p_n)] - \theta'(1 - \sigma)^2E(p_n)$

(5.36c) $Pr(A_{1,n+1} \mid S_{2,n+1}S_{1,n}) = (1 - \sigma)E(p_n) + \theta(1 - \sigma)^2[1 - E(p_n)]$

(5.36d) $Pr(A_{1,n+1} \mid S_{2,n+1}S_{2,n}) = (1 - \sigma)E(p_n) - \theta'(1 - \sigma)^2E(p_n).$

Asymptotic Sequential Predictions

Following the convention adopted earlier, we shall denote the limiting expression for $Pr(A_{i,n+1} \mid S_{j,n+1}S_{k,n})$ simply by deleting the trial subscripts; that is,

$$\lim_{n \to \infty} Pr(A_{i,n+1} \mid S_{j,n+1}S_{k,n}) = Pr(A_i \mid S_jS_k),$$

where the event order is understood. Of course, we know that

$$\lim_{n \to \infty} E(p_n) = p_\infty,$$
$$Pr(H) = \sigma + (1 - \sigma)p_\infty,$$
$$Pr(F) = (1 - \sigma)p_\infty.$$

Hence from Eq. 5.36, we can write

(5.37a) $Pr(A_1 \mid S_1S_1) = Pr(H) + \theta(1 - \sigma)^2(1 - p_\infty)$

(5.37b) $Pr(A_1 \mid S_1S_2) = Pr(H) - \theta'(1 - \sigma)^2 p_\infty$

(5.37c) $Pr(A_1 \mid S_2S_1) = Pr(F) + \theta(1 - \sigma)^2(1 - p_\infty)$

(5.37d) $Pr(A_1 \mid S_2S_2) = Pr(F) - \theta'(1 - \sigma)^2 p_\infty.$

Numerical predictions can be easily calculated once values for the parameters have been obtained. Further, independent of the parameter values, certain relations hold among the sequential probabilities. For example, it is obvious that

$$Pr(A_1 \mid S_1S_1) > Pr(H) > Pr(A_1 \mid S_1S_2),$$
$$Pr(A_1 \mid S_2S_1) > Pr(F) > Pr(A_1 \mid S_2S_2),$$

and

$$Pr(A_1 \mid S_1S_1) + Pr(A_1 \mid S_2S_2) = Pr(A_1 \mid S_1S_2) + Pr(A_1 \mid S_2S_1).$$

Also, the reader can prove for himself that the point

$$[Pr(A_1 \mid S_2S_1), \quad Pr(A_1 \mid S_1S_1)]$$

and the point

$$[Pr(A_1 \mid S_2S_2), \quad Pr(A_1 \mid S_1S_2)]$$

fall on the ROC curve; the point $[Pr(A_1 \mid S_2S_1), Pr(A_1 \mid S_1S_1)]$ will fall to the upper right of the point $[Pr(F), Pr(H)]$, whereas the point $[Pr(A_1 \mid S_2S_2), Pr(A_1 \mid S_1S_2)]$ will fall to the lower left.

Estimates of Sequential Effects

Let us now consider methods that can be used to obtain estimates of $Pr(A_i \mid S_jS_k)$. Suppose a given subject's data was as follows for, say, trials 200 to 212.

Trial	200	201	202	203	204	205	206	207	208	209	210	211	212
Stimulus	S_1	S_2	S_1	S_1	S_1	S_2	S_2	S_2	S_2	S_1	S_1	S_1	S_1
Response	A_1	A_2	A_1	A_1	A_2	A_2	A_1	A_2	A_2	A_2	A_1	A_1	A_2

In this array the combination $A_{1,n+1}S_{1,n+1}S_{1,n}$ occurs three times, the combination $A_{2,n+1}S_{1,n+1}S_{1,n}$ occurs once, etc. We can summarize the triplet information in this sequence of trials by the following frequency table.

	$A_{1,n+1}$	$A_{2,n+1}$
$S_{1,n}S_{1,n+1}$	3	2
$S_{2,n}S_{1,n+1}$	1	1
$S_{1,n}S_{2,n+1}$	0	2
$S_{2,n}S_{2,n+1}$	1	2

More generally, the frequency table above can be denoted as

	A_1	A_2
S_1S_1	x_{11}	y_{11}
S_2S_1	x_{21}	y_{21}
S_1S_2	x_{12}	y_{12}
S_2S_2	x_{22}	y_{22}

where x_{ij} is the number of $A_{1,n+1}S_{j,n+1}S_{i,n}$ events and y_{ij} is the number of $A_{2,n+1}S_{j,n+1}S_{i,n}$ events. If the frequency matrix above is obtained for a trial sequence at asymptote, then x_{ij} and y_{ij} can be used to estimate the asymptotic probability $Pr(A_k \mid S_jS_i)$. That is,

$$Pr(A_1 \mid S_jS_i) = \frac{x_{ij}}{x_{ij} + y_{ij}}$$

and

$$Pr(A_2 \mid S_jS_i) = \frac{y_{ij}}{x_{ij} + y_{ij}}.$$

In order to use Eq. 5.37 to generate theoretical predictions for the sequential statistics, values for σ, θ, and θ' are needed. Of course, estimates of σ and φ ($= \theta'/\theta$) already have been obtained from the analysis of $Pr(H)$ and $Pr(F)$, and therefore only an estimate of θ (or θ') is required. One method for estimating θ would be to take the observed value of $Pr(A_1 \mid S_1S_1)$ at asymptote and set it equal to the theoretical expression in Eq. 5.37a; that is,

$$\frac{x_{11}}{x_{11} + y_{11}} = Pr(H) + \theta(1 - \sigma)^2(1 - p_\infty).$$

If we now substitute the estimates of σ and φ into the expression above, we can solve for θ. Taking the resulting estimate of θ, θ' can be obtained by noting that $\varphi = \theta'/\theta$. With these estimates of σ, θ', and θ, sequential predictions can be generated for each of the presentation schedules.

For the moment, we shall not go further in our discussion of sequential effects. However, we return to this topic in Sec. 5.7 and at that time treat some data.

5.6 PROBABILITY LEARNING AND OUTCOME STRUCTURE

In recent years there has been considerable interest in a class of experimental situations that have come to be known as probability learning. As we have indicated, these experiments have many features in common with the typical signal detection task. Consequently, it will be instructive to describe some of the theoretical developments associated with probability learning and indicate their relevance to the model presented in this chapter.

The typical probability learning experiment involves a long series of discrete trials. Each trial is initiated by the onset of a warning signal. To this cue the subject is required to make one of two responses, denoted A_1 and A_2. The trial is then terminated with an E_1 or E_2 reinforcing event; the occurrence of E_i indicates that A_i was the correct response for that trial. Thus in a human learning situation, the subject is required on each trial to predict the reinforcing event he expects will occur by making the appropriate response—an A_1 if he expects E_1 and an A_2 if he expects E_2; at the end of the trial he is permitted to observe which event actually occurred. Initially the subject may have no preference between the two responses, but as information accrues to him over trials his pattern of choices undergoes systematic changes. The role of a model is to predict the detailed features of these changes.

The learning is called probabilistic because there is no single correct response. The reinforcing events are presented according to some schedule that precludes perfect prediction. For example, the probability of E_1 may be (1) some function of the trial number, (2) dependent on previous responses of the subject, (3) dependent on previous reinforcing events, or (4) some combination of the foregoing. One frequently used schedule for generating E_i events is called the *noncontingent* reinforcement schedule. This case is defined by the condition that the probability of E_1 is constant over trials and independent of previous responses and reinforcements. It is customary in the literature to call this probability π; thus $Pr(E_{1,n}) = \pi$ for all n.

One of the first models to be applied to probability learning experiments involved a two-operator linear process. If p_n denotes the probability of an A_1 response on trial n, then

$$(5.38a) \qquad p_{n+1} = \begin{cases} (1 - \theta)p_n + \theta, & \text{if } E_{1,n} \\ (1 - \theta')p_n, & \text{if } E_{2,n}. \end{cases}$$

That is, the probability of an A_1 response was assumed to increase if E_1 occurred and to decrease if E_2 occurred. By the methods of Sec. 5.3, an expression can be derived for the expected value of $Pr(A_{1,n})$ in the noncontingent case. Without verifying it here, we record this result:

$$(5.38b) \quad Pr(A_{1,n}) = \frac{\pi}{\pi + (1 - \pi)\varphi}$$

$$- \left[\frac{\pi}{\pi + (1 - \pi)\varphi} - p_1 \right] [1 - \theta\pi - \theta'(1 - \pi)]^{n-1}$$

where we retain the notation $\varphi = \theta'/\theta$. Similarly, using the techniques developed in Sec. 5.5, expressions can be derived for sequential effects.

$$(5.38c) \quad \begin{aligned} Pr(A_{1,n+1} \mid E_{1,n}) &= (1 - \theta)Pr(A_{1,n}) + \theta \\ Pr(A_{1,n+1} \mid E_{2,n}) &= (1 - \theta')Pr(A_{1,n}). \end{aligned}$$

Interestingly, the model specified by Eq. 5.38a for probability learning is identical to the signal detection model developed in Sec. 5.2 in the limiting case when $\sigma = 0$. That is, as the signal becomes increasingly weak, the detection process tends to be governed more and more by p_n. Hence the detection model's special case, defined by $\gamma = \pi$ and $\sigma = 0$, is equivalent to the probability learning model above. The reader can easily check that this is the case. For example, the expression for $Pr(H_n)$ and that for $Pr(F_n)$ reduce to Eq. 5.38b when $\gamma = \pi$ and $\sigma = 0$. Similarly, the equations for $Pr(A_{1,n+1} \mid S_{1,n+1}S_{1,n})$ and for $Pr(A_{1,n+1} \mid S_{2,n+1}S_{1,n})$ reduce to the appropriate probability learning expression $Pr(A_{1,n+1} \mid E_{1,n})$; and so forth. The reduction of the signal detection model to that for probability learning is desirable, for if the signal is omitted in the detection task, then (except for instructions) the experimental procedure is essentially the same one used in probability learning.

For most probability learning experiments, it is reasonable to assume that the increment in the probability of an A_1 response given an E_1 reinforcing event is the same as the increment in the probability of an A_2 response given an E_2 event. In fact, the experimenter usually selects the responses and experimental procedure in order to guarantee that this symmetry condition will be met to some reasonable degree of accuracy. The requirement of symmetry between the two responses implies that $\theta = \theta'$; hence, Eq. 5.38b reduces to

$$(5.39) \quad Pr(A_{1,n}) = \pi - [\pi - p_1](1 - \theta)^{n-1}.$$

Under these conditions $Pr(A_{1,n})$ approaches π in the limit.

The prediction that the asymptotic probability of an A_1 response will match the reinforcement parameter π is a stringent test of the model and one that could not be expected to hold for all probability learning experiments. As different parameters of the probability learning task have been varied from one experiment to the next, considerable information has accumulated as to when this prediction is reasonable. (For a systematic review of this research, see Estes, 1964.) Roughly speaking, probability matching is observed when the experimental task and instructions indicate that the subject is to express his expectation on each trial (Estes and Straughan, 1954; Friedman, Burke, Cole, Estes, and Millward, 1964; Greeno, 1962; Messick and Solley, 1957) or when they stress the desirability of being correct on every trial as in a problem solving situation (Goodnow, 1955a; Goodnow and Postman, 1955). On the other hand, the probability of the more frequently rewarded response is sometimes observed to exceed the matching value when the instructions lead the subject to believe that he is dealing with a random sequence of events (Edwards, 1961b; Morse and Runquist, 1960) or when they stress the importance of maximizing overall performance (Das, 1961; Rubenstein, 1959).

When probability matching is obtained, then the linear model specified by Eq. 5.38a does a reasonably accurate job of predicting the learning curve and much of the sequential data. Of particular interest in such analyses is what is called the *recency effect*. The model predicts that the greater the number of consecutive preceding occurrences of a given reinforcing event, the greater the likelihood that the subject will predict that event on the next trial. For example, by the methods developed in Sec. 5.5, it can be shown that

$$Pr(A_{1,n+v} \mid E_{1,n+v-1}E_{1,n+v-2} \cdots E_{1,n}E_{2,n-1})$$
$$= 1 - [1 - (1 - \theta)E(p_{n-1})](1 - \theta)^v.$$

That is, as the string of E_1 events lengthens, the probability of an A_1 increases approaching one as $v \to \infty$. Data relevant to this prediction were first reported by Jarvik (1951), and were clearly negative. The subjects did not follow the predicted function but instead responded in terms of what has been called the "gambler's fallacy"; that is, their likelihood of predicting an event increased with increasing numbers of trials since the last occurrence of that event. The recency curve, instead of corresponding to the predicted function, showed an initial increase in response probability for the first two or three reinforcements, and then a decrease as the run of consecutive reinforcements continued. This "negative recency" effect was also found by a number of subsequent investigators (Anderson, 1960; Feldman, 1959; Nicks, 1959). However, more recent experiments (Friedman et al., 1964; Edwards, 1961b) suggest that the bow-shaped recency curve is found primarily during the early trials of an experiment; for studies with a sufficiently long series of trials, the negative recency effect washes out and then the run data are adequately described by the linear model. An explanation of this finding has been offered by Estes (1962*b*); he argues that the negative recency function results from response tendencies the subject brings with him to the experiment (via generalization from other tasks) but which extinguish with experience in the experimental situation.

For appropriately contrived experimental situations, then, the model provides a reasonably accurate account of many aspects of probability learning data. However, even under these conditions there are certain shortcomings of the model that are quite consistently observed (Friedman et al., 1964). First of all, the estimate of θ fails to be invariant across various aspects of the data. The value of θ required to fit the learning curve tends to be smaller than the value that provides the best account of asymptotic sequential data. Also, the estimate of θ tends to be related to the reinforcement schedule; that is, θ tends to increase as the difference between π and $\frac{1}{2}$ increases. Another shortcoming of the model is that in general the predicted variance of response frequencies is far less than observed. This deficiency seems to be a weakness of the model that cannot be easily resolved. It is principally for this reason that a number of alternative models for probability learning have been proposed; we shall examine one such model in Chapter 8.

Monetary Payoffs

When differential payoffs are introduced in the probability learning situation, the probability of the most frequently rewarded response tends to overshoot the matching value, approaching an asymptote that is directly related to the payoff structure (Edwards, 1956; Siegel, 1961; Siegel and Goldstein, 1959; Taub and Myers, 1961). For example, consider a probability learning experiment using the following outcome structure

$$\begin{array}{cc} & \begin{array}{cc} E_1 & E_2 \end{array} \\ \begin{array}{c} A_1 \\ A_2 \end{array} & \begin{bmatrix} +u & -u \\ -u & +u \end{bmatrix}. \end{array}$$

A correct response (A_1E_1 or A_2E_2) leads to a gain of u units, and an incorrect response (A_1E_2 or A_2E_1) to a loss of u units. Then for $\pi > \frac{1}{2}$, it is generally the case that the observed asymptotic probability of an A_1 response increases with increasing values of u. To illustrate this result, let us examine a study by Suppes and Atkinson (1960). Three groups were run all using $\pi = 0.6$; the groups differed with respect to u, which took on the value 0, 5, and 10 cents. In their study the observed asymptotic probabilities of an A_1 response were 0.605, 0.648, and 0.695 for u equal to 0, 5, and 10 cents, respectively. Thus, for $u = 0$, the matching prediction was supported, but for the other values of u the probability of an A_1 exceeded π.

There are several ways of generalizing the notions embodied in Eq. 5.38a to handle probability learning experiments involving variable payoffs; in fact, considerable research already has been done on this topic. For example, Atkinson (1962) and Myers and Atkinson (1964) have proposed a model derived from stimulus sampling theory that gives a good account of a wide array of probability learning experiments involving quite general payoff structures. Their model makes use of the concept of regret (Simon, 1956; Savage, 1957) and assumes a monotonic relation between regret and the value of the conditioning parameters. Choice models of the sort described in Chapter 4 have also been used to analyze the problem of payoffs in probability learning (Estes, 1962c; Cole, 1965). However, there are many unresolved issues regarding all of the models that have been proposed to deal with variable outcome structures, and most psychologists are not very satisfied with current theoretical explanations.

As we have seen, the p_n function proposed for the signal detection process is one that has been extensively investigated in the context of probability learning, and therefore the model suggests a close relation between theories of decision and detection situations. If the signal detection model were generalized to situations involving monetary payoffs, then (as in the case of probability learning) a more complex theory of the decision process would be necessary. Obviously there are outcome structures that will displace the subject's performance point off the ROC curve specified by Eq. 5.10.* For example, consider the payoff matrix

$$\begin{array}{cc} A_1 & A_2 \end{array}$$
$$\begin{array}{c} S_1 \\ S_2 \end{array} \begin{bmatrix} -10 & +20 \\ +20 & -10 \end{bmatrix}.$$

In this case the subject is heavily rewarded for incorrect detection responses and penalized for correct responses. Hence over time the subject would undoubtedly generate a point $[Pr(F), Pr(H)]$ that fell in the lower right-hand sector of the ROC space. That is, the probability of a false alarm would exceed the probability of a hit for this payoff matrix. It is important to note that such effects cannot be predicted merely by generalizing the assumptions governing p_n. The reason is that no matter how p_n

---

* In fact, even for experiments of the type discussed here, it is likely that the observed point $[Pr(F), Pr(H)]$ will fall below the predicted ROC curve when γ is close to 0 or 1 (see Atkinson, 1963a).

is permitted to vary, the model still requires that performance points fall on a linear curve with intercept σ.

Several prospective modifications of the detection model are able to account for experimental manipulations that generate performance points off the ROC curve. One approach is to develop a more elaborate conceptualization of the decision process. For example, one can replace the matrix $\mathbf{D}_n$ in Eq. 5.7 with

$$
\begin{array}{cc}
 & A_1 \qquad\qquad A_2 \\
\begin{array}{c} s_0 \\ s_1 \\ s_2 \end{array} &
\left[
\begin{array}{cc}
p_n & 1 - p_n \\
a_n^{(1)} & 1 - a_n^{(1)} \\
1 - a_n^{(2)} & a_n^{(2)}
\end{array}
\right].
\end{array}
$$

For this process manipulations of the outcome structure might not only affect p_n but also $a_n^{(i)}$. Thus, depending on the postulated relation of $a_n^{(i)}$ to the outcome structure, it would be possible to generate virtually any ROC curve. Of course, when $a_n^{(1)} = a_n^{(2)} = 1$ we obtain the original model, and we would want the theory to specify the experimental conditions for which this model is appropriate.

Another possible modification of the theory would be to develop a more general formulation of the sensory process. Pursuing this line, one might assume that the subject's sensitivity level could vary within certain limits as a function of the outcome structure and other variables (Atkinson, 1963a).

Both of these alternatives represent potential lines of theoretical development. They raise an important question: can changes in performance induced by manipulation of the outcome structure be explained by elaborating the theory of the bias process or do they also necessitate postulating a more complex sensory mechanism?

5.7 AN EXPERIMENT INVOLVING BOTH SIGNAL DETECTION AND PROBABILITY LEARNING

In this section we consider two modifications of the forced-choice detection task which yield an experiment that is an interesting mixture of signal detection and probability learning. One modification involves the introduction of blank trials, and the other the use of false-information feedback. By *blank trials* we mean that on occasion a trial will occur for which the signal has been omitted entirely; a blank trial will be denoted as S_0. By *false-information feedback* we mean that on some trials the subject will be told that a signal occurred in a particular observation interval when in fact it did not.

In the experiment to be discussed here, the subject was given the same instructions that were used in the other detection experiment; that is, he was led to believe that a signal would occur on every trial and that the information events reliably indicated the interval in which the signal occurred. Actually the presentation schedule involved S_1, S_2 and S_0 trials. On S_1 trials an E_1 always occurred, and on S_2 trials an E_2 always occurred; on S_0 trials sometimes E_1 occurred and sometimes E_2 occurred. The tree in Fig. 5.8 characterizes the presentation schedule

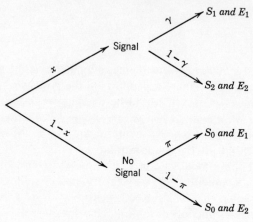

Figure 5.8.

used in the study: (1) with probability $x\gamma$ a signal was presented in the first interval and, after the response, event E_1 occurred; (2) with probability $x(1 - \gamma)$ a signal was presented in the second interval and followed by event E_2; and (3) with probability $1 - x$ a blank trial was presented. On a blank trial an E_1 information event occurred with probability π and an E_2 event with probability $1 - \pi$.

If $x = 1$, we have a typical forced-choice detection task; the S_1 or S_2 signal occurs with probability γ and $1 - \gamma$, respectively, and the information feedback is reliably correlated with the signal events. If $x = 0$, we have a pure probability learning experiment; a signal event never occurs, but still the subject is faced with the task of predicting the E_1 and E_2 events which are being generated with probabilities π and $1 - \pi$, respectively. If x takes on an intermediate value, the experiment involves concurrent signal detection and probability learning. As we shall see later, experiments using intermediate values of x permit us to make some very sharp predictions that differentiate the model developed in this chapter from several others with similar assumptions.

Theoretical Analysis

The model of Sec. 5.2 applies directly to this experiment. No new assumptions are necessary; we need only apply the axioms and carry out the appropriate derivations. First of all, consider the activation matrix for this experiment. In terms of the assumptions

$$
\mathbf{A}^* = \begin{array}{c} \\ S_1 \\ S_2 \\ S_0 \end{array} \overset{\begin{array}{ccc} s_0 & s_1 & s_2 \end{array}}{\begin{bmatrix} 1 - \sigma & \sigma & 0 \\ 1 - \sigma & 0 & \sigma \\ 1 & 0 & 0 \end{bmatrix}}.
$$

Stated in words, s_1 or s_0 can be activated on an S_1 trial; s_2 or s_0 can be activated on an S_2 trial; but only s_0 can be activated on an S_0 trial. Using the matrix $\mathbf{A}^*$ and the decision matrix $\mathbf{D}_n$ specified by Eq. 5.7, a performance matrix can be derived where the rows are the events S_1, S_2, and S_0 and the columns are the responses A_1 and A_2. The entries in the first column of this matrix are as follows:

(5.40a) $Pr(H_n) = Pr(A_{1,n} \mid S_{1,n}) = \sigma + (1 - \sigma)p_n$

(5.40b) $Pr(F_n) = Pr(A_{1,n} \mid S_{2,n}) = (1 - \sigma)p_n$

(5.40c) $Pr(A_{1,n} \mid S_{0,n}) = p_n.$

By inspection of Eqs. 5.40a and 5.40b, we can see that the ROC curve for this experiment is the same as before; namely,

(5.41) $Pr(H_n) = \sigma + Pr(F_n).$

Also, from Eqs. 5.40a and 5.40c it follows that

(5.42) $Pr(H_n) = \sigma + (1 - \sigma)Pr(A_{1,n} \mid S_{0,n}).$

Next, we derive an expression for the response bias. In Sec. 5.2 the axioms describing changes in p_n were presented; to repeat,

$$
p_{n+1} = \begin{cases} Q_1 p_n, & \text{if } s_{0,n} \ \& \ E_{1,n} \\ Q_2 p_n, & \text{if } s_{0,n} \ \& \ E_{2,n} \\ Q_0 p_n, & \text{otherwise.} \end{cases}
$$

These axioms are directly applicable to the present experiment. Given the equation above, we need only compute the likelihood of $(s_{0,n} \ \& \ E_{1,n})$, and $(s_{0,n} \& E_{2,n})$. The tree in Fig. 5.9 describes the possible events that can occur on a given trial. From the figure we read off that

$$Pr(s_{0,n} \& E_{1,n}) = x\gamma(1 - \sigma) + (1 - x)\pi$$

and

$$Pr(s_{0,n} \& E_{2,n}) = x(1 - \gamma)(1 - \sigma) + (1 - x)(1 - \pi).$$

Given the results above, we can now derive $E(p_n)$. We shall not go through all of the steps of the derivation, for they involve precisely the

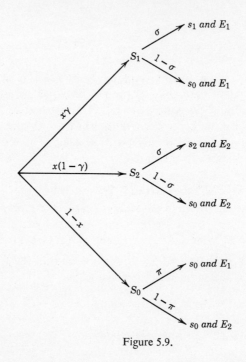

Figure 5.9.

same arguments that were employed in Sec. 5.3. Note first of all that if the bias parameter has fixed value p_n, then its expected value on trial $n + 1$ is simply

$$E(p_{n+1}) = Pr(s_{0,n} \& E_{1,n})Q_1 p_n + Pr(s_{0,n} \& E_{2,n})Q_2 p_n$$
$$+ [1 - Pr(s_{0,n} \& E_{1,n}) - Pr(s_{0,n} \& E_{2,n})]Q_0 p_n.$$

Carrying out the appropriate operations yields

$$E(p_{n+1}) = \{1 - \theta[x\gamma(1 - \sigma) + (1 - x)\pi] - \theta'[x(1 - \gamma)(1 - \sigma)$$
$$+ (1 - x)(1 - \pi)]\}p_n + \theta[x\gamma(1 - \sigma) + (1 - x)\pi].$$

Recall that for the first experiment, we proved that p_n could be replaced by $E(p_n)$, (see Eq. 5.16). By invoking the argument used there, we can prove that in the equation above p_n may be replaced by $E(p_n)$. After so doing, we have a difference equation in the variable $E(p_n)$. Employing the solution given by Eq. 5.19 yields

$$E(p_n) = p_\infty - [p_\infty - p_1]G^{n-1}.$$

Here G is the coefficient of p_n in the last equation on the preceding page, and

(5.43)
$$p_\infty = \frac{x\gamma(1 - \sigma) + (1 - x)\pi}{[x\gamma(1 - \sigma) + (1 - x)\pi] + [x(1 - \gamma)(1 - \sigma) + (1 - x)(1 - \pi)]\varphi},$$

where $\varphi = \theta'/\theta$. If $x = 1$, these equations reduce to those given in Sec. 5.3 for the signal detection model; and if $x = 0$, to the equations in Sec. 5.6 for the probability learning model.

Empirical Analysis

We now consider some data from an experiment using presentation schedules of the sort described in this section.* The same instructions and procedures were employed in this study as in the signal detection study described earlier, except that a pretraining phase was added. Pretraining lasted three days and involved running each subject on the schedule B routine used in the first experiment; that is, during pretraining a signal always occurred in one of the two observation intervals, information feedback was reliable, and $\gamma = \frac{1}{2}$. The signal intensity was fixed throughout the experiment, but the experimenter manipulated the noise level during pretraining in an attempt to establish a signal-to-noise ratio for each subject that yielded a correct response rate of approximately 79 per cent; the rationale for selecting this particular value will be given later. The manipulation of the noise level by the experimenter was done strictly by trial and error, but the procedure proved to be quite successful, since at the end of pretraining, a noise level for each subject had been established that yielded a correct response probability very close to the desired value. During the remainder of the experiment, the noise level was fixed for each subject at the value determined during pretraining. Also, during pretraining any subject who tended to strongly favor one response over the other was eliminated from the experiment. Only subjects whose overall proportion of A_1 responses was between 0.40 and 0.60 during

---

* This study is reported in more detail in Atkinson and Kinchla (1965).

pretraining were included in the main experiment. (Four subjects from a group of 18 were eliminated on this basis.) Since $\gamma = \frac{1}{2}$ during pretraining, this selection procedure guaranteed that φ would be close to one for all subjects.

Pretraining, therefore, involved two special features: (1) noise levels were determined individually for each subject, and (2) subjects who showed a strong preference for one or the other of the two response alternatives were eliminated from the experiment. The first requirement guaranteed that σ was approximately the same for all subjects. The second insured that φ was fairly close to one for all subjects. Thus, in a

Table 5.4   Predicted and Observed Response Probabilities

	Schedule A		Schedule B		Schedule C		Schedule D	
	Obs.	Pred.	Obs.	Pred.	Obs.	Pred.	Obs.	Pred.
$Pr(H)$	0.641	0.672	0.755	0.734	0.820	0.820	0.903	0.886
$Pr(F)$	0.086	0.100	0.174	0.162	0.227	0.248	0.344	0.314
$Pr(A_1 \mid S_0)$	0.213	0.234	0.401	0.378	0.553	0.578	0.765	0.733
$Pr(A_1)$	0.219	0.238	0.505	0.485	0.464	0.484	0.764	0.738

rough sense, a homogeneous group of subjects was formed via pretraining; homogeneous in the sense that all subjects were characterized by approximately the same values of σ and φ.

In the experiment proper, four presentation schedules were used. The probability, $1 - x$, of a blank trial was $\frac{1}{2}$ for all schedules, but the schedules differed on γ and π; namely,

$$\text{Schedule } A: \gamma = 0.25, \pi = 0.25$$
$$\text{Schedule } B: \gamma = 0.75, \pi = 0.25$$
$$\text{Schedule } C: \gamma = 0.25, \pi = 0.75$$
$$\text{Schedule } D: \gamma = 0.75, \pi = 0.75.$$

Test sessions of 400 trials were run on consecutive days. Each day a subject ran on one of the presentation schedules above for the entire session. In successive 4-day blocks a subject completed one day on each of the four schedules; within each 4-day block the order of schedules was randomly determined. The experiment involved 20 test sessions, and each schedule was repeated on five separate days.

Table 5.4 exhibits the average proportion of A_1 responses conditionalized on stimulus events. Proportions were computed for each subject based on the last 350 trials of replications two through five of a given presentation schedule; thus the estimates for each subject are based on $4 \times 350 = 1400$ trials. The average of these proportions over subjects are the quantities presented in the table. Although data were analyzed on an individual subject basis in the first experiment, there are at least two

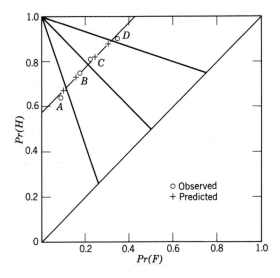

Fig. 5.10   Observed and predicted values for $Pr(H)$ and $Pr(F)$.

justifications for presenting group averages now. One reason is that it simplifies the analysis, and such simplification is welcomed for our present purpose, which is primarily to illustrate the theory. The second reason is that there is a theoretical rationale for treating group data in the present experiment. The rationale is based on the pretraining procedure, which was designed to insure that both σ and φ would be approximately the same for all subjects. By inspection of Eqs. 5.40 and 5.43, we see that asymptotic expressions for $Pr(H)$, $Pr(F)$ and $Pr(A_1 \mid S_0)$ depend only on σ and φ. If σ and φ are the same for all subjects, then the model makes the same predictions for the group average as for individual subjects.*

Figure 5.10 presents plots of the observed values of $Pr(H)$ and $Pr(F)$ as given in Table 5.4. The theory predicts that these points should fall on a straight line with slope 1 and intercept σ. We estimate σ from these data

---

* For an excellent discussion of the problems introduced by applying models of individual behavior to group averages see Estes (1956).

using the method of least squares (see Eq. 5.29); that is,

$$\sigma = \tfrac{1}{4}\{(0.641 + 0.755 + 0.820 + 0.903)$$

$$- (0.086 + 0.174 + 0.227 + 0.344)\}$$

$$= 0.572.$$

This estimate was used to generate the ROC curve displayed in Fig. 5.10. The four observed points, one from each schedule, do indeed fall virtually on a straight line.

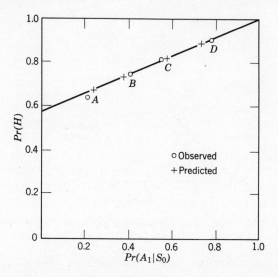

Fig. 5.11   Observed and predicted values for $Pr(H)$ and $Pr(A_1 \mid S_0)$.

Figure 5.11 presents a plot of $Pr(A_1 \mid S_0)$ versus $Pr(A_1 \mid S_1)$. As indicated in Eq. 5.42, these points should be related by a linear function with slope $1 - \sigma$ and intercept σ. Using our estimate of σ, we generated the straight line in Fig. 5.11. Once again the linear relation seems to be well supported.

In order to make numerical predictions for response proportions, we need (in addition to σ) an estimate of φ. Estimation of this parameter is attained using the same method employed in Sec. 5.4. The probability of an A_1 response is

$$Pr(A_1) = x\gamma Pr(A_1 \mid S_1) + x(1 - \gamma)Pr(A_1 \mid S_2) + (1 - x)Pr(A_1 \mid S_0)$$

$$= \sigma x\gamma + (1 - \sigma x)p_\infty.$$

Inserting the expression for p_∞ given in Eq. 5.43 and solving for φ yields

$$\varphi = \frac{[\gamma(1 - \sigma) + \pi](2 - \sigma)}{[2Pr(A_1) - \sigma\gamma][(1 - \gamma)(1 - \sigma) + 1 - \pi]}$$
$$- \frac{\gamma(1 - \sigma) + \pi}{(1 - \gamma)(1 - \sigma) + 1 - \pi}.$$

For each presentation schedule we have substituted the observed value of $Pr(A_1)$ in the equation above to obtain an estimate of φ. For example, for schedule A the observed value of $Pr(A_1)$ is 0.219; letting $\hat{\sigma} = 0.572$, $\gamma = 0.25$, $\pi = 0.25$, and $Pr(A_1) = 0.219$ in the equation above yields

$$\hat{\varphi}_A = 1.281.$$

Similarly, for the other schedules

$$\hat{\varphi}_B = 0.969$$
$$\hat{\varphi}_C = 1.229$$
$$\hat{\varphi}_D = 0.897.$$

Note that $\hat{\varphi}$ seems to be correlated more with γ than with π. Schedules A and C ($\gamma = 0.25$) both yield $\hat{\varphi} > 1$, whereas schedules B and D ($\gamma = 0.75$) yield $\hat{\varphi} < 1$. Recalling that $\varphi = \theta'/\theta$ and that γ is the probability of a signal in the first interval (if there is a signal), these estimates suggest that $\theta' > \theta$ if the probability of the signal being in the second interval exceeds $\frac{1}{2}$. Hence the change in the bias parameter p_n seems to be somewhat dominated by the interval with the higher probability of bracketing the signal. Despite this departure from independence of the parameters φ and γ, very little damage is done to the accuracy of the model's predictions, as will shortly be seen. To obtain an overall estimate of φ, we have taken the average of the individual values; that is,

$$\hat{\varphi} = \frac{1}{4}(\hat{\varphi}_A + \hat{\varphi}_B + \hat{\varphi}_C + \hat{\varphi}_D)$$
$$= 1.094.$$

With estimates of σ and φ, we can now use Eqs. 5.40 and 5.43 to generate predictions for $Pr(H)$, $Pr(F)$, $Pr(A_1 \mid S_0)$, and $Pr(A_1)$. These predicted quantities are given in Table 5.4; they also are graphically displayed in Figs. 5.10 and 5.11 as cross marks on the appropriate line segments. There are no constraints on the relations among the quantities $Pr(A_1 \mid S_1)$, $Pr(A_1 \mid S_2)$, and $Pr(A_1 \mid S_0)$, and therefore twelve independent predictions are being made on the basis of two parameter estimates. One need only inspect the array of observed and predicted quantities to realize that the correspondence between theoretical and observed values is quite satisfactory.

Recall that for both schedules B and C the E_1 and E_2 information-feedback events occurred equally often; that is, on both schedules the subject was being told (via the trial-to-trial feedback) that the signal was recurring equally often in the two observation intervals. However, the signal actually occurred more frequently in the first interval for schedule B than for schedule C. These experimental manipulations are reflected in the data. On an S_0 trial the probability of an A_1 response was greater for schedule C than for schedule B (0.553 versus 0.401), whereas over all trials the probability of an A_1 response was greater on schedule B than on schedule C (0.505 versus 0.464). Both of these relations are predicted by the model.

Sequential Effects*

For further testing of the model, the sequential data seem most germane. Employing the methods of Sec. 5.5, one can obtain expressions for sequential probabilities. In the present experiment the quantities $Pr(A_1 \mid S_k S_j)$ (for $j, k = 1, 2$) are identical to those presented in Eq. 5.37. Furthermore, using the same techniques expressions involving S_0 events on trials n and $n + 1$ can be easily derived, and are as follows:

(5.44a) $Pr(A_1 \mid S_1 S_0) = Pr(H) + (1 - \sigma)[\theta\pi(1 - p_\infty) - p_\infty \theta'(1 - \pi)]$

(5.44b) $Pr(A_1 \mid S_2 S_0) = Pr(F) + (1 - \sigma)[\theta\pi(1 - p_\infty) - p_\infty \theta'(1 - \pi)]$

(5.44c) $Pr(A_1 \mid S_0 S_1) = p_\infty + \theta(1 - \sigma)(1 - p_\infty)$

(5.44d) $Pr(A_1 \mid S_0 S_2) = p_\infty - \theta'(1 - \sigma)p_\infty$

(5.44e) $Pr(A_1 \mid S_0 S_0) = p_\infty[1 - \theta\pi - \theta'(1 - \pi)] + \theta\pi.$

We shall not examine the correspondence between these particular sequential effects and theoretical predictions, because there are 18 such independent quantities for each experimental condition and the analysis would involve us in too much detail. However, to illustrate the methods involved, two sequential predictions will be considered; namely, $Pr(A_{1,n+1} \mid E_{1,n})$ and $Pr(A_{1,n+1} \mid E_{2,n})$. Note that for these probabilities the stimulus events on trials n and $n + 1$ are suppressed, and we ask only for the overall likelihood of an A_1 response conditionalized on the information event of the preceding trial. The A_1 could occur in response to any of the stimulus events S_1, S_2, or S_0 on trial $n + 1$; similarly the information event E_1 on trial n could follow an S_1 or S_0 stimulus, and the

---

* This section treats a special topic and may be omitted on first reading.

Table 5.5   Predicted and Observed Sequential Quantities

	Schedule A		Schedule B		Schedule C		Schedule D	
	Pred.	Obs.	Pred.	Obs.	Pred.	Obs.	Pred.	Obs.
$Pr(A_{1,n+1} \mid E_{1,n})$	0.267	0.255	0.503	0.529	0.503	0.475	0.748	0.788
$Pr(A_{1,n+1} \mid E_{2,n})$	0.229	0.207	0.466	0.482	0.466	0.453	0.708	0.716

E_2 an S_2 or S_0 stimulus. Asymptotic expressions for these quantities can be obtained by appropriate combinations of Eq. 5.37 and 5.44 and are as follows:

$$\lim_{n \to \infty} Pr(A_{1,n+1} \mid E_{1,n})$$

$$= Pr(A_1) + (1 - \sigma x)\theta(1 - p_\infty)\left[\frac{\pi(1 - x) + x\gamma(1 - \sigma)}{\pi(1 - x) + x\gamma}\right]$$

$$\lim_{n \to \infty} Pr(A_{1,n+1} \mid E_{2,n})$$

$$= Pr(A_1) - (1 - \sigma x)\theta' p_\infty\left[\frac{(1 - \pi)(1 - x) + x(1 - \gamma)(1 - \sigma)}{(1 - \pi)(1 - x) + x(1 - \gamma)}\right]$$

where p_∞ is given by Eq. 5.43 and $Pr(A_1) = \sigma x \gamma + (1 - \sigma x)p_\infty$.

Table 5.5 presents the observed values for $Pr(A_{1,n+1} \mid E_{1,n})$ and $Pr(A_{1,n+1} \mid E_{2,n})$. Estimates of $Pr(A_{1,n+1} \mid E_{1,n})$ and $Pr(A_{1,n+1} \mid E_{2,n})$ were obtained for each subject; the average of these individual estimates are the quantities presented in the table. These estimates are based on the same set of trials as the data presented in Table 5.4 and will be regarded as asymptotic.

We can now use the equations above to yield predictions for these observed values. By inspection of the equations, we see that estimates are needed for σ, θ, and θ' before predictions can be made. Since we already have estimates of σ and $\varphi = \theta'/\theta$, we need estimate only θ' or θ. Suppose we fix on some value of θ'. Then θ is determined, because θ'/θ must equal the estimate of φ. For a fixed θ' we can calculate predictions for the eight statistics displayed in Table 5.5; these calculations are made for each experimental schedule by substituting the appropriate values of γ and π in the equations above, along with $\sigma = 0.572$, $\varphi = 1.094$, and $\theta = \theta'/1.094$. Once numerical predictions have been generated for a particular value of θ', the goodness-of-fit can be evaluated by computing the sum of squared deviations between predicted and observed values; that is, for a specific value of θ', define the quantity

$$S(\theta') = \sum (\text{predicted} - \text{observed})^2,$$

where the sum is over the eight entries in Table 5.5.

One method for estimating θ' is to select its value so as to minimize $S(\theta')$. To carry out this minimization analytically would yield unwieldy expressions. In order to avoid this complication, we have resorted to a high-speed computer and have simply calculated $S(\theta')$ for θ' ranging from 0.01 to 1 in successive increments of 0.01. Over this range of values the function $S(\theta')$ takes on a minimum at $\theta' = 0.08$. The predicted quantities presented in Table 5.5 were obtained using this value of θ'.

By and large, the correspondence displayed in Table 5.5 is not too bad. In evaluating the goodness-of-fit it should be kept in mind that all of the quantities in the table are independent, and thus there are eight degrees of freedom. The model requires that $Pr(A_{1,n+1} \mid E_{1,n}) > Pr(A_{1,n+1} \mid E_{2,n})$ for admissible values of θ and θ', and this prediction is upheld for all four schedules. Note also that

$$Pr(A_{1,n+1} \mid S_{1,n+1}E_{1,n}) > Pr(A_{1,n+1} \mid S_{1,n+1}E_{2,n})$$

$$Pr(A_{1,n+1} \mid S_{2,n+1}E_{1,n}) > Pr(A_{1,n+1} \mid S_{2,n+1}E_{2,n})$$

$$Pr(A_{1,n+1} \mid S_{0,n+1}E_{1,n}) > Pr(A_{1,n+1} \mid S_{0,n+1}E_{2,n}).$$

Although not presented here, a breakdown of the data into this form indicates that these three inequalities hold for each of the four schedules.

5.8   ALTERNATIVE MODELS FOR THE BIAS PROCESS

The reader who has followed the development to this point may by now have some of his own ideas regarding modifications and improvements of the model. Of course, the development and testing of alternative models is precisely the type of enterprise that permits us to make progress in understanding a challenging phenomenon. Once a model has achieved a level of descriptive accuracy acceptable to psychologists who are actively investigating the area, further progress must come largely via differential tests of alternative models.

One formulation of the bias process in signal detection that originally appealed to us involved changes in p_n that were determined solely by the information events E_1 and E_2. Formally stated, the proposal is that

$$p_{n+1} = \begin{cases} (1 - \theta)p_n + \theta, & \text{if } E_{1,n} \\ (1 - \theta')p_n, & \text{if } E_{2,n}. \end{cases}$$

This formulation (which we shall refer to as Model II) is to be contrasted with Eq. 5.12 (Model I), where changes in p_n can occur only when the

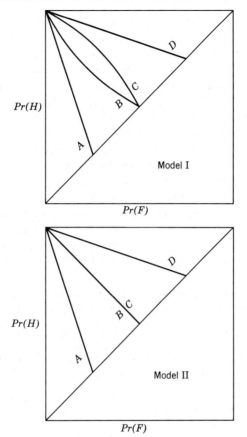

Fig. 5.12 Theoretical iso-bias curves.

s_0 sensory state is activated.* In spite of the marked difference between these two sets of assumptions, the models yield identical predictions in the first signal detection experiment for the asymptotic probabilities of a hit and of a false alarm. Only by a detailed analysis of the sequential statistics and the pre-asymptotic data can it be shown that Model I is somewhat superior to Model II.

However, the two models make strikingly different predictions for the study reported in the last section, even for hit and false alarm proportions. For example, applying Model II to that study yields

$$p_\infty = \frac{x\gamma + (1 - x)\pi}{[x\gamma + (1 - x)\pi] + [x(1 - \gamma) + (1 - x)(1 - \pi)]\varphi}.$$

* Both Models I and II reduce to the probability learning model discussed in Sec. 5.6 when $\sigma \to 0$.

By inspection of the above equation, we see that p_∞ is identical for both schedules B and C of the second experiment; whereas, using Model I, p_∞ is greater for schedule C than for schedule B. This relation is reflected in $Pr(H)$ and $Pr(F)$. For Model II we predict that these quantities will be the same for both schedules B and C; whereas for Model I they both will be greater for schedule C than for schedule B. The ordering relation predicted by Model I for schedules B and C is borne out by the group averages presented in Table 5.4; it also is the case that the relation holds individually for all of our subjects. Therefore, Model I, but not Model II, appears to be substantiated by the data.

To illustrate further the relations between Models I and II, we have presented theoretical iso-bias curves in Fig. 5.12. For each model the curves were plotted assuming $\varphi = 1$. From the figure we see that the iso-bias curves for Model II are all linear and that they are identical for schedules B and C. For Model I, the iso-bias curves for schedules A and D also are linear; however, schedules B and C generate different, nonlinear curves.

Adopting Model I, a distance function can be defined between corresponding points on the iso-bias curves of schedules B and C; namely,

$$\Delta = \sqrt{[Pr(H_B) - Pr(H_C)]^2 + [Pr(F_B) - Pr(F_C)]^2},$$

where $Pr(H_B)$ denotes the asymptotic probability of a hit for schedule B, and so forth. To simplify the expressions let $\varphi = 1$; then by Eqs. 5.40 and 5.43

$$Pr(H_B) = \sigma + (1 - \sigma)\left[\frac{0.75(1 - \sigma) + 0.25}{2 - \sigma}\right]$$

$$Pr(F_B) = (1 - \sigma)\left[\frac{0.75(1 - \sigma) + 0.25}{2 - \sigma}\right]$$

$$Pr(H_C) = \sigma + (1 - \sigma)\left[\frac{0.25(1 - \sigma) + 0.75}{2 - \sigma}\right]$$

$$Pr(F_C) = (1 - \sigma)\left[\frac{0.25(1 - \sigma) + 0.75}{2 - \sigma}\right].$$

Substituting these expressions in Δ yields a distance measure that is a function of σ. The maximum of this function can be obtained by taking its derivative with respect to σ and setting the result equal to zero. Carrying out these steps yields

$$\sigma = 2 - \sqrt{2} \approx 0.59.$$

Hence, under the assumptions of Model I, the maximum difference between corresponding points on the iso-bias functions of schedules B and C will be observed for this value of σ.

One of the reasons for running the study reported in the last section was to determine whether such a difference would be observed. Therefore, to increase our chances of discovering an effect if it existed, we wanted to set the noise level at a value for which $\sigma = 0.59$. Recall that pretraining involved only S_1 and S_2 trials and they were presented with equal likelihood; hence (see Eq. 5.4)

$$Pr(C) = \sigma + (1 - \sigma)\tfrac{1}{2}.$$

Consequently, to fix σ at 0.59 required adjusting the noise level during pretraining to yield a correct-response probability of

$$0.79 \approx 0.59 + (0.41)\tfrac{1}{2}.$$

The pretraining procedure was fairly successful, inasmuch as the estimate of σ for the actual experiment was 0.572.

A natural generalization of the ideas presented in this section involves a simple combination of Models I and II. Namely to assume that changes in p_n are as follows:

$$(5.45) \qquad p_{n+1} = \begin{cases} (1 - \theta)p_n + \theta, & \text{if } s_{0,n} \ \& \ E_{1,n} \\ (1 - \theta')p_n, & \text{if } s_{0,n} \ \& \ E_{2,n} \\ (1 - \alpha)p_n + \alpha, & \text{if } s_{1,n} \ \& \ E_{1,n} \\ (1 - \alpha')p_n, & \text{if } s_{2,n} \ \& \ E_{2,n}. \end{cases}$$

Here, p_n is assumed to change on every trial but in different amounts depending on which sensory state is activated. Of course, Models I and II are special cases of this equation. When $\alpha' = \theta'$ and $\alpha = \theta$ the equation above reduces to Model II; similarly when $\alpha = \alpha' = 0$, it reduces to Model I. Therefore, if we were to use Eq. 5.45 in analyzing data, the correspondence between predicted and observed quantities would have to be at least as good as the best fit obtained for either Model I or Model II. In this regard, it must be kept in mind that the combined model has five parameters which need to be estimated, whereas the other models each have only three parameters. The basic question is whether estimating two additional parameters will yield an account of the data that is significantly better than the fit obtained for the best three-parameter model. The statistical problems involved in making such comparisons between models are discussed in Chapter 9.

5.9 CONCLUDING REMARKS

The model presented in this chapter is primarily concerned with a dynamic account of decision making and, as we have seen, can be applied to certain types of signal detection problems and to probability learning. Its limitations as a theory of probability learning have already been discussed, and we now want to add some similar remarks regarding signal detection. As the model was presented here, nothing was said about parameters of the signal as they affect behavior. However, one would like a theory of detection to predict what behavioral changes will occur when physical characteristics of the signal are manipulated. For example, how is performance influenced if the duration, frequency, or waveform of the signal is changed? Or, more importantly, how are differences between auditory and visual detection tasks reflected in the data? Obviously, such manipulations influence performance, but they have no precise interpretation in our model; they can affect the estimate of σ, but the details of the relationship are not made explicit. Although we shall not discuss them here, there are a number of theories about the sensory system that can be incorporated into the framework of the present model to give a more nearly complete interpretation of the activation process of Eq. 5.6. A discussion of these theories and their relation to our model falls outside the domain of this book; nevertheless, a few remarks are appropriate concerning the two major theoretical developments. One formulation has been labeled the neural quantum theory (Békésy, 1930); and the other signal detectability theory (Swets, Tanner and Birdsall, 1961). For a review of these theories, see Luce (1963b). In the neural quantum theory, the sensory system is assumed to be activated in discrete steps called quanta. Thus, although the stimulus input may be continuous, it is recorded by the sensory mechanism as a countable sequence of discrete events. Further, in some formulations of the quantum hypothesis, the probability distribution can be specified for the number of quantal units activated given a particular stimulus (Mueller, 1954; Pirenne and Marriott, 1959). In contrast, signal detectability theory rejects the notion of a sensory mechanism with discrete outputs, and argues for the concept of a criterion range of acceptance. It assumes that on each trial the reaction of the sensory system to an external stimulus can be characterized by a number (a likelihood ratio, or a function defined on likelihood ratios), and the subject's response depends on whether or not the number falls in the criterion range. The process is not deterministic, for repeated presentations of the stimulus do not generate the same number, but rather a distribution of numbers; under certain conditions this distribution can be specified in terms of the physical parameter of the signal. The determination of the criterion range is assumed to be under the control of the subject and to vary as a function of psychological variables that influence motivation and set.

As indicated at the outset, this chapter constitutes a very limited account of theoretical developments in signal detection and probability learning. However, the topics that have been examined were treated in considerable detail, and a fair amount of technique has been developed that should enable the reader to pursue other material on his own. For a general review of theoretical developments in signal detection we recommend Chapter 3 by Luce in Volume I of the *Handbook of Mathematical Psychology*;* a collection of contemporary readings edited by Swets (1964); and survey articles by Green (1960) and Mueller and McGill (1963). For a review of theoretical work in probability learning see a survey article by Estes (1964). Also certain sections of the following chapters in the *Handbook of Mathematical Psychology:* Chapter 9 (Volume II) by Sternberg, Chapter 10 (Volume II) by Atkinson and Estes, and Chapter 16 (Volume III) by Luce and Suppes.

---

* For a general survey of theoretical developments in psychophysics, also see Chapters 1, 4, and 5 in the *Handbook of Mathematical Psychology* (Vol. I).

CHAPTER 6

AVOIDANCE
CONDITIONING

In this chapter we consider the application of theoretical models to a traditional area of research on animal learning, namely, avoidance conditioning. As the name implies, in avoidance conditioning experiments the subject must learn to make an appropriate response to a warning signal (the conditioned stimulus or CS) in order to avoid a noxious or pain-producing stimulus, usually electric shock. If the animal fails to respond to the CS, the painful stimulus is administered. In this case, the painful stimulus is usually left on until the subject escapes it by performing the desired response. Avoidance conditioning procedures involve what Logan (1959) has called "conditions of correlated punishment," where the probability of punishment varies with response time (latency). The class of avoidance responses is defined in terms of those behaviors which achieve a certain end-result and do so before a criterion time has elapsed since the warning signal initiating the trial.

The following experiment will serve as a useful prototype for the ensuing discussion. The apparatus consists of two compartments separated by a guillotine door that can be raised or lowered. One compartment is painted white and has a grid floor through which painful electric shock may be delivered to the rat's feet. The other compartment is painted black and has a solid wooden floor. A naïve adult rat is placed in the white compartment with the guillotine door closed. After a few seconds, the door opens, a light goes on in the white compartment, and a buzzer sounds. This complex set of events constitutes the CS. If the rat runs into the black compartment before five seconds elapses, then no shock is administered and the CS terminates at the instant the response occurs. But if the rat is still in the white compartment at the end of five seconds, then the shock comes on and stays on until the rat runs into the black compartment. The events above characterize a single trial. After a trial, the rat is permitted to rest in the black compartment for a minute or so. It is then picked up and replaced in the white compartment for the beginning of the next trial. On each trial the experimenter records whether the rat responded before five seconds (thus avoiding shock) or after five seconds, recording perhaps zero for an avoidance and one for a shock trial. Initially, of course, the rat fails to avoid and receives several shocks. But he soon learns to the point where he avoids consistently on every trial. The mathematical model to be discussed in Sec. 6.1 provides an analysis of the data obtained during acquisition of this simple habit.

Avoidance conditioning, using either this simple paradigm or the more complex ones treated in later sections, has been extensively studied, and much is known about the process and the variables affecting it. At one time the fact that avoidance probabilities attained a high level was puzzling, since on successful trials the shock or "reinforcing stimulus" is omitted. An answer to this question was provided in the duo-process theories of Mowrer (1939) and Miller (1948). The learning of avoidance responses was conceived as resulting from two separate learning processes that are intertwined in the usual procedure. The first consists of the classical conditioning of an emotional response (fear) to the CS as a result of the contiguous pairing of this CS with the primary noxious event (shock) that elicits the fear reaction. The second consists of the learning of an instrumental response which is reinforced by virtue of the fact that it terminates the fear-inducing CS. In brief, then, the CS comes to arouse fear, and the avoidance response is reinforced and strengthened by fear reduction. A large body of evidence can be adduced for this duo-process view of avoidance learning, but it is not our purpose here either to review or evaluate these formulations (cf. Mowrer, 1960 for an extensive review).

One may accept this duo-process view of avoidance learning with its many qualitative implications but still feel the need for a satisfactory quantitative description of avoidance data. If one is concerned with quantitative descriptions of the detailed aspects of avoidance data, then the duo-process theory is not particularly helpful because it imposes too few constraints. That is, a variety of mathematical models can be proposed that are interpretable in terms of the constructs of the duo-process theory, and the theory by itself provides no way of differentiating an appropriate from an inappropriate representation. Rather than following that approach, we have set forth an alternative strategy in this chapter: we seek first for a satisfactory quantitative model for avoidance data. If an acceptable candidate can be found, we then will attempt to coordinate its constructs to the duo-process theory.

If we examine the array of avoidance experiments in the literature, we find that procedures differ to a fair degree in the complexity of the task confronting the subject. Also, the appropriate descriptive model will be clearly different for the simple tasks, as compared to the more complex tasks. In certain simple arrangements, such as those studied by Essman and Jarvick (1960), Madsen and McGaugh (1961), and Maatsch (1959), the avoidance response is apparently learned in all-or-none manner, much like the one-element model in Chapter 3 would suppose. In those experiments, the response designated as the avoidance response was evidently one having a very high initial probability of occurrence to fear; also, in Maatsch's situation, the avoidance response was effective in totally removing the rat from the frightening situation. An experiment by Theios (1963), conducted in a one-way shuttle box much like the prototype experiment described earlier, gave results that deviated from the strict all-or-none pattern; we shall shortly examine a generalization of the all-or-none model that describes his data with fair accuracy.

At another level of complexity is the two-way shuttle avoidance procedure. In this procedure, the subject is required to shuttle back and forth between two shock compartments in response to an external warning signal. That is, the subject runs in one direction on odd-numbered trials and in the opposite direction on even-numbered trials. This procedure places the subject in a stimulus discrimination problem and a response conflict problem. The response conflict arises because for successful avoidance, the procedure requires the animal to run back into that compartment where it had been punished on the prior trial. Thus, the response of avoiding the site of the most recent shock is in conflict with approaching it now to avoid shock from the compartment where the subject is sitting. The stimulus discrimination problem arises because fear and the shuttle response soon become conditioned to all the common cues throughout the apparatus (resulting in a fair number of spontaneous shuttle responses between CS trials), whereas the problem for the animal is to concentrate all this conditioning upon a single component of the stimulus complex (namely, the CS) so that this stimulus alone cues the fear and the shuttle response. As a result of this early diffuse fear conditioning, responses are very poorly reinforced in the beginning, since practically no fear reduction or relief follows the response. Until the relevant stimulus discrimination has been made, from the subject's point of view there is nothing he can do to escape this aversive situation. As one might expect from this informal analysis, the two-way shuttle procedure produces rather slow learning, a fair amount of oscillation between avoidance and nonavoidance, occasional cases of nonunity asymptotes, and even some cases of total failure to learn. The

Solomon and Wynne (1953) data to be considered later in this chapter is one experiment in which all animals (dogs, in this case) were successfully conditioned.

6.1 THE TWO-ELEMENT MODEL

Theios (1963) trained 50 naïve rats on a one-way shuttle response. During initial learning, the rat was placed in the white compartment; the CS was the opening of the door separating compartments and the onset of a light and buzzer; a high intensity shock was delivered to the floor of the white compartment within three seconds if the rat had not run into the black compartment before that time. The shock and CS continued until the rat entered the black side. After 20 seconds, the rat was returned to the white side for another trial. Trials continued in this massed fashion until the rat met a criterion of 20 consecutive successful avoidance responses. After a rat met this initial criterion, he was trained to run in the reverse direction by the same procedure; that is, he would be placed in the black side, presented with the CS and shocked if he failed to cross over to the white side within three seconds. Surprisingly, the reversal learning data were very similar to the original learning data. Hence, the two series from each rat were pooled, yielding 100 response sequences. These 100 sequences (of ones for errors or shocks, zeros for successes or avoidances) will be considered as independent random samples from a common stochastic process, although this assumption is probably only approximately correct.

Theios applied to his data the two-element model derived from stimulus sampling theory (cf. Sec. 8.1). The gist of the theory is that an individual's learning curve can be characterized as consisting of two steps. Starting at an initial avoidance probability of zero, the animal learns part of the task and as a consequence his response probability takes a discrete jump from zero to some intermediate level p. From this intermediate p-level, the subject eventually learns the second part of the task and this is accompanied by a second discrete jump in response probability from p to one. At this point learning is completed and the subject consistently produces successful avoidance responses. It is not too difficult to identify the two stages of learning with the constructs of the duo-process theory. The intermediate performance level might be identified with the subject's state after fear has been conditioned to the CS, but the instrumental response has not yet been totally conditioned to the CS or to the feedback stimulation from fear.

Theios assumed that the stimulus situation for the subject consists of two stimulus elements, one of which is sampled on each trial. Initially neither of the stimulus elements is conditioned to the avoidance response, so the animal is always shocked. The shock forces the shuttle response to occur, and it is assumed that with probability c the stimulus element sampled on that trial becomes conditioned to the avoidance response. Once such a conditioning trial is effective, the subject enters the inter-mediate performance state in which one stimulus element is conditioned while the other is not. Assume that with probability p the conditioned element is sampled so that an avoidance occurs, whereas with probability $q = 1 - p$ the unconditioned element is sampled so that the animal fails to avoid and receives shock. The net probability of a one-trial transition from the intermediate state into the terminal state (where both elements are conditioned) is qc, the probability of sampling and conditioning the formerly unconditioned element. Once both elements are conditioned, they stay conditioned so that perfect learning has been achieved.

The process described above can be represented as an absorbing Markov chain. The states 0, 1, 2 represent the number of elements conditioned to the avoidance response. The subject begins in state 0, enters state 1, and eventually moves into state 2 where he is absorbed. The matrix of one-trial transition probabilities is

$$
\begin{array}{c}
\text{State on} \\
\text{trial } n+1
\end{array}
$$

$$
(6.1) \quad
\begin{array}{cc}
 & \text{State on} \\
 & \text{trial } n
\end{array}
\begin{array}{c}
2 \\ 1 \\ 0
\end{array}
\begin{array}{ccc}
2 & 1 & 0 \\
\left[\begin{array}{ccc}
1 & 0 & 0 \\
qc & 1-qc & 0 \\
0 & c & 1-c
\end{array}\right]
\end{array}
\begin{array}{c}
Pr(A_1 \mid \text{row state}) \\
1 \\
p \\
0.
\end{array}
$$

Here A_1 denotes the avoidance response. We will shortly derive a number of predictions of interest from this model for comparison with Theios' data. The derivations make use of the convenient assumption that each subject is run an infinite number of trials. However, we digress momentarily to consider a fairly powerful parameter-free test of this special model.

Intermediate Responses as a Binomial Series

The state of conditioning (0, 1, or 2) on a particular trial is unobservable. That is, given an error, the subject can be in state 0 or 1; given a success, he can be in state 1 or 2. But suppose that we consider only responses on trials between the first success for a subject and his last error. The first success means that he has left state 0 and is now in either state 1 or 2;

the later error means that he was not in state 2 at that time, but rather must have been in state 1. Thus the model says that responses between the first success and last error are being generated while the subject is in the intermediate state. We will call these the intermediate trials or intermediate responses.

We will see that these intermediate responses should form a stationary binomial sequence of observations much like successive flips of a penny. Stationarity of this type was discussed in reference to the concept identification model in Sec. 2.5; the difference is that for the two-element model used here, only the intermediate responses are expected to form a binomial sequence. This means, in particular, that successive intermediate responses are expected to be statistically independent, and that a plot of success probabilities over the intermediate trials should yield a horizontal line.

Turning to the Theios data, we find that the intermediate responses can in fact be represented as a stationary binomial sequence. Stationarity of avoidance probability over intermediate trials can be tested, of course, for only those subjects that have at least two intermediate trials. Because the overall learning was quite rapid, only 48 of the 100 sequences satisfy this requirement. The intermediate trials were divided into a first and second half, throwing away an odd trial in the middle if necessary, and a paired t test was computed to determine whether the probability of a success was larger in the second than in the first half. The value of t was 0.19 which, with 47 degrees of freedom, is not significant. Thus, we are not inclined to reject the hypothesis that response probabilities are stationary over the intermediate trials.

The mean proportion of avoidance responses over all intermediate trials was 0.572, based on a total of 231 trials. By a derivation that will not be given here, the model in Eq. 6.1 implies that this proportion of successes should be

$$\frac{p}{1 - c(1 - p)}.$$

In other words, the percentage of successes between the first success and last error is expected to be somewhat larger than p. The bias away from p results from the assumption that the probability of leaving state 1 is different on success than on error trials. To simplify matters, Theios assumed that $p = \frac{1}{2}$, and this led to fairly accurate predictions of his data, as will be seen shortly.

To complete discussion of the properties of the intermediate responses, Table 6.1 gives the results relevant to testing whether the intermediate responses occur independently of one another. Table 6.1 gives the frequencies of transitions from success or error on trial n to success or

Table 6.1 Transition Frequencies for
Intermediate Trials

| | Trial $n + 1$ | |
Trial n	Success	Error
Success	90	118
Error	44	54

error on trial $n + 1$, including the trial of last error. The test for independence of Table 6.1 gave $\chi^2 = 0.07$ which with one degree of freedom is not significant. Thus, we cannot reject the hypothesis of statistical independence on successive intermediate responses.

A further test is provided by the distribution of the number of successes in blocks of four intermediate trials; the model expects this to conform to the law of the binomial distribution. Utilizing nonoverlapping blocks of four intermediate trials, the results in Table 6.2 were obtained. The estimate of the binomial parameter was taken from the percentage of successes (0.536) for those trial blocks represented in Table 6.2. The fit of the predicted binomial law to the observed distribution of successes is quite satisfactory ($\chi^2 = 0.345$, $df = 3$).

In summary, it appears that the intermediate responses approximate a stationary, independent sequence of binomial events. This is what is predicted by the two-element model, which asserts that individual performance is described by discrete steps in response probability from zero to p and then from p to one. Without benefit of the model, we probably would not have been led to examine this particular aspect of the data and hence would not have uncovered this surprisingly simple structure.

Table 6.2 Number of Successes in Blocks of
Four Intermediate Trials

Number of Successes	Observed Frequency	Predicted Frequency
0	2	2.3
1	12	10.7
2	17	18.5
3	15	14.4
4	4	4.1

Distribution of Total Errors

Now we wish to derive the distribution of total errors (shocks) for the two-element model. The total errors T may be divided into a number t_0

which occur while the subject is in state 0 and a number t_1 which occur while the subject is in state 1. Since there is a probability c that the subject leaves state 0 on each error, the probability distribution of t_0 is given by the geometric law, namely,

$$Pr(t_0 = j) = c(1 - c)^{j-1} \qquad \text{(for } j > 0)$$

with mean and variance

$$E(t_0) = \frac{1}{c}, \quad \text{Var}(t_0) = \frac{1 - c}{c^2}.$$

Similarly, once state 1 has been entered the only opportunity for the subject to leave state 1 is on an error trial, and for each error he has a constant probability c of moving into state 2. Thus, the probability distribution of t_1 will be the same as that of t_0.

To find the distribution of $T = t_0 + t_1$, we *convolute* the separate distributions of t_0 and t_1. The probability that $T = k$ may be written as the sum (over j) of the probabilities that j errors occur in state 0 and the remaining $k - j$ errors occur in state 1. Note that t_0 and t_1 must be at least one, thus eliminating the terms in the sum for $j = 0$ and $j = k$.

$$(6.2) \qquad Pr(T = k) = \sum_{j=1}^{k-1} Pr(t_0 = j) \cdot Pr(t_1 = k - j)$$

$$= \sum_{j=1}^{k-1} c(1 - c)^{j-1} c(1 - c)^{k-j-1}$$

$$= \sum_{j=1}^{k-1} c^2 (1 - c)^{k-2}$$

$$= (k - 1) c^2 (1 - c)^{k-2} \qquad \text{(for } k \geq 2).$$

The j in the exponent of $1 - c$ cancels, so we are left with the sum of $k - 1$ constant terms, each term being $c^2(1 - c)^{k-2}$. This leads to our final expression in Eq. 6.2 for the probability distribution of total errors. We note that it requires that T be two or larger, which was true in the Theios data.

By standard methods, we may find the expectation and variance of T; namely,

$$(6.3) \qquad E(T) = \sum_{k=2}^{\infty} k Pr(T = k) = \sum_{k=2}^{\infty} k(k - 1) c^2 (1 - c)^{k-2} = \frac{2}{c}$$

$$\text{Var}(T) = \sum_{k=2}^{\infty} k^2 Pr(T = k) - [E(T)]^2 = \frac{2(1 - c)}{c^2}.$$

We note that the mean and variance of T are consistent with the fact that T is the sum of t_0 and t_1, and these latter two are independent of one another. Hence,

$$E(T) = E(t_0) + E(t_1) = \frac{2}{c}$$

and

$$\mathrm{Var}(T_0) = \mathrm{Var}(t_0) + \mathrm{Var}(t_1) = \frac{2(1-c)}{c^2}.$$

Estimating the c Parameter

We may use the distribution of T to obtain an estimate of c. T can be shown to be a sufficient statistic for c; this means, roughly, that once T is known, no further information about c can be gathered from consideration of other statistics. We use the maximum likelihood method (cf. Chapter 9) to estimate c from the distribution of total errors. We let f_k be the observed frequency of sequences having exactly k errors, and we let $N = \sum f_k$ be the total number of cases. The estimated mean, $\bar{T}$, will be $\dfrac{\sum k f_k}{N}$. We first write the likelihood function

$$L(c) = \prod_{k=2}^{\infty} Pr(T = k)^{f_k}$$

$$= \prod_{k=2}^{\infty} [(k-1)c^2(1-c)^{k-2}]^{f_k}.$$

We wish to find that value of c which maximizes this likelihood function. We take the logarithm of $L(c)$ to convert the product into a sum of the form

$$\log L(c) = \sum_{k=2}^{\infty} f_k \log(k-1) + \sum_{k=2}^{\infty} 2f_k \log c + \sum_{k=2}^{\infty}(k-2)f_k \log(1-c),$$

or

$$\log L(c) = K + 2N \log c + N(\bar{T} - 2) \log(1 - c),$$

where K is a constant independent of c. The value of c that maximizes $\log L(c)$, and hence maximizes $L(c)$, is found by setting its partial derivative equal to zero:

$$\frac{\partial \log L(c)}{\partial c} = \frac{2N}{c} - \frac{N(\bar{T} - 2)}{1 - c} = 0.$$

The solution to this equation is our estimate of c; namely,

(6.4) $$\hat{c} = \frac{2}{\bar{T}}.$$

Thus, finding the maximum likelihood estimate of c consists essentially of solving for c in the theoretical expression for $E(T)$ in Eq. 6.3.

The theoretical variance of the maximum likelihood estimate (see Sec. 9.2) is

$$\mathrm{Var}(\hat{c}) = \frac{-1}{E\left[\dfrac{\partial^2 \log L}{\partial c^2}\right]}.$$

But

$$\frac{\partial^2 \log L}{\partial c^2} = -N\left[\frac{2}{c^2} + \frac{\bar{T} - 2}{(1 - c)^2}\right].$$

The only random variable in this expression is $\bar{T}$, which has expectation $2/c$. Hence,

$$-E\left[\frac{\partial^2 \log L}{\partial c^2}\right] = N\left[\frac{2}{c^2} + \frac{\dfrac{2}{c} - 2}{(1 - c)^2}\right].$$

Simplifying and taking the reciprocal yields

(6.5) $$\mathrm{Var}(\hat{c}) = \frac{c^2(1 - c)}{2N}.$$

We may substitute our estimate $c = 2/\bar{T}$ into Eq. 6.5 to arrive at

$$\mathrm{Var}(\hat{c}) = \frac{2\bar{T} - 4}{N\bar{T}^3}.$$

We will now consider these estimates for the avoidance data reported by Theios. There were 100 protocols, so we set $N = 100$. The observed average value of T was 4.68. Equating $\bar{T}$ to 4.68, we obtain

$$\hat{c} = \frac{2}{4.68} = 0.427$$

$$\mathrm{Var}(\hat{c}) = \frac{(0.427)^2(0.573)}{200} = 0.0005.$$

We will use the estimate $\hat{c} = 0.427$ in predicting these data. By the relatively small value of $\mathrm{Var}(\hat{c})$, we are assured that the estimate is probably close to its true value.

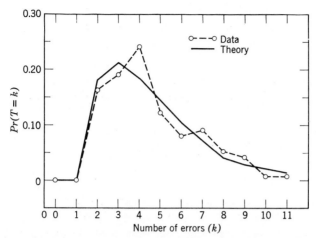

Fig. 6.1 Probability distribution of total errors (adapted from Fig. 3 in Theios, 1963).

As a first prediction from the model, we try to fit the distribution of total errors using the theoretical expression derived in Eq. 6.2. The observed and predicted relative frequencies of T are shown in Fig. 6.1. We see that the model's predictions closely approximate the observed values. The observed standard deviation of T was 2.34, and the prediction from Eq. 6.3 is

$$\sigma(T) = \frac{\sqrt{2(1-c)}}{c} = 2.52.$$

Mean Learning Curve and Trial of Last Error

For further derivations we need to know the probability, called $w_{i,n}$, that the subject is in state i ($i = 0, 1, 2$) at the start of trial n, given that he started in state 0 on trial 1. Since on any trial n the subject must be in one of the three states, we require that

$$w_{0,n} + w_{1,n} + w_{2,n} = 1.$$

Hence, once $w_{0,n}$ and $w_{1,n}$ are found, $w_{2,n}$ may be obtained by subtraction.

We find $w_{0,n}$ by examining our matrix of transition probabilities in Eq. 6.1. From the matrix we see that there is a constant probability, $1 - c$, that the subject remains in state 0 on each trial. Thus, given that the subject is in state 0 on trial n (with probability $w_{0,n}$), then the likelihood that he is still in state 0 at the start of trial $n + 1$ is given by

$$w_{0,n+1} = (1 - c)w_{0,n}.$$

This is a linear difference equation of the type encountered in previous chapters (see Eq. 5.18 with $A = 0$). Assuming that the subject starts in state 0 on trial 1, so that $w_{0,1} = 1$, the solution has the form

$$(6.6) \qquad w_{0,n} = (1 - c)^{n-1}w_{0,1} = (1 - c)^{n-1}.$$

It may be noted that the mean number of trials that the subject will be in state 0 is given by the sum of $w_{0,n}$; namely,

$$n_0 = \sum_{n=1}^{\infty} w_{0,n} = \frac{1}{c}.$$

Since each trial in state 0 leads to an error, the mean errors in state 0 is also $1/c$, which agrees with our former calculation of $E(t_0)$.

To obtain $w_{1,n}$, we begin by summing the probabilities of all the possible ways by which the subject could stay in state 0 for k trials, then move into state 1 and remain there for the remaining $n - k - 1$ trials. The mathematical expression is

$$w_{1,n} = \sum_{k=1}^{n-1} c(1 - c)^{k-1}(1 - qc)^{n-k-1}.$$

The first terms, $c(1 - c)^{k-1}$, give the probability that the move from state 0 into state 1 occurs on trial k, whereas the second term $(1 - qc)^{n-k-1}$ gives the probability of staying in state 1 until trial n. Since the subject must have at least one trial in each state, the index k starts at one rather than zero. To carry out this summation, we first alter the exponent of $1 - qc$ so that it reads $n - 2 - (k - 1)$ and rewrite $w_{1,n}$ as

$$w_{1,n} = \sum_{k=1}^{n-1} c(1 - qc)^{n-2} \left[\frac{(1 - c)}{(1 - qc)}\right]^{k-1}.$$

The first two terms are constants when we sum over k, so they can be brought outside the summation. We are left with the sum of the first $n - 1$ terms of a geometric series with common ratio $(1 - c)/(1 - qc)$. The result of this sum is

$$w_{1,n} = c(1 - qc)^{n-2} \left[\frac{1 - \left(\dfrac{1 - c}{1 - qc}\right)^{n-1}}{1 - \left(\dfrac{1 - c}{1 - qc}\right)}\right].$$

Clearing fractions yields

$$(6.7) \qquad w_{1,n} = \frac{1}{p}\left[(1 - qc)^{n-1} - (1 - c)^{n-1}\right].$$

Note that $w_{1,n}$ is given by the difference between two exponentially decaying terms. To visualize the function, refer to Fig. 6.2, which has been calculated for $p = q = 0.5$ and $c = 0.427$. Panel A of the figure displays the two exponential curves, one decaying at the rate $1 - c$ and the other at a slower rate $1 - qc$. The difference between these two curves (shaded in) is small at first, then becomes larger, then gets small again as both curves approach zero. This difference times the constant $1/p$ is shown in panel B. The curve in panel B corresponds to our intuition concerning what the function $w_{1,n}$ should look like. Since we begin the process in state 0, $w_{1,1} = 0$ and generally $w_{1,n}$ will be small at first. As trials continue, the probability increases that the subject will be found in state 1. But as trials continue further, the likelihood increases that the subject has entered and then left state 1 and has been caught in state 2, the absorbing state; hence, $w_{1,n}$ eventually returns to zero as n becomes large. In general, the function in panel B will not be perfectly symmetrical. If c is substantially greater than qc, the subject will enter state 1 more rapidly than he leaves it, producing a positively skewed curve. It should be mentioned that the equation for $w_{1,n}$ can be arrived at by solving the difference equation

$$w_{1,n+1} = (1 - qc)w_{1,n} + cw_{0,n} = (1 - qc)w_{1,n} + c(1 - c)^{n-1}.$$

Our result in Eq. 6.7 will be seen to satisfy this difference equation.

If we inquire about the average number of trials that the process is in state 1, the answer is given by summing the values of $w_{1,n}$; namely

(6.8)
$$n_1 = \frac{1}{p}\sum_{n=1}^{\infty}(1 - qc)^{n-1} - \frac{1}{p}\sum_{n=1}^{\infty}(1 - c)^{n-1}$$

$$= \frac{1}{p}\left[\frac{1}{qc} - \frac{1}{c}\right] = \frac{1}{qc}.$$

This result arises in a direct manner. Every subject must enter state 1. Once state 1 has been entered, there is a constant probability, qc, that it will be left on each trial. Hence, the number of trials in state 1 will be geometrically distributed as

$$Pr(k \text{ trials in state 1 before entering state 2}) = qc(1 - qc)^{k-1},$$

which has a mean of $1/qc$. We note too that for each trial the subject is in state 1, he has probability q of making an error. Hence, the mean number of errors committed in state 1 will be

$$q\left(\frac{1}{qc}\right) = \frac{1}{c},$$

which agrees with the result for $E(t_1)$ given earlier.

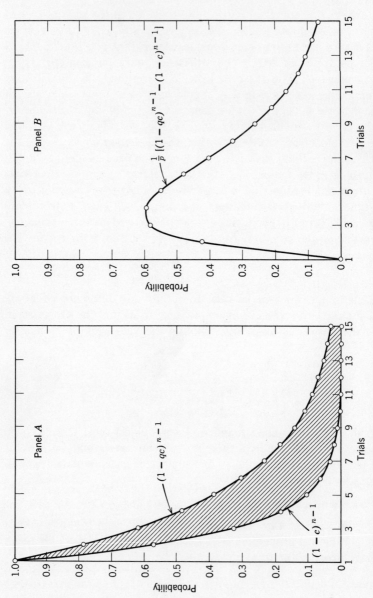

Fig. 6.2 Panel A graphs the exponential decay functions $(1 - c)^{n-1}$ and $(1 - qc)^{n-1}$. Panel B is the graph of $1/p$ times their difference. For these curves, the parameter values are $p = q = 0.50$ and $c = 0.427$.

Having obtained $w_{0,n}$ and $w_{1,n}$, the remaining term, $w_{2,n}$, may be obtained by subtraction.

(6.9)
$$w_{2,n} = 1 - w_{0,n} - w_{1,n}$$
$$= 1 - (1-c)^{n-1} - \frac{1}{p}[(1-qc)^{n-1} - (1-c)^{n-1}].$$

Because the model requires an error on the trial marking transition from state 1 to state 2, we may employ $w_{2,n}$ for making a direct prediction. By assumption, once a subject arrives in state 2 he makes no further

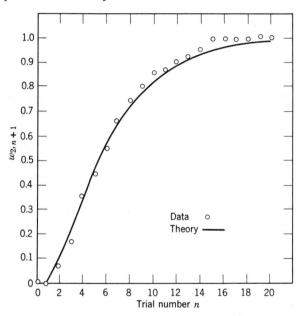

Fig. 6.3   Proportion of sequences with no errors following trial n (adapted from Fig. 4 in Theios, 1963).

errors. Hence, $w_{2,n}$ may be interpreted as the probability that there are no errors in the sequence following trial $n-1$. Alternatively, it is the probability that a subject's last error occurs on or before trial $n-1$. So employing the estimates $p = 0.50$ and $c = 0.427$, we substitute into Eq. 6.9 to predict the proportion of sequences having their last error on or before trial $n-1$. As Fig. 6.3 shows, the fit to the data is quite satisfactory.

Suppose we define L to be a random variable denoting the trial number on which the last error occurs. From the remarks above, we can see that $w_{2,n}$ is the probability that L is less than or equal to $n-1$. From this observation, the probability distribution of L may be obtained by taking successive differences between $w_{2,n+1}$ and $w_{2,n}$.

(6.10)
$$Pr(L = n) = Pr(L \leq n) - Pr(L \leq n - 1)$$
$$= w_{2,n+1} - w_{2,n}$$
$$= \frac{qc}{p} [(1 - qc)^{n-1} - (1 - c)^{n-1}].$$

The reader may have recognized that there is an alternative and more direct way to obtain the probability above. For L to equal n, the subject (1) must be in state 1 on trial n, with probability $w_{1,n}$, (2) must sample the unconditioned element and make an error, with probability q, and (3) must effectively condition that element, with probability c. Hence

$$Pr(L = n) = w_{1,n}qc,$$

which gives the same result as in Eq. 6.10. The mean value of L may be obtained by standard methods:

$$E(L) = \sum_{n=1}^{\infty} nPr(L = n) = \frac{1}{c} + \frac{1}{qc} = n_0 + n_1.$$

As expected, the mean value of L turns out to be the sum of the mean trials in states 0 and 1, the n_0 and n_1 derived previously. For the Theios data, the observed mean trial of last error was 6.56; with $q = 0.50$ and $c = 0.427$, our equation for $E(L)$ predicts 7.02.

Another prediction easily derived once the $w_{i,n}$ are known is the equation for the mean learning curve. We let q_n denote the average probability of an error on trial n, and $p_n = 1 - q_n$ the probability of a success. Errors can occur only if the subject is in state 0 or state 1. Thus,

(6.11)
$$q_n = w_{0,n}Pr(\text{error} \mid \text{state 0}) + w_{1,n}Pr(\text{error} \mid \text{state 1})$$
$$= (1 - c)^{n-1} + \frac{q}{p} [(1 - qc)^{n-1} - (1 - c)^{n-1}].$$

In case $p = q = 0.5$ this equation reduces to

$$q_n = (1 - 0.5c)^{n-1}.$$

We note that the mean total errors is given by the infinite sum of q_n, which is $\dfrac{1}{0.5c}$ as obtained previously. The probability of an avoidance response on trial n will be

$$p_n = 1 - (1 - 0.5c)^{n-1}.$$

Figure 6.4 shows the fit of p_n with $c = 0.427$ to the observed learning curve in Theios' experiment. The predicted values correspond closely to those observed.

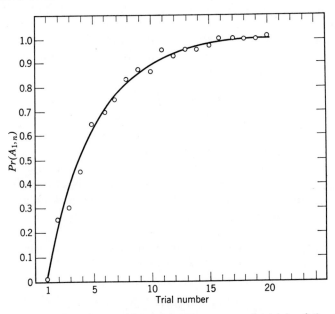

Fig. 6.4   Probability of an avoidance response on successive trials of the experiment (adapted from Fig. 5 in Theios, 1963).

Sequential Statistics

Finally we derive from the model some predictions about properties of the error-successs equences for an individual subject. As in Secs. 2.5 and 3.2, we wish to predict the mean number of error runs of length j. To achieve this result, we first derive the expected number of times a string of j errors (a j-tuple) occurs in a single learning sequence. As before, a response indicator random variable, x_n, is defined to equal one if an error occurs on trial n and to equal zero otherwise. We define $u_{j,n}$ as

$$u_{j,n} = x_n x_{n+1} \cdots x_{n+j-1}.$$

The quantity $u_{j,n}$ counts the occurrence of a j-tuple of errors running from trial n through trial $n + j - 1$. Since each x_n is one or zero, the product of j of them is also one or zero. The expectation of $u_{j,n}$ is the probability that $u_{j,n} = 1$, which is in turn the probability that each x_n in the product is one.

To find $Pr(u_{j,n} = 1)$, we first conditionalize upon whether the subject is in state 0 or in state 1 when he makes the leading error on trial n.

First consider him to be in state 1 on trial n. The probability that he is in state 1 and makes an error is $w_{1,n}q$. The probability that he makes another error on the next trial is $(1 - c)q$; that is, with probability $1 - c$ the sampled element was not conditioned on trial n and with probability q it is sampled again on trial $n + 1$, leading to another error. Since we are concerned with j errors in succession, he must make "another error" $j - 1$ times after the first one. Thus, the probability of starting in state 1 and making j consecutive errors is

$$w_{0,n}q[q(1 - c)]^{j-1}.$$

This is one component of $Pr(u_{j,n} = 1)$. The other component of $Pr(u_{j,n} = 1)$ arises when we consider that the subject begins in state 0 on trial n, with probability $w_{0,n}$. From state 0 there are a number of paths that the subject might follow while putting out j consecutive errors. The simplest of these paths is the one in which the subject stays in state 0 for the remaining $j - 1$ trials, each trial necessarily making an error. This path has probability $w_{0,n}(1 - c)^{j-1}$. The other paths are those in which the subject stays in state 0 for k of the $j - 1$ trials, then moves into state 1; after moving to state 1 he makes an error, and then stays there and errs on each of the $j - 1 - k$ remaining trials of the string. This particular path has probability

$$w_{0,n}[(1 - c)^{k-1}c]q[(1 - c)q]^{j-1-k}.$$

The possible values of k in this equation are the integers from 1 through $j - 1$.

We may summarize the discussion above by writing the following:

$$E(u_{j,n}) = Pr(u_{j,n} = 1) = w_{1,n}q[q(1 - c)]^{j-1} + w_{0,n}(1 - c)^{j-1}$$
$$+ w_{0,n}\sum_{k=1}^{j-1}(1 - c)^{k-1}cq[q(1 - c)]^{j-1-k}.$$

The third-term summation can be carried out easily since the exponents of $1 - c$ add to $j - 2$, so $(1 - c)^{j-2}$ can be brought out in front of the sum over k. The result in this case, after some simplification, is

$$E(u_{j,n}) = w_{1,n}q[q(1 - c)]^{j-1} + w_{0,n}(1 - c)^{j-1}$$
$$+ w_{0,n}\frac{qc}{p}(1 - c)^{j-2}(1 - q^{j-1}).$$

We are interested in finding the average number of j-tuples of errors over all trials. We define u_j to be the sum over all n of the $u_{j,n}$'s. The expectation of u_j is simply the sum of the separate $E(u_{j,n})$ determined above. In summing $E(u_{j,n})$ over n, the only factors that vary with n are

$w_{1,n}$ and $w_{0,n}$. The sums over n of $w_{1,n}$ and $w_{0,n}$ are $1/qc$ and $1/c$, the n_1 and n_0 determined previously. Hence, if in $E(u_{j,n})$ we replace $w_{1,n}$ by $1/qc$ and $w_{0,n}$ by $1/c$, we obtain $E(u_j)$, that is,

$$(6.12) \quad E(u_j) = \sum_{n=1}^{\infty} \prod_{i=0}^{j-1} x_{n+i}$$

$$= \frac{[q(1-c)]^{j-1}}{c} + \frac{(1-c)^{j-1}}{c} + \frac{q}{p}(1-c)^{j-2}(1-q^{j-1})$$

$$= \frac{(1-c)^{j-1}}{c}\left[1 + q^{j-1} + \frac{qc(1-q^{j-1})}{p(1-c)}\right].$$

As a check on Eq. 6.12, notice that u_1 should be just the total errors made by the subject. Evaluating Eq. 6.12 at $j = 1$, we find that $E(u_1)$ equals $2/c$, which is indeed the $E(T)$ derived previously.

We saw in Sec. 2.5 that the expected number of error runs of length j is related to the expected values of the u_j's by the formula

$$E(r_j) = E(u_j) - 2E(u_{j+1}) + E(u_{j+2}).$$

The total number of error runs of any length is

$$(6.13) \qquad E(R) = \sum_{j=1}^{\infty} E(r_j) = E(u_1) - E(u_2) = 1 + \frac{p}{c}.$$

For the Theios data, using the estimates of $p = 0.50$ and $c = 0.427$, the predicted mean number of error runs per sequence is 2.17; this comes very close to the observed total runs which was 2.18. The values predicted for $E(r_1)$, $E(r_2)$, and $E(r_3)$ are 1.05, 0.51, and 0.27; the corresponding observed numbers of runs of length 1, 2, 3 were 1.05, 0.46, and 0.30. Thus, we see that the model gives a remarkably close fit to the sequential features of these data.

This concludes our discussion of the Theios data and of the two-element model. In summary, we see that the model provides an excellent quantitative account of these data. In retrospect this finding can be attributed in large part to the stability of the data ensured by the large sample size and by the simplified conditions and care with which the experiment was run. It is worth mentioning that similar avoidance learning conditions run in later experiments by Theios and his associates have continued to support the general two-stage model, although the p estimates have differed from 0.50. We have derived here only a few predictions from the two-element model. A technical report by Theios (1961) may be consulted for derivations of many other predictions that he fit to his data. A generalization of the two-stage model was utilized in a paper by Bower and Theios (1964), who fit the model to a number of sets of data from a variety of different learning situations. The generalization consisted simply of postulating that the subject could move out of the intermediate state with probability s on a success trial and with probability e on an error trial.

6.2 THE LINEAR MODEL

We now consider two-way shuttle-avoidance learning. As mentioned at the beginning of this chapter, this provides a more complex learning task for the subject and produces what appears to be more gradual learning. The data to be discussed here are those reported by Solomon and Wynne (1953), because these data have already been extensively analyzed according to the linear model (cf. Bush and Mosteller, 1955, Chapter 11). The relevant experimental conditions were as follows: each of 30 mature dogs was trained to shuttle between two compartments to avoid electric shock. The two compartments had grid floors and were separated by a barrier with a guillotine door on the top of it. The *CS* consisted of turning out the lights above the compartment the dog was in and simultaneously raising the gate. The other compartment was still illuminated. The *CS* was presented for ten seconds and then followed by electric shock if the dog had not already jumped over the barrier into the other compartment. If the animal failed to avoid, the shock was left on until it escaped by jumping across the barrier. The intensity of the shock was set at a very high level, just below that which would tetanize the dog's leg muscles. Each dog was given ten trials per day until well past the point of learning (consistent avoidance). None of the dogs made an error after trial 25. The fact that all subjects learned to a high level is probably attributable to the very intense shock level used in the experiment. The original protocols are reproduced in Bush and Mosteller (1955, p. 239) and may be consulted for more detailed information.

The major theoretical interest in this section is in how well the two-operator version of the linear model describes the dog data. One operator expresses the effect of a shock trial and the other that of an avoidance trial. The single-operator linear model was treated in Sec. 3.4, and a three-operator linear model in Chapter 5. Later, in Sec. 6.4, we will again take up the Solomon-Wynne experiment, applying the two-operator form of Luce's (1959a) beta model.

An intuitive rationale for the linear model comes from inspecting the learning curve for the dog data. Figure 6.5 shows the proportion of dogs that avoided shock over trials. The proportion of avoidances was close to zero on trial 1 and reached an asymptote of one over the last few trials. The curve in Fig. 6.5 is increasing and negatively accelerated;

that is, the increment from one trial to the next decreases with increasing n. If we let p_n be the proportion of dogs who avoid shock on trial n, then (according to Fig. 6.5) the increment $p_{n+1} - p_n$ should be positive and a decreasing function of n. Hence it is natural to assume that the trial-to-trial increment is proportional to the amount of improvement still

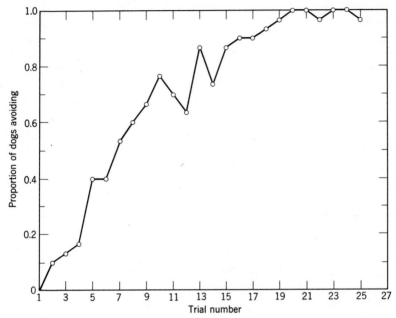

Fig. 6.5 Proportion of dogs that avoided shock on each trial in the Solomon-Wynne experiment.

possible, which is $1 - p_n$. These considerations suggest that the mean learning curve can be described by the equation

$$(6.14) \qquad p_{n+1} - p_n = (1 - \alpha)(1 - p_n).$$

In Eq. 6.14 both of the differences $p_{n+1} - p_n$ and $1 - p_n$ are nonnegative, so $(1 - \alpha) \geq 0$, or $\alpha \leq 1$. The condition that p_{n+1} be less than or equal to one for all n also implies (by substituting one for p_{n+1} in Eq. 6.14) that

$$1 - p_n \geq (1 - \alpha)(1 - p_n).$$

This equation means that $(1 - \alpha) \leq 1$, or $\alpha \geq 0$. Combining the two bounds, we have $0 \leq \alpha \leq 1$. The upper bound $\alpha = 1$ corresponds to the case where no learning occurs. The lower bound $\alpha = 0$ yields $p_2 - p_1 = 1 - p_1$, or $p_2 = 1$; likewise, $p_n = 1$ for $n > 2$. Hence, the smaller α is, the faster learning occurs.

We digress momentarily to point out that Eq. 6.14 can be generalized to the case where the asymptote is λ, such that $0 \leq \lambda \leq 1$. This generalization, although not needed for the avoidance data, is of importance. Bush and Mosteller (1955) have demonstrated that the general form of this equation can be applied to a wide range of experimental situations by appropriately identifying the operators with experimental events (that is, assigning different α and λ to different events). The generalization of Eq. 6.14 is obvious. If the asymptotic proportion correct is λ, then $\lambda - p_n$ is the amount of increase still possible after trial n. Hence, the increment on the next trial, $p_{n+1} - p_n$, should be proportional to this maximum possible increment; that is,

$$p_{n+1} - p_n = (1 - \alpha)(\lambda - p_n).$$

Rewriting yields

(6.15)
$$p_{n+1} = p_n + (1 - \alpha)(\lambda - p_n)$$
$$= \alpha p_n + (1 - \alpha)\lambda.$$

This is a linear difference equation of the form encountered in Eq. 5.18. By Eq. 5.19 the solution is

(6.16)
$$p_n = \alpha^{n-1} p_1 + (1 - \alpha^{n-1})\lambda.$$

Since $\lim_{n \to \infty} \alpha^{n-1} = 0$, we have $\lim_{n \to \infty} p_n = \lambda$, proving the foregoing statement that the proportion correct tends to λ as n approaches infinity.

The Two-Operator Linear Model

Returning to the problem of developing a linear model for the avoidance data, we ask how the linear relation in Eq. 6.15 can be adapted to that situation. On any trial, the dog can receive or avoid shock. There is no reason to expect that the increment $p_{n+1} - p_n$ will be the same after a shock trial as after an avoidance trial. Hence two operators are assumed. The Q_a operator is applied following an avoidance trial, and Q_s following a shock trial. That is,

(6.17)

$$p_{n+1} = \begin{cases} Q_a p_n = \alpha_a p_n + (1 - \alpha_a)\lambda_a, & \text{if the dog avoids shock on trial } n \\ Q_s p_n = \alpha_s p_n + (1 - \alpha_s)\lambda_s, & \text{if the dog is shocked and then escapes shock on trial } n. \end{cases}$$

These equations represent the general formulation of the linear model with operators Q_a and Q_s. Various special cases of Eq. 6.17 are classified according to constraints on the α's and λ's.

From an examination of the Solomon-Wynne data, Bush and Mosteller concluded that for shock-avoidance learning the restrictions $\lambda_a = \lambda_s = 1$ are appropriate. The assumption that $\lambda_a = 1$ is justified by the observation that all dogs ultimately learned to avoid on every trial. Therefore, a run of avoidances must maintain p_n close to one, so λ_a must be close to one. The argument that λ_s must be virtually one is derived from Eq. 6.15 by substituting λ_s for λ:

$$p_{n+1} - p_n = (1 - \alpha)(\lambda_s - p_n).$$

Late in learning p_n is near one, because the dogs ultimately exhibited perfect learning. But if λ_s is noticeably less than one, then late in learning p_n will exceed λ_s and by the above equation the effect of a shock trial will be to make p_{n+1} less than p_n. The data contradict the hypothesis that p_n decreases late in learning, so λ_s cannot be appreciably less than one. Consequently, we assume that both λ_s and λ_a are one. Making these restrictions in Eq. 6.17 yields

$$p_{n+1} = \begin{cases} \alpha_a p_n + (1 - \alpha_a), & \text{if the dog avoids shock on trial } n \\ \alpha_s p_n + (1 - \alpha_s), & \text{if the dog is shocked and then} \\ & \text{escapes shock on trial } n. \end{cases}$$

The equations can be written more compactly in terms of q_n, the probability of shock on trial n. Substituting $q_n = 1 - p_n$ into the two lines above, we have

$$1 - q_{n+1} = \begin{cases} \alpha_a(1 - q_n) + 1 - \alpha_a \\ \alpha_s(1 - q_n) + 1 - \alpha_s. \end{cases}$$

Simplifying,

$$(6.18) \qquad q_{n+1} = \begin{cases} \alpha_a q_n, & \text{if the dog avoids shock on trial } n \\ \alpha_s q_n, & \text{if the dog is shocked and then escapes} \\ & \text{shock on trial } n. \end{cases}$$

These equations are crucial for all subsequent work with the two-operator linear model. It appears reasonable to take $q_1 = 1$, since none of the dogs in the Solomon-Wynne experiment avoided shock on trial 1. This behavior is to be expected, since they had had no previous opportunities to learn.

An important property of Eq. 6.18 is that the shock and avoidance operators commute with each other; that is, if the two operators are to be applied once each, the order in which they are applied makes no difference in the resulting value of q. To illustrate this statement, suppose that two dogs have the same probability q_n of failing to avoid on trial n. Suppose further that one dog is shocked on trial n and avoids on trial $n + 1$, whereas the other dog avoids on trial n and is shocked on trial

$n + 1$. Then q_{n+2} will be the same for both dogs. The effect on q_n of a shock-avoidance sequence is identical to the effect of an avoidance-shock sequence; that is, $Q_a Q_s p_n = Q_s Q_a p_n$.* Therefore, the theoretical probability that a dog will avoid on a particular trial depends only on his total number of past shocks and avoidances, and does not depend on his particular shock-avoidance history.

Derivations from the Two-Operator Linear Model

Mathematical analysis of the two-operator model is complicated by the fact that the trial-sequence of operators applied to q is under the control of the subject. Whether the Q_a or Q_s operator is applied to q_n depends on whether the animal avoids or gets shocked on trial n, and this depends on q_n. Because of this subject-control feature of the process, we will have a distribution of q-values on each trial. Distributions of response probabilities were discussed previously in Chapters 3 and 5. Recall that the distribution of q-values on trial n may be reconstructed by writing out the tree of events (shocks and avoidances) that could take place during the first $n - 1$ trials. In this case, each path of this tree corresponds to a particular sequence of shocks and avoidances. We suppose that path v of the tree terminates at the end of trial $n - 1$ (or beginning of trial n) with a q-value denoted by $q_{v,n}$. The probability of this particular path, obtained by multiplying the probabilities of the individual branching points, will be denoted as $P_{v,n}$. Thus, we have a random variable, q_n, with probability distribution specified by $Pr(q_n = q_{v,n}) = P_{v,n}$. Because of the commutativity of the shock and avoidance operators, some of the paths of this tree give the same value of $q_{v,n}$. In particular, those paths having the same number of shocks up through trial $n - 1$ lead to the same value of $q_{v,n}$.

The rth raw moment of the q_n distribution will be denoted as $V_{r,n}$, where

(6.19) $$V_{r,n} = \sum_v q_{v,n}^r Pr(q_n = q_{v,n}) = \sum_v q_{v,n}^r P_{v,n}.$$

The first raw moment, $V_{1,n}$, is the average error probability on trial n and is to be compared with the observed mean error probability. We would like to find an explicit expression for $V_{1,n}$. The method to be used was illustrated in Secs. 3.6 and 5.3; we first try to find a difference equation relating $V_{1,n+1}$ to $V_{1,n}$, and then solve the equation.

To find the relevant difference equation, we begin by considering a

---

* More generally, for $\alpha_a < 1$ and $\alpha_s < 1$, two linear operators commute if their limit points (the λ in Eq. 6.16) are identical (Bush and Mosteller, 1955, pp. 64–65).

subject who has a q_n-value of $q_{v,n}$ on trial n. If this subject fails to avoid and is shocked on trial n (which happens with probability $q_{v,n}$), then his new q-value on trial $n + 1$ will be $\alpha_s q_{v,n}$. On the other hand, if this subject avoids successfully on trial n, (which he does with probability $1 - q_{v,n}$), then the q-value on trial $n + 1$ will be $\alpha_a q_{v,n}$. The mean value of q on trial $n + 1$ for this subject will be a weighted combination of $\alpha_s q_{v,n}$ and $\alpha_a q_{v,n}$, where the weighting coefficients are $q_{v,n}$ and $1 - q_{v,n}$.

$$E(q_{v,n+1}) = q_{v,n}[\alpha_s q_{v,n}] + (1 - q_{v,n})[\alpha_a q_{v,n}].$$

To find the mean value over the entire population of subjects, denoted $V_{1,n+1}$, we sum over all values of $q_{v,n}$, each weighted by its probability of occurrence:

$$V_{1,n+1} = \sum_v [\alpha_s q_{v,n}^2 + \alpha_a(q_{v,n} - q_{v,n}^2)]P_{v,n}$$

or

(6.20) $$V_{1,n+1} = \alpha_a V_{1,n} + (\alpha_s - \alpha_a)V_{2,n}.$$

We see that $V_{1,n+1}$ depends not only on $V_{1,n}$ but also on the next higher moment, $V_{2,n}$. A similar recursion for the rth raw moment will depend upon the $(r + 1)$st moment from the preceding trial; namely,

$$V_{r,n+1} = \sum_v [q_{v,n}(\alpha_s q_{v,n})^r + (1 - q_{v,n})(\alpha_a q_{v,n})^r]P_{v,n}$$

or

$$V_{r,n+1} = \alpha_a^r V_{r,n} + (\alpha_s^r - \alpha_a^r)V_{r+1,n}.$$

At this point we have encountered a rather fundamental difficulty. We cannot solve Eq. 6.20 because we do not know $V_{2,n}$. If we try to solve a similar difference equation for $V_{2,n}$, we are stymied by the fact that $V_{2,n+1}$ depends on $V_{3,n}$, and we do not know $V_{3,n}$, and so on. There is no simple way to find the mean learning curve for this case with two operators, and the difficulty arises because the sequence of operator applications is subject-controlled. Of course, if $\alpha_s = \alpha_a$ then the $V_{2,n}$ term in Eq. 6.20 disappears and an explicit solution for $V_{1,n}$ is available. But we cannot take this out since, as will be seen later, the data require different values for α_s and α_a.

The Expected Operator Approximation*

Failing to obtain an exact solution to $V_{1,n}$, we may consider an approximate solution. What we will do is to approximate the troublesome $V_{2,n}$

---

* This section treats a special topic and may be omitted.

in Eq. 6.20 by the expression $(V_{1,n})^2$. The closeness of this approximation depends on the amount of dispersion or variance of the $q_{v,n}$ values. Recall the variance of q_n is defined as

$$\text{Var}(q_n) = V_{2,n} - (V_{1,n})^2.$$

The approximation is exact only if the variance is zero—in fact, only if all $q_{v,n}$ are identically equal to the mean $V_{1,n}$. The reason for the label "expected operator approximation" is seen when we use operator notation. As before, let Q_s represent the shock operator and Q_a the avoidance operator, and define the expected operator Q_n as $V_{1,n}Q_s + (1 - V_{1,n})Q_a$. Then, our result in Eq. 6.20 may be thought of as arising when the expected operator, Q_n, is applied to $V_{1,n}$. The calculation is:

$$(6.21) \quad V_{1,n+1} = Q_n V_{1,n} = [V_{1,n}Q_s + (1 - V_{1,n})Q_a]V_{1,n}$$
$$= V_{1,n}[Q_s(V_{1,n})] + (1 - V_{1,n})[Q_a(V_{1,n})]$$
$$= V_{1,n}[\alpha_s V_{1,n}] + (1 - V_{1,n})[\alpha_a V_{1,n}]$$
$$= \alpha_a V_{1,n} + (\alpha_s - \alpha_a)(V_{1,n})^2.$$

Equation 6.21 will be seen as the same as Eq. 6.20 except that $(V_{1,n})^2$ has replaced $V_{2,n}$.

Now, Eq. 6.21 is a difference equation relating $V_{1,n+1}$ to $V_{1,n}$. Unfortunately, an exact solution to this difference equation is not available because of the $(V_{1,n})^2$ term. Thus, we have to make a second approximation, converting Eq. 6.21 into a differential equation. This corresponding differential equation can then be solved explicitly for $V_{1,n}$. To obtain the differential equation, first subtract $V_{1,n}$ from both sides of Eq. 6.21 and write it as

$$V_{1,n+1} - V_{1,n} = -(1 - \alpha_a)V_{1,n} - (\alpha_a - \alpha_s)(V_{1,n})^2.$$

Then replace $V_{1,n+1} - V_{1,n}$ by the differential element

$$(6.22) \quad \frac{dV_1}{dn} = \lim_{\Delta n \to 0} \frac{\Delta V_{1,n}}{\Delta n} = -V_1(a + bV_1),$$

where $a = 1 - \alpha_a$ and $b = \alpha_a - \alpha_s$. The solution for this differential equation is found as follows:

$$\int_{V_{1,1}}^{V_{1,n}} \frac{dV_1}{V_1(a + bV_1)} = -\int_1^n dn = -(n - 1).$$

Consulting a table of indefinite integrals, the left-hand integral is seen to be

$$-\frac{1}{a} \ln\left(\frac{a + bV_1}{V_1}\right) + C,$$

where C is the constant of integration and $\ln x$ denotes the logarithm of x to the base e. When the integral is evaluated between the limits of $V_{1,1}$ and $V_{1,n}$, the result is

$$\frac{1}{a} \ln \left(\frac{a + bV_{1,1}}{V_{1,1}} \right) \left(\frac{V_{1,n}}{a + bV_{1,n}} \right) = -(n - 1).$$

Taking the antilog of both sides and simplifying, yields

(6.23)
$$V_{1,n} = \frac{aKe^{-a(n-1)}}{1 - bKe^{-a(n-1)}},$$

where

$$K = \frac{V_{1,1}}{a + bV_{1,1}}.$$

For the particular case under consideration, $V_{1,1} = 1$ since all subjects begin on trial 1 with a q-value of one. Substituting $V_{1,1} = 1$, $a = 1 - \alpha_a$ and $b = \alpha_a - \alpha_s$ into Eq. 6.23, we obtain the following expression after simplification:

(6.24)
$$V_{1,n} = \frac{(1 - \alpha_a)e^{-(1-\alpha_a)(n-1)}}{1 - \alpha_s + (\alpha_s - \alpha_a)e^{-(1-\alpha_a)(n-1)}}.$$

Thus have we arrived at an explicit equation for $V_{1,n}$. The reader should keep in mind the two approximations involved in arriving at this point.

Applying this equation to the Solomon-Wynne data, we predict $1 - V_{1,n}$, the mean probability of an avoidance response on trial n. For these purposes we use the parameter estimates $\alpha_a = 0.80$ and $\alpha_s = 0.92$. It will be explained later how these parameter estimates were obtained. Figure 6.6 shows the observed proportion of avoidance responses on each trial (circles joined by solid lines). The smooth curve gives the theoretical mean, $1 - V_{1,n}$, computed from Eq. 6.24. The open circles joined by dashed lines are predictions from Monte Carlo runs and will be discussed later. The important point here is that Eq. 6.24 gives a reasonably accurate fit to the observed learning curve in Fig. 6.6.

We will use Eq. 6.24 for one further purpose, namely, to derive an estimation equation from it. The expected total errors during learning is just the sum (or integral) of the error probabilities over all trials n. Thus, interpreting $V_{1,n}$ as the error probability on trial n, the expected total errors is found by integration (from $n = 1$ to ∞) of Eq. 6.24:

(6.25)
$$E(T) \approx \int_1^\infty V_{1,n} \, dn = \frac{1}{\alpha_s - \alpha_a} \ln \left(\frac{1 - \alpha_a}{1 - \alpha_s} \right).$$

Once one of the parameters is known, the observed mean errors along with Eq. 6.25 may be used in estimating the other parameter. Tables of this

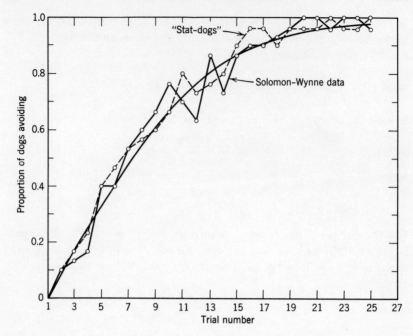

Fig. 6.6 Proportion of avoidance responses on each trial, comparing data with stat-dogs and with the expected operator approximation from Eq. 6.24 (adapted from Fig. 11.1 in Bush and Mosteller, 1955).

function for a grid of α_s and α_a values are to be found in Bush and Mosteller (1955, pp. 344–345).

Parameter Estimates

We turn now to the important task of estimating the parameters of the linear model. Estimates are more difficult to obtain for this model than for any other model considered in this chapter. The maximum likelihood method (cf. Chapter 9) yields extremely cumbersome expressions that do not simplify. Method of moments estimates are difficult because explicit expressions for only a few statistics can be derived, and these usually involve complicated functions. Bush and Mosteller (1955) consider several estimation methods for α_s and α_a in their discussion of the Solomon-Wynne data, and the reader may consult their book for details. We adopt the strategy of estimating α_s from the data prior to the first avoidance response, since these data do not depend on α_a. Once an estimate of α_s has been obtained, we then use α_s and the mean number of errors in Eq. 6.25 to estimate the avoidance parameter, α_a.

To obtain an estimation equation for α_s, we try to derive an expression for the mean number of shocks before the first avoidance response. Let F be this random variable; its possible values are $0, 1, 2, \ldots$. To find its mean, we first determine its distribution. The probability that there are n errors before the first avoidance can be written as

$$Pr(F = n) = 1 \cdot \alpha_s \cdot \alpha_s^2 \cdot \alpha_s^3 \cdots \alpha_s^{n-1}(1 - \alpha_s^n)$$

$$= \prod_{i=0}^{n-1} \alpha_s^i - \prod_{i=0}^{n} \alpha_s^i.$$

In taking products, the exponents of α_s are summed. We use the formula for the sum of the first k integers,

$$1 + 2 + 3 + \cdots + k = \frac{k(k + 1)}{2}.$$

Thus, the distribution of F may be written as

(6.26)　　　　　$Pr(F = n) = \alpha_s^{(n/2)(n-1)} - \alpha_s^{(n/2)(n+1)}.$

To find an expression for the average value of F, we proceed as follows:

$$E(F) = \sum_{n=0}^{\infty} nPr(F = n) = \sum_{n=0}^{\infty} n\alpha_s^{(n/2)(n-1)} - \sum_{n=0}^{\infty} n\alpha_s^{(n/2)(n+1)}.$$

We write out the first few terms of each sum to show the result:

(6.27)　　$E(F) = [1 + 2\alpha_s + 3\alpha_s^3 + 4\alpha_s^6 + 5\alpha_s^{10} + \cdots]$

$$- [\alpha_s + 2\alpha_s^3 + 3\alpha_s^6 + 4\alpha_s^{10} + 5\alpha_s^{15} + \cdots]$$

$$= 1 + \alpha_s + \alpha_s^3 + \alpha_s^6 + \alpha_s^{10} + \cdots$$

$$= \sum_{v=0}^{\infty} \alpha_s^{(v/2)(v+1)}.$$

The sum in this last line can be reduced no further. However, the function has been tabled by Bush and Mosteller (1955, p. 339).

　Turning to the data, we find that the average number of errors before the first avoidance was 4.50 in the Solomon-Wynne study. Referring to the tables given in Bush and Mosteller's book, it is found that the function for $E(F)$ will equal 4.50 if α_s has a value of about 0.923. This gives one estimate of α_s. On the basis of this plus evidence from other estimation methods, Bush and Mosteller decided to use $\alpha_s = 0.92$ as the appropriate estimate. Once α_s has been estimated, we then use the observed mean errors (7.80) along with the theoretical expression in Eq. 6.25 to obtain an estimate of α_a. By consulting the tables of the $E(T)$ function, it is found that an estimate of $\alpha_a = 0.80$ will fit the observed mean errors. We next try to predict other features of the data using the estimates $\alpha_a = 0.80$

and $\alpha_s = 0.92$. Since $(0.92)^{2.7} \approx 0.80$, the model says that a single avoidance trial reduces the error probability about as much as three (2.7) successive shock trials.

Predictions from Monte Carlo Runs

We wish now to use the model to predict various aspects of the Solomon-Wynne data. In principle, this is done by deriving theoretical expressions for a number of statistics of interest, evaluating these expressions for our particular numerical estimates of α_a and α_s, and comparing the predicted values to the observed values. As the reader may already have inferred from the preceding derivations, this procedure runs into considerable mathematical difficulties; that is, explicit expressions for many statistics of interest are not available because of the analytic problems encountered. Of course, the model does make a prediction about every statistic of the data; but frequently it is devilishly difficult to determine analytically what that prediction is.

It happens that the Monte Carlo method can be used to generate numerical predictions in those instances where analytic methods fail to yield explicit results. The Monte Carlo method consists of "running" a number of artificial subjects (called "stat-dogs" here) through the hypothetical experiment, using the rules of the model; whenever a probabilistic choice is encountered, a random number generator is consulted. The artificial learning sequences generated by the model are then compared to the real data by computing any desired statistic on both sets of sequences.

An illustration is necessary to clarify the method. We trace out the running of one stat-dog through the artificial experiment. The rules of the model are

$$
\begin{align}
&\text{(6.28a)} \\
&\text{(6.28b)}
\end{align}
\quad
q_{v,n+1} =
\begin{cases}
0.80 q_{v,n} & \text{if dog } v \text{ avoids on trial } n \\
0.92 q_{v,n} & \text{if dog } v \text{ is shocked on trial } n.
\end{cases}
$$

The stat-dog, who responds as prescribed by the model, receives shock on trial 1 because he starts with $q_1 = 1$. His error probability on trial 2, by Eq. 6.28b, is $q_2 = 0.92 q_1 = 0.92$. We use a random number table to decide whether he avoids or is shocked on trial 2. Considering the two-digit random numbers from 01, 02, . . . , 99, 00, we associate the numbers from 01 to 92 with a failure to avoid, and the numbers 93, . . . , 99, 00 with an avoidance. Since random numbers are uniformly distributed, the probability of obtaining a random number within the first set is 0.92 and of obtaining a number within the second set is 0.08. Consulting the

Table 6.3

Computation of Shock-Avoidance Sequence, Using $\hat{q}_1 = 1.00$,

$$\alpha_a = 0.80, \ \alpha_s = 0.92.$$

Trial No.	$\hat{q}_n$	Random No.	Response
1	1.000	—	S
2	0.920 (1.000) = 0.920	15	S
3	0.920 (0.920) = 0.846	63	S
4	0.920 (0.846) = 0.779	98	A
5	0.800 (0.779) = 0.623	97	A
6	0.800 (0.623) = 0.498	70	A
7	0.800 (0.498) = 0.398	17	S
8	0.920 (0.398) = 0.366	31	S
9	0.920 (0.366) = 0.337	73	A
10	0.800 (0.337) = 0.270	81	A
11	0.800 (0.270) = 0.216	36	A
12	0.800 (0.216) = 0.173	48	A
13	0.800 (0.173) = 0.138	60	A
14	0.800 (0.138) = 0.110	33	A
15	0.800 (0.110) = 0.088	62	A
16	0.800 (0.088) = 0.070	27	A
17	0.800 (0.070) = 0.056	81	A
18	0.800 (0.056) = 0.045	20	A

random number table, we (or the stat-dog) happened to draw the number 15 which lies within the first set, so this stat-dog fails to avoid and is shocked on trial 2. By Eq. 6.28b, his new error probability after this shock and at the beginning of trial 3 should be $q_3 = 0.92q_2 = (0.92)^2 = 0.846$. On trial 3, we would associate the random numbers from 01 to 85 with failure to avoid and those from 86 to 00 with avoidance. The next entry in our random number table happened to be 63, so the stat-dog is shocked on trial 3. This yields $q_4 = 0.92q_3 = 0.694$ for his error probability on trial 4. Continuing in this fashion, this stat-dog was run for 18 trials; his protocol and the relevant computations are shown in Table 6.3. Inspection of the table indicates that the major features of the protocol can be summarized by the following statistics:

Number of trials before first avoidance	3
Number of trials before second avoidance	4
Total number of shocks	5
Trial number of last shock	8
Number of alternations of shocks and avoidances	3
Longest run of shocks	3
Number of trials before first run of four consecutive avoidances	8

The calculations in Table 6.3 demonstrate the random element inherent in any probabilistic model. A second stat-dog would have produced a protocol different from that in the table, because his sequence of random numbers undoubtedly would differ from that of the first dog. After running a group of stat-dogs, all with $\hat{q}_1 = 1$, $\hat{\alpha}_a = 0.80$, and $\hat{\alpha}_s = 0.92$, we can readily compute distributions and moments of the various statistics. We must run enough stat-dogs to obtain estimates that would not change significantly if additional runs were made. The use of a high-speed computer markedly facilitates this Monte Carlo procedure. In the present example Bush and Mosteller ran 30 stat-dogs, which number appeared sufficient for producing reliable theoretical values. Recall that the number of real dogs also was 30.

Table 6.4   Comparisons of the Stat-Dog Data and the Solomon-Wynne Data

	Stat-Dogs		Real Dogs	
	Mean	S.D.	Mean	S.D.
Trials before first avoidance	4.13	2.08	4.50	2.25
Trials before second avoidance	6.20	2.06	6.47	2.62
Total shocks	7.60	2.27	7.80	2.52
Trial of last shock	12.53	4.78	11.33	4.36
Alternations	5.87	2.11	5.47	2.72
Longest run of shocks	4.33	1.89	4.73	2.03
Trials before first run of four avoidances	9.47	3.48	9.70	4.14

From the Monte Carlo runs, the mean proportion of avoidances on each trial was calculated. The dashed line in Fig. 6.6 shows the learning curve for the 30 stat-dogs. The curves for the real dogs and stat-dogs agree closely with each other. It appears that the model gives a satisfactory account of the mean learning curve.

Table 6.4 compares the stat-dogs with the Solomon-Wynne data. For each statistic in the table the mean for the real dogs is closely approximated by the mean for the stat-dogs. There is a slight but consistent tendency for the standard deviations to be higher for the real dogs than for the stat-dogs. However, the disparity is small and does not detract from the overall satisfactory fit of the model. In general, the standard deviation is a useful comparison statistic, since it tells us to what extent the observed individual differences between dogs can be handled by the theory. As a rule, one would expect the observed standard deviations to exceed the predicted values somewhat, even if the goodness of fit to other statistics is adequate. The model only incorporates one source of variability among dogs, namely, variation imposed by the probabilistic rule for responding. On the other hand, in the actual experimental situation a number of plausible sources of inter-dog variability can be suggested.

For instance, the dogs undoubtedly differ somewhat in factors such as sensitivity to electric shock and general activity level.

Prediction of Response Trigrams

As mentioned earlier, there are some statistics that can be calculated explicitly from the two-operator model so that the theorist has some recourse besides Monte Carlo simulations for testing the model. We illustrate this by predicting the probability of occurrences of the eight possible sequences of responses on three consecutive trials, n, $n + 1$ and $n + 2$. By summing these probabilities over trials n from, say, 1 to M, we thereby predict the trigram frequencies over that block of trials. Admittedly, such trigram frequencies are not included in the conventional descriptive statistics of a typical learning experiment and may seem a bit strained; yet, in fact, there are no model-free arguments for why some statistics are more "natural" than others, and conventions are merely that.

We begin by deriving from the model the probability of a particular sequence of three responses starting on trial n. We let S_n represent "shock on trial n" and A_n "avoid on trial n." Consider first the probability of a shock on all three trials:

$$(6.29) \qquad Pr(S_n S_{n+1} S_{n+2}) = \sum_v Pr(S_n S_{n+1} S_{n+2} \mid q_{v,n}) P_{v,n}$$

$$= \sum_v q_{v,n} (\alpha_s q_{v,n})(\alpha_s^2 q_{v,n}) P_{v,n}$$

$$= \alpha_s^3 \sum_v q_{v,n}^3 P_{v,n}$$

$$= \alpha_s^3 V_{3,n}.$$

We first conditionalize upon the possible values of $q_{v,n}$. The probability of S_n is $q_{v,n}$; given a shock on trial n, the probability of S_{n+1} is $\alpha_s q_{v,n}$; given a second shock on trial $n + 1$, the probability of a third shock is $\alpha_s^2 q_{v,n}$. Thus, this trigram depends on $V_{3,n}$.

Consider one more of the eight possible trigrams: an avoidance on trial n, a shock on trial $n + 1$, and another avoidance on trial $n + 2$. The probability of this sequence is

$$(6.30) \quad Pr(A_n S_{n+1} A_{n+2}) = \sum_v (1 - q_{v,n}) \alpha_a q_{v,n} (1 - \alpha_a \alpha_s q_{v,n}) P_{v,n}$$

$$= \alpha_a \sum_v q_{v,n} P_{v,n} - \alpha_a (1 + \alpha_a \alpha_s) \sum_v q_{v,n}^2 P_{v,n}$$

$$+ \alpha_a^2 \alpha_s \sum_v q_{v,n}^3 P_{v,n}$$

$$= \alpha_a V_{1,n} - \alpha_a (1 + \alpha_a \alpha_s) V_{2,n} + \alpha_a^2 \alpha_s V_{3,n}$$

$$= \alpha_a (V_{1,n} - V_{2,n}) - \alpha_a^2 \alpha_s (V_{2,n} - V_{3,n}).$$

This trigram depends on V_1, V_2 and V_3.

By continuing along these lines, one generates expressions for all eight trigrams. The results are listed below where for convenience in notation $s = \alpha_s$, $a = \alpha_a$ and $V_r = V_{r,n}$.

	Trigram			
	n	$n+1$	$n+2$	Trigram Probability
	S	S	S	$s^3 V_3$
	S	S	A	$sV_2 - s^3 V_3$
(6.31)	S	A	S	$as(V_2 - sV_3)$
	S	A	A	$V_1 - saV_2 - s(V_2 - saV_3)$
	A	S	S	$sa^2(V_2 - V_3)$
	A	S	A	$a(V_1 - V_2) - a^2 s(V_2 - V_3)$
	A	A	S	$a^2(V_1 - V_2) - a^3(V_2 - V_3)$
	A	A	A	$1 - V_1 - a(1 + a)(V_1 - V_2) + a^3(V_2 - V_3)$.

The expressions listed in Eq. 6.31 are to be interpreted as the probability that a single subject (or group of subjects) outputs a particular trigram starting on trial n. With only 30 subjects, the frequency of each trigram for any n is too small to permit serious testing. Instead we consider the total number of occurrences of each trigram in the first M trials summed over all 30 subjects.

To illustrate the method of tabulating the trigram frequencies, consider the particular protocol $SSSASAAS$. This consists of eight trials, from which we can count six trigrams. The first trigram is SSS, the second is SSA, the third SAS, and so forth. Thus, the trigrams overlap with adjacent ones. In analyzing the Solomon-Wynne protocols (cf. Bush and Mosteller, 1955, p. 239), we consider the first 19 trials, after which only one dog had two shocks (so we include most of the error data). For each subject we tabulate 17 trigrams for n from 1 up through 17. Thus there is a total of $17 \times 30 = 510$ frequencies in our trigram table. The observed frequencies are given in Table 6.5.

We shall try to predict these data using the theoretical expressions in Eq. 6.31. The relevant prediction equations may be obtained by summing the expressions in Eq. 6.31 over n from 1 to 17 and multiplying by the number of subjects. For example,

$$\text{freq}(SSS) = 30 \sum_{n=1}^{17} s^3 V_{3,n} = 30s^3(17\bar{V}_3) = 510s^3 \bar{V}_3,$$

where $\bar{V}_3$ is to be interpreted as the mean value of V_3 over trials 1 through 17. In similar fashion, V_1 and V_2 are replaced by $\bar{V}_1$ and $\bar{V}_2$ in the relevant lines of Eq. 6.31.

The trigram predictions are now a function of five parameters—a, s, $\bar{V}_1$, $\bar{V}_2$, and $\bar{V}_3$. We use the shock and avoidance parameters determined previously, namely, $a \equiv \alpha_a = 0.80$, $s \equiv \alpha_s = 0.92$. The other three parameters are estimated from the table of observed frequencies. We

Table 6.5 Observed and Predicted Trigram
Frequencies in Solomon-Wynne Data

	Trigram		Frequency	
n	$n+1$	$n+2$	Observed	Predicted
S	S	S	92	92
S	S	A	43	43
S	A	S	39	28
S	A	A	55	66
A	S	S	16	17
A	S	A	50	49
A	A	S	28	37
A	A	A	187	178

estimate $\bar{V}_1$ by the proportion of trigrams having a shock in the first position; note that the first four lines of Eq. 6.31 sum to $\bar{V}_1$. Our estimate is

$$V_1 = \frac{229}{510} = 0.448.$$

The estimate of $\bar{V}_2$ comes from the proportion of trigrams having a shock on the first two trials, namely, lines one and two in Table 6.5.

$$Pr(S_n S_{n+1}) = s\bar{V}_2 = \frac{92 + 43}{510} = 0.265.$$

From the prior estimate of $s = 0.92$, we then obtain

$$\bar{V}_2 = \frac{0.265}{0.920} = 0.288.$$

Finally, $\bar{V}_3$ is estimated from the SSS trigram (line 1).

$$Pr(SSS) = s^3\bar{V}_3 = \frac{92}{510} = 0.1805.$$

But $s^3 = (0.92)^3 = 0.78$, so

$$\bar{V}_3 = \frac{0.1805}{0.78} = 0.232.$$

Thus, with the estimates $a = 0.80$, $s = 0.92$, $\bar{V}_1 = 0.448$, $\bar{V}_2 = 0.288$ and $\bar{V}_3 = 0.232$, we try to predict the observed trigram frequencies using the theoretical expressions in Eq. 6.31. The observed and predicted values (rounded to nearest integer) are compared in Table 6.5. The χ^2

for goodness of fit of observed to predicted frequencies is 8.87, which with four degrees of freedom falls between the five and ten per cent levels of significance.

The reader may ask how we arrive at the four degrees of freedom for the χ^2 test. It arises because we have placed four constraints on the two columns of frequencies. First, both columns must add to 510, the number of observations. Second, due to our $\bar{V}_1$ estimate, the first four lines in the two columns must add to 229. Third, due to our $\bar{V}_2$ estimate, the first two lines in each column must add to 135. Fourth, to obtain our $\bar{V}_3$ estimate, we required that line one equal 92 in both columns. Putting together these constraints, we see that lines one and two must be identical in the two columns, the sum of lines three and four must equal 94, and the sum of lines five through eight must be 281 in both columns. Thus, we have lost four degrees of freedom, leaving $8 - 4 = 4$ for the test. We have not subtracted any degrees of freedom for the estimates of a and s, since those were obtained from other statistics and not directly from this table. The mathematical theory of parameter estimation is unclear on this latter point since it seems that the statistics used in estimating a and s (that is, errors to first success and total errors) place some constraints on the trigram frequencies; on the other hand, if the $\bar{V}_i$ had been known functions of a and s, then only two degrees of freedom would have been subtracted for estimation of parameters. (We return to this point in Sec. 9.5.)

Comparing predicted and observed frequencies in Table 6.5, the fit is not particularly good (except for lines five and six), given the number of constraints imposed on the table. The fit could probably be improved by using all eight trigram frequencies in obtaining minimum χ^2 estimates of the three parameters $\bar{V}_1$, $\bar{V}_2$, $\bar{V}_3$ (see Sec. 9.5); in serious tests of the model, where the fit is of major concern, this procedure would be advisable. However, our purpose here has been served by the intuitive estimates used. The intent was to show how some explicit analytic predictions can be made with the two-operator model and compared with data even though the process is complicated by subject-controlled events. For that purpose, the illustration in this section is adequate.

6.3 THE LINEAR MODEL FOR EXPERIMENTER-CONTROLLED EVENTS*

We do not wish to leave the reader with the mistaken impression that the two-operator linear model always runs into mathematical difficulties

---

* This section treats a special topic and may be omitted.

when applied to avoidance conditioning. The problems encountered in the application to the Solomon-Wynne data stemmed from the fact that the subject himself had control over the sequence of operators applied to q_n; it was this feature of the situation that brought in the higher moments of the q-distribution. We consider now an application of the two-operator model to avoidance conditioning, where no major analytic difficulties arise in generating the predictions of interest. The difficulties are avoided because for experimenter-controlled events certain assumptions can be made to simplify the structure of the model.

The experiment to be considered is one reported by Brody (1957) utilizing college students as subjects. We will provide only a very brief sketch of the experimental conditions; for details, the original report should be consulted. The subject sat before a device displaying a short vertical-line segment that, over time, rapidly and randomly weaved back and forth in its position along a horizontal slot. The subject's task was to keep a small pointer upon this weaving line by turning, with his right hand, a knob which moved the pointer along the horizontal slot. At random times during the experiment, a buzzer would sound and two seconds later the light illuminating the weaving line would be extinguished. Since the subject was motivated to achieve a high tracking score, these periods of darkness may be considered as "aversive" because during such periods the subject lost track of the moving line and his score deteriorated. We might then suppose that given the opportunity the subject would make some response which terminates or escapes a dark period (that is, which turns the light on again) and moreover would learn to make some response which avoids the onset of a dark period. Brody's subjects did indeed do this, so we may infer that dark periods were acting as aversive stimuli in this context. The escape and avoidance responses were recorded from a knob, which the subject could rotate to the left or right with his left hand. We identify a left or a right turn of the knob with the two response classes, A_1 and A_2, in our model. By preliminary training, all subjects learned to respond to the buzzer to avoid darkness, and if darkness occurred, to turn the knob in either direction to escape darkness. In the main experiment, Brody manipulated the probabilities that A_1 or A_2 avoided and, failing to avoid, that A_1 or A_2 escaped darkness.

During the brief warning signal, the subject had time to make only one response to try to avoid darkness. The experiment was designed so that with probability π_1 an A_1 response would successfully avoid (with probability $1 - \pi_1$, A_1 failed to avoid) and with probability π_2 an A_2 response would avoid (with $1 - \pi_2$, A_2 failed). Given that the response to the buzzer failed to avoid the onset of darkness, the darkness continued until the subject escaped it by making an A_1 or A_2. On a proportion φ

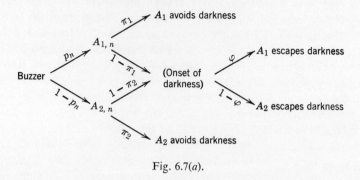

Fig. 6.7(a).

of the trials, darkness was terminated by an A_1 response, whereas on the remaining proportion $1 - \varphi$ of the trials an A_2 response led to escape. A correction procedure was used during dark periods; that is, darkness continued during errors and terminated only when the correct response occurred. Figure 6.7a summarizes in a tree the schedule of events on a trial and Fig. 6.7b displays a few sample events that might occur on a trial.

Suppose we were to list all possible response sequences that could occur on a trial. They are as follows: A_1, A_2, A_1A_1, A_1A_2, A_2A_1, A_2A_2, $A_1A_2 \cdots A_2A_1$, $A_1A_1 \cdots A_1A_2$, $A_2A_2 \cdots A_2A_1$ and $A_2A_1 \cdots A_1A_2$. The

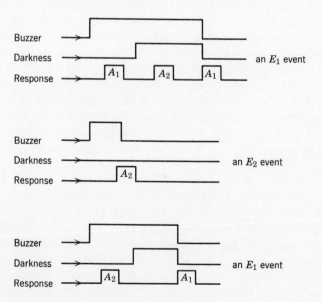

Fig. 6.7(b) Some event sequences on a trial. Read from left to right in time.

first member of the sequence is the avoidance response to the buzzer; the remaining members in the sequence are the escape responses to darkness. The abbreviation $A_1A_2 \cdots A_2A_1$ means "replace the dots by any number of extra A_2 responses." The model to be presented concentrates upon predicting the probability of the response to the buzzer (the first response in the trial sequences above). We let p_n denote the probability that on trial n the first response is A_1.

Derivations

In applying the linear model to predicting p_n, we could in principle identify a different operator for each possible within-trial sequence of events, but this would lead to analytic complications. Brody introduced two quite powerful simplifying assumptions. The first assumption was that all within-trial sequences ending with a common response would have a common incremental effect upon the probability of that terminal response occurring as the first response on the next trial. Thus reinforcement is concentrated solely upon the last response performed in the presence of the buzzer. The assumption, reminiscent of Guthrie's contiguity theory of reinforcement, reduces all the within-trial sequences to two classes, those ending in A_1 and those ending in A_2. When a member of the first class occurs, we say that reinforcing event E_1 has occurred (A_1 was reinforced); when a member of the second class occurs, we say that reinforcing event E_2 has occurred (A_2 was reinforced). The second simplifying assumption Brody proposed was that the incremental effect of an E_1 trial on p_n was complementary to the incremental effect of an E_2 trial on $1 - p_n$. Thus we may write the linear operators as:

$$p_{v,n+1} = \alpha p_{v,n} + 1 - \alpha, \qquad \text{if an } E_1 \text{ occurs on trial } n \text{ for subject } v$$

$$1 - p_{v,n+1} = \alpha(1 - p_{v,n}) + 1 - \alpha, \qquad \text{if an } E_2 \text{ occurs on trial } n \text{ for subject } v.$$

The two operators are written in a manner that clearly exhibits the assumed complementarity. This second equation, for an E_2 event, can be rewritten in standard form. When this is done, the pair of equations becomes

$$(6.32) \qquad p_{v,n+1} = \begin{cases} \alpha p_{v,n} + 1 - \alpha, & \text{if } E_{1,n} \text{ for subject } v \\ \alpha p_{v,n}, & \text{if } E_{2,n} \text{ for subject } v. \end{cases}$$

For this model, we will derive the mean learning curve $V_{1,n}$; and as a consequence, obtain predictions for the asymptotic value of $V_{1,\infty}$ for the four different experimental conditions run by Brody. We first derive a difference equation relating the mean response probability on trial $n + 1$, denoted $V_{1,n+1}$, to its former value on trial n, denoted $V_{1,n}$. As was the case in Sec. 5.3, we begin by considering a particular subject whose history of reinforcements through the first $n - 1$ trials has brought him to a p-value of $p_{v,n}$ at the beginning of trial n. The likelihood of this past history will be denoted as $P_{v,n}$. For this subject, the likelihood of an E_1 event on trial n is

$$Pr(E_{1,v,n}) = p_{v,n}\pi_1 + p_{v,n}(1 - \pi_1)\varphi + (1 - p_{v,n})(1 - \pi_2)\varphi.$$

This equation lists the probabilities of all ways by which the trial can terminate with an A_1 response and may be verified by referring to the tree diagram in Fig. 6.7a. The probability of an E_2 event for this particular subject is just $1 - Pr(E_{1,v,n})$.

We ask, what is the expected value of $p_{v,n+1}$ for this subject? It is obtained as follows:

$$
\begin{aligned}
(6.33) \quad E(p_{v,n+1}) &= [\alpha p_{v,n} + 1 - \alpha]Pr(E_{1,v,n}) + [\alpha p_{v,n}]Pr(E_{2,v,n}) \\
&= [\alpha + (1 - \alpha)\pi_1 + (1 - \alpha)\varphi(\pi_2 - \pi_1)]p_{v,n} \\
&\quad + (1 - \alpha)(1 - \pi_2)\varphi.
\end{aligned}
$$

To find the population mean, $V_{1,n+1}$, each value of $E(p_{v,n+1})$ is weighted by its probability of occurrence in the population $P_{v,n}$ and summed over v. In doing this, we arrive at the following expression

$$
\begin{aligned}
(6.34) \quad V_{1,n+1} &= G \sum_v p_{v,n} P_{v,n} + A \sum_v P_{v,n} \\
&= GV_{1,n} + A
\end{aligned}
$$

where A and G are the respective constants in Eq. 6.33. Equation 6.34 is a linear difference equation; using the solution given in Eq. 5.19 yields

$$(6.35) \qquad V_{1,n} = \frac{A}{1 - G} - \left(\frac{A}{1 - G} - V_{1,1}\right)G^{n-1}.$$

Thus an exponential learning curve is predicted, rising from an initial value of $V_{1,1}$ to an asymptote of $A/(1 - G)$. Let us examine this asymptote in more detail. It is

$$V_{1,\infty} = \frac{A}{1 - G} = \frac{(1 - \alpha)(1 - \pi_2)\varphi}{1 - [\alpha + (1 - \alpha)\pi_1 + (1 - \alpha)\varphi(\pi_2 - \pi_1)]}.$$

Simplification yields

$$(6.36) \qquad V_{1,\infty} = \frac{\varphi(1 - \pi_2)}{\varphi(1 - \pi_2) + (1 - \varphi)(1 - \pi_1)}.$$

We note that the predicted asymptote does not depend upon α, the learning parameter, but does depend upon the values of φ and the ratio

$(1 - \pi_1)/(1 - \pi_2)$, which are set by the experimenter and hence are known in advance.

Returning to the experiment, Brody ran four groups of 32 subjects each for 100 trials, the groups differing in their values of φ, π_1, and π_2. He found that the mean learning curves were fit very well by the function for $V_{1,n}$ derived in Eq. 6.35. Using Eq. 6.36, the asymptotic percentages of A_1 avoidance responses may be predicted. The average proportions of A_1 responses during the last 20 trials are given in Table 6.6 along with the theoretical values. The predictions correspond closely to the observed values. We note that the observed values are slightly low for groups 1, 2, and 4; the agreement probably would have been better had more trials been run to ensure that the subjects had reached their asymptotic levels.

Table 6.6   Proportion of A_1 Responses over Trials
81–100 in Brody's Experiment

Group	φ	π_1	π_2	Predicted	Observed
1	1.00	0.66	0.34	1.00	0.92
2	0.66	0.66	0.34	0.79	0.72
3	0.34	0.66	0.34	0.50	0.53
4	0.30	0.90	0.10	0.79	0.77

Let us consider some further implications of Eq. 6.36 for $V_{1,\infty}$. If $\pi_1 = \pi_2 = 1$, then the expression has the indeterminate form $0/0$. The cause of this indeterminacy may be seen by reference to our starting point, Eq. 6.33. When $\pi_1 = \pi_2 = 1$, Eq. 6.33 yields $E(q_{v,n+1}) = q_{v,n}$ and Eq. 6.34 yields $V_{1,n+1} = V_{1,n}$. The result in this special case is that the average A_1 probability remains at the initial value $V_{1,1}$. However, theoretical analyses, not presented here, indicate that individual subjects will absorb on A_1 or A_2; the predicted percentage absorbed on A_1 is $V_{1,1}$.

We note too that $V_{1,\infty}$ in Eq. 6.36 will be one whenever $\varphi = 1$ (and $\pi_2 < 1$). Thus, independent of the avoidance probabilities π_1 and π_2, the model predicts that the escape contingency $\varphi = 1$ will dominate and determine the choice of avoidance responses. A particularly interesting case from an experimental point of view arises when $\varphi = 1$, $\pi_1 = 0$ and π_2 is arbitrarily close to one. In words, A_2 almost always avoids, A_1 never avoids, but A_1 always escapes the aversive stimulus. The model (Eq. 6.36) predicts that the subject will not learn to avoid (make A_2) in this condition. In general, the model says that the subject cannot be taught to make one response to avoid and a different, incompatible response to escape. This prediction is counterintuitive and undoubtedly wrong for a large number of cases. In everyday life, in anticipation of some danger we commonly take appropriate preventive actions that differ from the actions taken when the danger is actually present. For example, we buy fire insurance and check the electrical insulation because we anticipate that our house might burn down; but if the house is burning around us, we run to the nearest exit.

The problem, of course, is that the model as formulated does not take account of the discrimination possible between warning signal alone and warning signal-plus-aversive event. It assumes complete transfer to the former stimulus of responses reinforced to the latter stimulus complex. Such discrimination factors can be incorporated into the model, but at the cost of added complexity.

The simple model with the complete-transfer assumption clearly does a good job in accounting for Brody's four experimental conditions. Other situations may be represented well enough by the complete-transfer assumption. For example, unpublished experiments by Bower showed that the model's counterintuitive predictions were actually correct in a two-choice shock avoidance situation involving rats as subjects. If the rat went to the left side of a choice apparatus (T-maze) within five seconds of being released, it avoided shock; otherwise shock came on and the rat had to go to the right side to turn it off. None of the animals learned to avoid in this condition, whereas all did when the escape and avoidance responses were to the same side. In another condition, the rats were initially trained to avoid to the left side by having the escape and avoidance contingency there. After that, conditions were switched so that the left turn continued to avoid, but if the rat failed to avoid, a right turn was required for escape (namely, the first conditions studied). After an initial string of avoidances (due to the initial training), the rats would fail, get shocked and have to escape to the other side. After a few trials of this kind, all of the rats in this condition stopped going to the left (the avoidance side) so that eventually their behavior was indistinguishable from that of subjects in the first condition run. Thus, we see that in these particular experimental conditions the stupid behavior predicted by the complete-transfer assumption was found; we can be assured, however, that other experimental conditions undoubtedly can be arranged for rats to produce the intelligent behavior that agrees with our common-sense expectations.

6.4   THE BETA MODEL*

At the end of Sec. 6.2 we concluded that the two-operator linear model gave a quantitatively accurate account of the Solomon-Wynne data.

---

* This section treats a special topic and may be omitted.

To what extent are we justified in citing this conclusion as empirical support for the axioms of the model? Obviously, they would be only weakly supported if equally accurate predictions could be generated from rather different axioms. Therefore, we now consider the beta model (Luce, 1959a) as an alternative explanation of two-way avoidance learning.

Following the pattern by which the linear model was developed, we introduce the basic notions of the beta model first in the context where the same operator applies on each trial and there are two response alternatives available to the subject. Next we generalize the model, letting one operator express the effect of a shock and the other that of an avoidance. Then we take up the question of estimating parameter values of the beta model from the dog data. Having obtained estimates, we note some immediately ensuing implications, making comparisons with the data and with the corresponding predictions of the two-operator linear model.

Single-Operator Beta Model

Unlike the linear model, the beta model assumes that response probability is one manifestation of a more fundamental but unobservable entity which we shall call *response strength*. Experimental manipulations, it is asserted, influence behavior if they produce a change in the relative strengths of the various response alternatives available to the organism. If behavior is indeed determined by a unitary strength factor, then presumably the current strength will be reflected in other response measures, for example, latency, amplitude, threshold, as well as in probability of occurrence. But to delimit this discussion, we shall confine our analysis to response probabilities in a two-choice situation (cf. Luce, 1960a, for an extension of the beta model to predict latencies). Hull (1952) was one of the first psychologists to use response strength as a construct in a deductive model. A similar identification of this term has been given by Spence (1956); however, in Luce's beta model response strength is envisioned in a more highly formalized way, and is given a stochastic interpretation.

The first step in our exposition is to state an assumption for a "static" situation; we want to advance a plausible assumption about how the probability of a particular response depends on the present strengths of the two competing alternatives. Then the next step is to append a suitable assumption about how strengths, and hence response likelihoods, change over trials in an experiment where the trial outcomes are contingent on the subject's response. Of course, typical avoidance conditioning experiments fall into this category.

To begin, suppose that at the start of some trial the response strengths are $v(1)$ and $v(2)$ for alternatives 1 and 2, respectively. Then, according to the beta model,

(6.37a) $$Pr(1) = \frac{v(1)}{v(1) + v(2)},$$

where $Pr(1)$ is the probability that the subject makes response 1, and $0 < v(1), v(2) < \infty$. The reader will recognize that the assumption above is identical to the corresponding axiom in Eq. 4.6, where its implications for choice behavior in a steady-state condition were spelled out. One important consequence of Eq. 6.37a becomes apparent when we divide the numerator and the denominator of the right side by $v(1)$, obtaining

(6.37b) $$Pr(1) = \frac{1}{1 + \dfrac{v(2)}{v(1)}}.$$

Hence the ratio $v(2)/v(1)$ can be inferred from choice data. The absolute magnitudes of the strengths are known only up to a multiplicative constant, because

$$\frac{kv(2)}{kv(1)} = \frac{v(2)}{v(1)},$$

where k is any arbitrary positive constant. This ratio, which will be used extensively in the sequel, is abbreviated as v:

$$v = \frac{v(2)}{v(1)}.$$

In order to specify a learning model, it is necessary to propose assumptions about how $v(1)$ and $v(2)$ change from one learning trial to the next. We use the notation $v_n(1)$ and $v_n(2)$ to permit reference to response strengths at the start of trial n. What are reasonable assumptions to make about how a trial outcome changes $v_n(1)$ and $v_n(2)$? It seems natural to suppose that the strength of alternative 1 on trial $n + 1$ should depend on its own strength on trial n; in other words, $v_{n+1}(1)$ should be a function of $v_n(1)$. Further, mathematical convenience persuades us to adopt the path-independence assumption that $v_{n+1}(1)$ is independent of $v_k(1)$ for $k < n$, and likewise for $v_{n+1}(2)$. There remains the critical question of whether to assume that $v_{n+1}(1)$ depends on $v_n(2)$ as well as on $v_n(1)$. Basic to the beta model is the assumption that $v_{n+1}(1)$ does *not* depend on $v_n(2)$, and vice versa. After further restricting the form of the functional relationship between $v_{n+1}(1)$ and $v_n(1)$, Luce proves that the theoretical effect of a learning trial is to multiply the response strength by a constant. In general, one trial outcome might be more effective than the other in altering strengths, so we assume that the constants for alternatives 1 and 2 can be unequal.

Calling these constants k_1 and k_2, a trial is said to yield these response strength transformations:

$$v_{n+1}(1) = k_1 v_n(1),$$
$$v_{n+1}(2) = k_2 v_n(2).$$

Dividing the second line by the first, letting $\beta = k_2/k_1$, and denoting by v_n the value of $v_n(2)/v_n(1)$ on trial n, we have the fundamental equality:

(6.38) $$v_{n+1} = \beta v_n.$$

This result is reminiscent of Eq. 6.18 in the linear model. We can see that the single-operator beta model is path-independent and linear in the strength ratio v_n. Note that v_n increases over trials for $\beta > 1$ and decreases for $\beta < 1$. The bounds on $v_n(1)$ and $v_n(2)$ imply that $0 < v_n < \infty$.

Equation 6.37 gave $Pr(1)$ in terms of v_n and in turn Eq. 6.38 states how v_n varies with n. From these two equations we can derive the trial-to-trial changes in $Pr(1)$. Affixing the trial subscript n to the terms in Eq. 6.37b and using q_n as an abbreviation for the probability of response 1 on trial n gives

(6.39a) $$q_n = \frac{1}{v_n + 1}.$$

For any trial n this equation expresses q_n as a function of v_n, the present strength ratio. Conversely, simple rearrangement of Eq. 6.39a yields

(6.39b) $$v_n = \frac{1 - q_n}{q_n}.$$

The result above is what we might have expected, because if, in a two-response situation, alternatives 1 and 2 were equiprobable ($q_n = \frac{1}{2}$), then by Eq. 6.39b we have $v_n = 1$, or $v_n(1) = v_n(2)$. Likewise, it is clear from Eq. 6.39a that if $v_n(1) = v_n(2)$, then $q_n = \frac{1}{2}$.

Now let us derive the recursion for trial-to-trial changes in q_n. Replacing n by $n + 1$ in Eq. 6.39a,

$$q_{n+1} = \frac{1}{v_{n+1} + 1}.$$

Substituting from Eq. 6.38

$$q_{n+1} = \frac{1}{\beta v_n + 1}.$$

But now we can eliminate v_n via Eq. 6.39b to obtain the desired result:

$$(6.40) \qquad q_{n+1} = \frac{1}{\beta \dfrac{1 - q_n}{q_n} + 1} = \frac{q_n}{q_n + \beta(1 - q_n)}.$$

By contrast with Eq. 6.18 of the linear model, the equation above says that q_{n+1} is a nonlinear transform of q_n. We might surmise that this nonlinearity imposes difficulties in deriving theoretical expressions. Later it will become evident that this suspicion is correct.

Successive applications of Eq. 6.40 generate the response probabilities on trials after trial $n + 1$. Extending the result to trial $n + 2$,

$$q_{n+2} = \frac{q_{n+1}}{q_{n+1} + \beta(1 - q_{n+1})} = \frac{q_n}{q_n + \beta^2(1 - q_n)},$$

where the second equality comes from Eq. 6.40. The same argument shows that for any positive integers k and n,

$$(6.41) \qquad q_{n+k} = \frac{q_n}{q_n + \beta^k(1 - q_n)}.$$

If we exclude the cases $\beta = 1$ or 0, $q_n = 1$ or 0, then q_n will change over trials. Preliminary to discussing the asymptote of q_n, we identify q_n as the probability of an error on trial n. (We could just as well have let $1 - q_n$ be the probability of an error; the choice merely determines whether $\beta > 1$ or $\beta < 1$ but has no effect on the derivations.)

Denoting by q_∞ the asymptotic value of q_n, Eq. 6.41 implies

$$q_\infty = \lim_{k \to \infty} \frac{q_n}{q_n + \beta^k(1 - q_n)}.$$

Now as k increases, if $\beta > 1$ then β^k approaches infinity, whereas if $\beta < 1$ then β^k approaches zero. Hence

$$(6.42) \qquad q_\infty = \begin{cases} 0, & \text{if } \beta > 1, \\ 1, & \text{if } \beta < 1. \end{cases}$$

If $\beta = 1$, q_n remains at the initial level q_1.

The Two-Operator Beta Model

Paralleling the generalization of the linear model, we assume one operator Q'_a following an avoidance, and another operator Q'_s after a shock. The primes distinguish these operators from those of the linear model. That is, for a single dog the assumption is:

$$q_{n+1} = \begin{cases} Q'_s q_n = \dfrac{q_n}{q_n + \beta_s(1 - q_n)}, & \text{if shock on trial } n \\[4mm] Q'_a q_n = \dfrac{q_n}{q_n + \beta_a(1 - q_n)}, & \text{if avoidance on trial } n. \end{cases}$$

(6.43a)

(6.43b)

The reader can verify that the operators Q'_a and Q'_s commute, that is,

$$\text{(6.44)} \qquad Q'_a Q'_s q_n = Q'_s Q'_a q_n = \frac{q_n}{q_n + \beta_a \beta_s(1 - q_n)}.$$

The special case of Eq. 6.44 when $Q'_a = Q'_s$ was derived preceding Eq. 6.41.

Since learning occurs, we require $q_{n+1} < q_n$, or from Eq. 6.40,

$$\frac{q_n}{q_n + \beta(1 - q_n)} < q_n,$$

which simplifies to $1 - q_n < \beta(1 - q_n)$. Hence $\beta > 1$; in particular, we expect that $\beta_a > 1$ and $\beta_s > 1$. Also, learning is faster the more the β values exceed one.

Parameter Estimation

Recall from Eq. 6.40 that q_1 must be less than one in order for learning to occur. Therefore, not only β_a and β_s, but q_1 as well, must be estimated from the data, making one more parameter than was needed with the linear model. We present a maximum likelihood technique (Bush, 1963, pp. 440–447) which relies on a relationship between q_n for an individual dog and his cumulative numbers of shocks and avoidances through trial $n - 1$.

Let the indicator random variable $x_{i,n}$ equal one if subject i makes an error (receives a shock) on trial n, and zero if he is correct (avoids) on trial n. Further, let $q_{i,n}$ be his probability of an error on trial n. The value of $q_{i,n}$ will depend in an as yet unspecified manner on his total numbers of shocks and avoidances through trial $n - 1$; we defer the calculation of this function until it is needed. For the ith dog, the likelihood, $L_i(q_1, \beta_a, \beta_s)$ of his observed N-trial response sequence is

$$L_i(q_1, \beta_a, \beta_s) = \prod_{n=1}^{N} q_{i,n}^{x_{i,n}}(1 - q_{i,n})^{1-x_{i,n}}.$$

If the number of dogs is D, the overall likelihood is

$$L(q_1, \beta_a, \beta_s) = \prod_{i=1}^{D} \prod_{n=1}^{N} q_{i,n}^{x_{i,n}}(1 - q_{i,n})^{1-x_{i,n}}.$$

We shall show that $q_{i,n}$ is a function of the three parameters to be estimated, namely, q_1, β_a, and β_s. The objective is to find the values of these parameters which jointly maximize L. Now L attains its maximum when $\log L$ is maximal, and by taking logs the unwieldy products in the above equation convert into sums. Carrying out this operation gives

$$\log L = \sum_{i=1}^{D} \sum_{n=1}^{N} [x_{i,n} \log q_{i,n} + (1 - x_{i,n}) \log (1 - q_{i,n})].$$

To find the maximum likelihood estimate of, say, q_1 we take the partial derivative of $\log L$ with respect to q_1 and equate the resulting expression to zero

(6.45)
$$\frac{\partial \log L}{\partial q_1} = \sum_{i=1}^{D} \sum_{n=1}^{N} \left[\frac{x_{i,n}}{q_{i,n}} \frac{\partial q_{i,n}}{\partial q_1} - \frac{(1 - x_{i,n})}{(1 - q_{i\,n})} \frac{\partial q_{i,n}}{\partial q_1} \right]$$

$$= \sum_{i=1}^{D} \sum_{n=1}^{N} \left[\frac{x_{i,n} - q_{i,n}}{q_{i,n}(1 - q_{i,n})} \right] \frac{\partial q_{i,n}}{\partial q_1} = 0.$$

Turning to the calculation of this partial derivative, the exposition is facilitated if we temporarily suppress the subscript i, and so for the moment q_n is understood as being $q_{i,n}$. Let a_n and s_n be the numbers of shocks and avoidances, respectively, that a dog has received in his first $n - 1$ trials. Clearly, $s_n + a_n = n - 1$. The numbers s_n and a_n will, of course, vary from dog to dog; but q_1, β_s and β_a are assumed to be equal for all dogs in the experiment.

Setting $n = 1$ in Eq. 6.44 and extending that result to s_n applications of Q'_s and a_n applications of Q'_a gives

(6.46)
$$q_n = \frac{q_1}{q_1 + \beta_a^{a_n}\beta_s^{s_n}(1 - q_1)}.$$

Letting $d = \beta_a^{a_n}\beta_s^{s_n}$,

(6.47)
$$q_n = \frac{q_1}{q_1 + d(1 - q_1)}.$$

Differentiating with respect to q_1 and simplifying yields

$$\frac{\partial q_n}{\partial q_1} = \frac{d}{[q_1 + d(1 - q_1)]^2}.$$

Fortunately, this equation can be rewritten so as to extract a $q_n(1 - q_n)$ factor, which can later be cancelled against the denominator of Eq. 6.45. Algebraic manipulation of Eq. 6.47 gives

$$q_n(1 - q_n) = \frac{q_1(1 - q_1)d}{[q_1 + d(1 - q_1)]^2} .$$

But this expression is just $q_1(1 - q_1)$ times the foregoing result for $\partial q_n / \partial q_1$; hence

$$\frac{\partial q_n}{\partial q_1} = \frac{q_n(1 - q_n)}{q_1(1 - q_1)} .$$

Now we can effect a simplification of the likelihood equation. Reinstating the subscript i on q_n and inserting from the above equation into Eq. 6.45:

(6.48)
$$\sum_{i=1}^{D} \sum_{n=1}^{N} \frac{x_{i,n} - q_{i,n}}{q_1(1 - q_1)} = 0.$$

Hence the terms in the numerator must sum to zero. Reversing the order of summation, we are first required to evaluate

$$\sum_{i=1}^{D} x_{i,n} - \sum_{i=1}^{D} q_{i,n}.$$

Letting

$$\frac{1}{D} \sum_{i=1}^{D} x_{i,n} = \bar{x}_n$$

and

$$\frac{1}{D} \sum_{i=1}^{D} q_{i,n} = \bar{q}_n,$$

we next insert these averages into Eq. 6.48, cancelling the $1/D$ factor. Equation 6.48 then becomes

(6.49)
$$\sum_{n=1}^{N} (\bar{x}_n - \bar{q}_n) = 0.$$

This completes the derivation of one of the maximum likelihood estimation equations. The average $\bar{x}_n$ is computed from the observed $x_{i,n}$ values. Also, $\bar{q}_n$ is the average over subjects of the theoretical values $q_{i,n}$ which are computed by affixing the subscript i to the q_n terms in Eq. 6.46.

The same method of derivation yields the other two estimation equations, as the reader can verify. One equation would come from replacing $\partial q_{i,n} / \partial q_i$ by $\partial q_{i,n} / \partial \beta_a$ in Eq. 6.45 and then using Eq. 6.46 to calculate the latter derivative. The third equation would come from handling the

β_s derivative in the same fashion. The estimation equations, then, are

(6.50a)
$$\sum_{n=1}^{N} (\bar{x}_n - \bar{q}_n) = 0,$$

(6.50b)
$$\sum_{n=1}^{N} a_n(\bar{x}_n - \bar{q}_n) = 0,$$

(6.50c)
$$\sum_{n=1}^{N} s_n(\bar{x}_n - \bar{q}_n) = 0.$$

At this stage we have three equations to solve for the three unknowns $\hat{q}_1$, $\hat{\beta}_a$, and $\hat{\beta}_s$. Some analytical difficulties can arise, however, because the $\bar{q}_n$'s are functions both of the data (the a_n and s_n quantities) and of the model's parameters. One numerical recourse is to employ Monte Carlo computations as in Sec. 6.2. Grids of values of $\hat{q}_1$, $\hat{\beta}_a$, and $\hat{\beta}_s$ are scanned; the quantities $\sum_{n=1}^{N} \bar{q}_n$, $\sum_{n=1}^{N} a_n\bar{q}_n$, and $\sum_{n=1}^{N} s_n\bar{q}_n$ are then computed from the stat data. According to Eq. 6.50a, we seek to minimize $\sum_{n=1}^{N} \bar{q}_n - \sum_{n=1}^{N} \bar{x}_n$, where the latter is computed from the data. Equations 6.50b and c are similarly interpreted. The computation routine finds values of $\hat{q}_1$, $\hat{\beta}_a$, and $\hat{\beta}_s$ such that Eq. 6.50 are satisfied, and these values are taken as the parameter estimates.

A second method of solving Eq. 6.50 for the maximum likelihood estimates begins by making an exponential transformation of Eq. 6.46. Letting $v_1 = e^{-f}$, $\beta_a = e^{-g}$, and $\beta_s = e^{-h}$, we have for an individual subject:

$$q_n = \frac{1}{1 + \beta_a^{a_n}\beta_s^{s_n}v_1}$$
$$= \frac{1}{1 + \exp - (f + ga_n + hs_n)},$$

where $\exp - (f + ga_n + hs_n)$ denotes $e^{-(f+ga_n+hs_n)}$, and the subscript i is suppressed. The above equation is a (three-parameter) *logistic* function. Its relevance to other areas is discussed by Barucha-Reid (1960) and Rapoport (1963). A major advantage of the logistic is that the function

$$\log \left(\frac{q_n}{1 - q_n} \right),$$

known as *logit* q_n, is linear. Denoting the logit as λ_n:

$$\lambda_n = \log \left(\frac{q_n}{1 - q_n} \right) = \log \left(\frac{1}{\exp - (f + ga_n + hs_n)} \right)$$
$$= f + ga_n + hs_n.$$

Since the equation is linear, there are no difficulties in using group averages. The remaining steps are to estimate f, g, and h, because then $\hat{v}_1$, $\hat{\beta}_a$, and $\hat{\beta}_s$ will be known. A convenient maximum likelihood routine is available. It involves making initial rough estimates of the parameters, thereby estimating $\bar{x}_n$ in Eq. 6.50. Then an iteration scheme (based on a Taylor's expansion of the logit around the initial estimate of $\bar{x}_n$) is used to generate successively more accurate approximations to $\hat{f}$, $\hat{g}$, and $\hat{h}$. In the present case, using the expansion to replace $\bar{x}_n$ in the three equations of Eq. 6.50 will yield three equations linear in $\Delta\hat{f}$, $\Delta\hat{g}$, and $\Delta\hat{h}$, where the latter are the adjustments to be made in the provisional estimates. These equations are then solved simultaneously for $\Delta\hat{f}$, $\Delta\hat{g}$, and $\Delta\hat{h}$. Usually one or two iterations suffice to produce convergence. Readers unfamiliar with series expansions may consult Berkson (1957) for more details and computational examples (see also Hodges, 1958; Bush, 1963, pp. 447–454).

Sternberg (1963) applied this maximum likelihood technique to the Solomon-Wynne data, obtaining the estimates $\hat{q}_1 = 0.86$, $\hat{\beta}_a = 1.36$ and $\hat{\beta}_s = 1.23$. From these values, we can get an idea of the adequacy of the beta model for these data. The estimate $\hat{q}_1 = 0.86$ is certainly too low. In fact, the observed proportion of failures to avoid on trial 1 was 1.00. This unrealistic prediction of q_1 means that the model will deviate systematically from the data (at least over the early trials); presumably more so than the linear model. Of course, the difficulty originates in that in the beta model, q_1 cannot be set equal to one, because then the model would predict no learning.

By a quite different estimation method, a more empirically accurate estimate of q_1 can be obtained (Bush, Galanter, and Luce, 1959, p. 386); the estimates are: $\hat{q}_1 = 0.94$, $\hat{\beta}_a = 1.20$, and $\hat{\beta}_s = 1.69$. However, this method has several drawbacks. First, the routine is rather involved and does not yield maximum likelihood estimates. Second, with $\hat{\beta}_s > \hat{\beta}_a$ the model predicts that the increment in avoidance probability will be greater after a shock than after an avoidance. On the contrary, the maximum likelihood estimates of the beta model, and also the estimates of the linear model, imply that the increment in avoidance probability will be greater after an avoidance than after a shock. Sternberg (1963, p. 109) found that, assuming the linear and beta models for the Solomon-Wynne data, an avoidance was indeed more effective than a shock. More precisely, he found that if there are no individual differences in parameter values, then we should have $\hat{\beta}_a > \hat{\beta}_s$, which is the reverse of the order found by the Bush, Galanter, and Luce method. Hence, the advantage of the latter method (that it comes closer to the observed q_1) is offset by the fact that its ordering of $\hat{\beta}_a$ and $\hat{\beta}_s$ is the reverse of that indicated by Sternberg's analysis.

In summary, either method of estimating the beta model's parameters seems to produce estimates that conflict with the dog data. Moreover, the discrepancies exceed those observed with the linear model, which required only two parameter estimates. At least insofar as these data are concerned, the two-operator linear model appears to be preferable to the two-operator beta model. Linearity, as expressed in these models, gains more empirical support at the level of response probability than at the level of response strength.

6.5   A MODEL FOR EXTINCTION OF AVOIDANCE HABITS

A problem with both the two-element model and the two-operator linear and beta models is that, as formulated, they do not account for extinction of a learned avoidance habit. Extinction procedures differ from acquisition only in what is done on trials when the animal fails to respond to the CS: in acquisition, a response failure is followed by shock which forces the response to occur; in extinction, a response failure is "accepted" by the experimenter, no shock is given, and the CS is terminated.

In some cases, avoidance habits are highly resistant to extinction, the response persisting perhaps 500 to 1000 trials without any sign of decrement. However, in other circumstances, the response can be extinguished within a relatively small number of trials, say, 30 to 70. Investigators still are engaged in determining the variables that influence resistance to extinction in these various cases. For instance, Solomon and Wynne (1953) found with dogs that very intense shock during training produced avoidance habits of extraordinary persistence; in fact, after many hundreds of trials some of their dogs showed no decrement in performance and they concluded that the habit would "never" extinguish in these animals without the introduction of special procedures. Another important variable appears to be the aforementioned complexity of the performance. Using a simple one-way shuttle response, Miller (1951) found that rats may take from 300 to 600 trials to extinguish; contrariwise, a fair number of studies using rats in the two-way shuttle situation have typically found extinction to occur in 30 to 100 trials or thereabouts. The exact number of trials to extinction varies with specific training factors, but we wish to emphasize the magnitude of differences between extinction of the one-way and two-way shuttle habits.

The duo-process theory has a neat way of accounting for extinction of avoidance habits. Each successful avoidance trial is alleged to result in some extinction of fear to the warning signal, since on that trial the CS

is not reinforced by being paired with shock. Because of extinction over nonshock trials of the fear response, there eventually is insufficient drive to motivate the instrumental response, so the response fails to occur. This weakening effect of a string of successful avoidances is expected during acquisition too, of course, but there when the response fails it is boosted up again by the shock forcing its occurrence. An experiment by Sheffield (1948) confirmed these expectations in a situation resembling the two-way shuttle; however, other experimenters have not found this phenomenon of progressive weakening (that is, slower speeds) of responses over a string of avoidances. Thus, the facts of the issue are not unequivocal at this time.

If we were to apply the various models presented in this chapter to extinction, we would find them inadequate. In the two-element model, for example, once both stimulus elements are conditioned during acquisition, the subject would be expected to respond perfectly forever after, since the probability of avoidance is one in the absorption state. Similarly, in the linear model, the effect of a long string of avoidances, such as might occur at the end of training and the beginning of extinction, would be to drive the avoidance probability arbitrarily close to the limit points which are one. The closer the avoidance probability was to one, the more likely another avoidance would occur, driving this probability even closer. Thus, the linear model would "trap" the subject into an endless string of avoidances, and extinction would be impossible. The same argument applies to the beta model.

To handle this problem, we will discuss a modification of the two-element model that permits its application to extinction experiments; similar modifications could be proposed for the linear and beta models. This modified model has the advantage of covering some of the obvious facts about extinction, although it has not been tested as yet in quantitative detail. Our purpose here is to illustrate how a model can be modified in directions appropriate to handle data differing from that on which it was based; we would be surprised if the modification were actually correct in detail.

Assumptions for Extinction

Only one axiom of the two-element model has to be changed, namely, the response rule. We shall assume that if the sampled stimulus element is conditioned, then the subject makes the avoidance response with probability $1 - f$, and fails to make the avoidance response (or rather, makes some response incompatible with avoidance) with probability f. One way to interpret f is in terms of the distribution of response times to the *CS*. To say that a stimulus element "is conditioned to" the avoidance response may be interpreted to mean that when this stimulus element is sampled, the subject's response latencies conform to some density function, $g(t)$. In this interpretation, then, $1 - f$ is just the probability that the latency selected from $g(t)$ is less than the criterion time (the *CS-US* interval), so that a successful avoidance is recorded on that trial. For fixed $g(t)$, this probability $1 - f$ is clearly an increasing function of the criterion time, whereas $g(t)$ itself would be determined by learning variables like shock intensity, the *CS-US* interval during training, the complexity of the task, etc. For the simple two-element model discussed earlier, it was assumed that $f = 0$. In the following, we shall investigate the consequences of assuming that f is greater than zero.

As before, we adopt the assumption of conditioning by contiguity; that is, the last response performed on a trial has some probability of becoming associated to the stimulus element sampled on that trial if it was not already so associated. This holds in particular for those in-compatible behaviors that occur on extinction trials when the experimenter records a "failure of avoidance," terminates the *CS*, and gives no shock. If shock occurs following a failure, it forces the shuttle response and so this last response can be conditioned to the stimulus if it is not already so. Extinction, then, is interpreted as the conditioning by contiguity of the stimulus elements to behavior incompatible with the avoidance pattern (that is, relaxing or just sitting still). We will lump all such competing behaviors into a single class denoted as A_2, whereas A_1 will denote the class of avoidance responses (response times less than the criterion). We will let θ represent the probability that when the trial terminates with an A_2, that response of failing to avoid becomes associated to the stimulus element sampled on the trial; θ then plays the same role during conditioning of A_2 responses (extinction) as c plays during conditioning of A_1 responses on shock trials (acquisition). We assume that a stimulus element connected to A_2 never elicits an avoidance response A_1.

In the following, we develop the model for the general case where the probability of delivering a shock given a failure to avoid has some arbitrary value π. The case $\pi = 1$ is customarily studied in acquisition, and $\pi = 0$ defines an extinction procedure. Unpublished work by Bower and Haller has explored intermediate π's of 0.20, 0.50 and 0.70 with results qualitatively in accord with the model's predictions.

Derivations for Extinction

We begin by finding the state-to-state transition probabilities for the associated three-state Markov chain. Figure 6.8 shows the within-trial

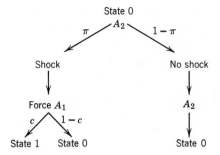

Fig. 6.8 Diagram of the possible transitions out of state 0.

tree of possible events when the subject begins in state 0, where neither stimulus element is associated to avoidance (that is, both elements are connected to A_2).

Recall that state 1 characterizes the process when one stimulus element is conditioned, and in this state the conditioned element is sampled with probability p. The tree for transitions out of state 1 is a bit more complicated. It is shown in Fig. 6.9. Let us verbally trace the second and fourth paths (counting from the right) to show the principles involved. With probability p the conditioned element is sampled, but it leads to a failure to avoid with probability f. With probability π shock occurs, forcing an A_1 response; because the element is already conditioned to A_1, the trial terminates with the process still in state 1. But with probability $1 - \pi$, no shock is delivered and the CS is terminated following an A_2. Hence with probability θ, the stimulus element becomes conditioned to A_2, giving up its former connection to A_1.

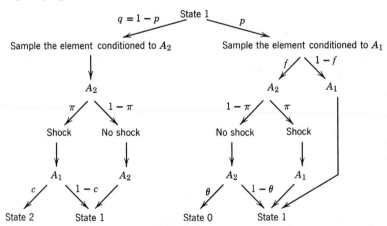

Fig. 6.9 Diagram of the possible transitions out of state 1.

Finally consider the tree for transitions out of state 2 wherein both elements are connected to the avoidance response, A_1. The intratrial tree of events is shown in Fig. 6.10.

To summarize the model as depicted in Figs. 6.8 to 6.10, transitions to a higher numbered state can occur only if the initial response on the trial is a failure to avoid and this nonavoidance is followed by shock. Transitions to a lower state can occur only if the animal samples a conditioned element but fails to avoid and "gets away with it" by not being shocked for the failure.

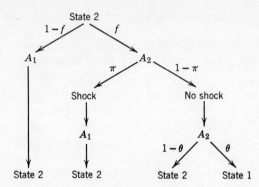

Fig. 6.10 Diagram of the possible transitions out of state 2.

The state-to-state transition probabilities are summarized in the following matrix, where the rows give the conditioning state at the beginning of trial n and the columns give the state on trial $n + 1$.

(6.51)

$$
\begin{array}{c}
\\
2\\
1\\
0
\end{array}
\begin{bmatrix}
2 & 1 & 0 \\
1 - f(1 - \pi)\theta & f(1 - \pi)\theta & 0 \\
q\pi c & 1 - q\pi c - pf(1 - \pi)\theta & pf(1 - \pi)\theta \\
0 & \pi c & 1 - \pi c
\end{bmatrix}
\begin{array}{c}
Pr(A_1 \mid \text{row state}) \\
1 - f \\
p(1 - f) \\
0
\end{array}
$$

To the right of the matrix, we have indicated the probability of an avoidance response given the row state. A naive subject presumably starts in state 0 on trial 1 of the experiment.

Let us examine various special cases of this transition matrix. First, if $f = 0$ and $\pi = 1$, we obtain the matrix displayed in Eq. 6.1 for the original two-element model. In this case, the transition probability from state 2 back to itself is one. This identifies state 2 as absorbing, and hence the subject would eventually enter it and be trapped there. More generally, state 2 is absorbing whenever either $f = 0$ or $\pi = 1$. For the $\pi = 1$ case, we note that the asymptotic avoidance probability, denoted P_T, is $1 - f$. Second, if $\pi = 0$ and $f > 0$, then state 0 is absorbing. This would be the matrix applied to extinction data, where at the end of training the subject is in state 2. Acquisition is viewed as the gradual advance of the subject up through the chain of conditioning states, whereas extinction is viewed as his descending the ladder from state 2 to 1 to 0 where he is trapped. Finally, we note that if $f > 0$ and π is between 0 and 1, then none of the states are absorbing and the subject will continually drift up and down among the conditioning states. In this case, we have an *ergodic* Markov process. This case is of theoretical and experimental interest, but we will not deal with it here; the theory of ergodic Markov chains is discussed in Sec. 7.3. After studying the analytic methods discussed there, the reader can apply them to the matrix in Eq. 6.51 to obtain predictions of interest.

Since we are primarily concerned with predictions for extinction, let us rewrite the matrix in the appropriate form when $\pi = 0$; namely,

$$
(6.52) \quad
\begin{array}{cccc}
 & 2 & 1 & 0 & Pr(A_1 \mid \text{row state}) \\
2 & \left[\begin{array}{ccc} 1 - f\theta & f\theta & 0 \\ 0 & 1 - pf\theta & pf\theta \\ 0 & 0 & 1 \end{array}\right] & & & \begin{array}{c} 1 - f \\ p(1 - f) \\ 0. \end{array}
\end{array}
$$

Let us assume that training with $\pi = 1$ has been carried to the degree necessary to ensure that the subject is in state 2 (that is, $P_T = 1 - f$) at the beginning of extinction. The extinction matrix in Eq. 6.52 is practically the mirror-image of the acquisition matrix given in Eq. 6.1 and the analysis proceeds in an analogous manner.

Suppose that we number our trials so that $n = 1$ is the first trial of the extinction series. Starting the subject off in state 2 on trial 1, the probability that he is still there at the start of trial n is

$$(6.53) \qquad w_{2,n} = (1 - f\theta)^{n-1}.$$

The mean number of trials before leaving state 2 will be

$$(6.54) \qquad n_2 = \sum_{n=1}^{\infty} (1 - f\theta)^{n-1} = \frac{1}{f\theta}.$$

In similar fashion, the probability that the subject is in state 1 on trial n is given by the sum of the probabilities of staying in state 2 for i trials, then moving to state 1 and remaining there for $n - 1 - i$ trials, that is,

$$w_{1,n} = \sum_{i=1}^{n-1} (1 - f\theta)^{i-1} f\theta (1 - pf\theta)^{n-1-i}.$$

Of course, the exponents sum to $n - 1$, the number of preceding opportunities for transition. By the methods used to derive Eq. 6.7, this expression reduces to

$$(6.55) \qquad w_{1,n} = \frac{1}{q}[(1 - pf\theta)^{n-1} - (1 - f\theta)^{n-1}].$$

The expected number of trials that the subject is in state 1 before leaving it will be

$$(6.56) \qquad n_1 = \sum_{n=1}^{\infty} w_{1,n} = \frac{1}{pf\theta},$$

the reciprocal of the one-trial probability of a transition from state 1.

Let p_n denote the probability of an avoidance reponse on the nth trial of the extinction series. The theoretical expression for p_n is

$$(6.57) \quad p_n = (1 - f)w_{2,n} + p(1 - f)w_{1,n}$$
$$= \left(1 - \frac{p}{q}\right)(1 - f)(1 - f\theta)^{n-1} + \frac{p(1 - f)}{q}(1 - pf\theta)^{n-1}.$$

We note that if $p = q = \frac{1}{2}$, as was the case for the Theios acquisition data, then the expression for p_n reduces to

$$p_n = (1 - f)(1 - pf\theta)^{n-1} = P_T[1 - 0.50(1 - P_T)\theta]^{n-1},$$

where we recall that $P_T = 1 - f$.

We may derive the mean number of avoidance responses before an extinction criterion is attained by summing the p_n of Eq. 6.57 over all trials n.

$$(6.58) \qquad \sum_{n=1}^{\infty} p_n = (1 - f)n_2 + p(1 - f)n_1$$
$$= \frac{2}{\theta} \frac{P_T}{1 - P_T}.$$

Thus, the number of avoidance responses before extinction bears a direct relation to the asymptotic response probability at the end of training. Because P_T may be very close to unity in some cases, it would be necessary to run the subject for a large number of asymptotic trials to estimate P_T. For example, P_T cannot be estimated in the Theios acquisition data, since training was stopped for each rat when 20 consecutive avoidances were given. A practical estimate of P_T may be obtained from the asymptotic mean length of runs of avoidances between failures. Once state 2 is entered, the probability that j avoidances intervene between any two failures is

$$Pr(\text{run of } j \text{ avoidances}) = (1 - f)^j f$$

and the average length of a run, denoted $\bar{R}$, will be

$$(6.59) \quad \bar{R} = \sum_{j=0}^{\infty} jf(1-f)^j = (1-f)f\sum_{j=1}^{\infty} j(1-f)^{j-1} = \frac{1-f}{f} = \frac{P_T}{1-P_T}.$$

For example, if $f = 0.01$ so that the asymptotic $P_T = 0.99$, then on the average we would observe a run of 99 avoidances before a failure was recorded. The equation for $\bar{R}$ can be substituted into the total-avoidances expression in Eq. 6.58 to obtain the result

$$(6.60) \qquad\qquad \sum_{n=1}^{\infty} p_n = \frac{2\bar{R}}{\theta}.$$

We note that the relationship found here between the training asymptote and resistance to extinction jibes with the informal evidence presented earlier. The simple one-way shuttle procedure employed by Theios gives a very high asymptote that is practically impossible to distinguish from unity, and this training procedure also produces extreme resistance to extinction. A similar comment applies to the Solomon-Wynne study employing traumatic shock levels, which also may be interpreted as forcing f close to zero. Using rats in a two-way shuttle experiment with moderate shock levels, mean training asymptotes are about 0.85 to 0.95; so $\bar{R}$ is around 5.5 to 19. In these conditions, the model predicts extinction within a relatively small number of trials (30 to 100 trials). Thus, the data and the model lend support to the same conclusion; the response that is most resistant to extinction is the one that can occur for a great many trials without having to be boosted occasionally by shocks (which are absent during extinction). Stated in this manner, the conclusion is obvious and we would want any theory of extinction to imply something like it.

The model for extinction proposed in this section has not been tested in quantitative detail, and there is a good chance *a priori* that many of its features are incorrect. To reiterate, our purpose here has been to illustrate how one may extend the range of potential applications of a theory by introducing only a small change in the basic axioms.

CHAPTER 7

SOCIAL AND
ECONOMIC BEHAVIOR

So far our exposition has been confined to models for the behavior of individual subjects. Now we want to describe how some of these ideas can be extended to the realm of social phenomena. A comprehensive treatment of quantitative theories of social behavior would require an entire volume.* But many of the theories do not seek to describe actual behavior, and among those that do, some restrict attention to terminal performance rather than learning phenomena. It is important that we now elaborate on this classification, since it forms the basis for our selection of models to be discussed in this chapter.

Roughly speaking, theoretical developments in the behavioral sciences can be characterized as normative or descriptive. A *normative theory* prescribes how an individual should behave in order to maximize the likelihood of attaining some end goal. In contrast, *descriptive theories* seek to describe and predict the actual behavior of the individual, and not what he should do. Of course, in most situations the observed behavior is usually quite different from that dictated by normative considerations. Both classical theory in economics and the more recent development of game theory (von Neumann and Morgenstern, 1944) are examples of normative theories; both are concerned with the ideal behavior of a "rational man."** Normative theories have played an

---

* For a general survey of mathematical models for social processes see Rapoport (1963).
** Luce and Raiffa's book (1957) is suggested as an excellent introduction to game theory. Experimental tests of game theory are reviewed by Rapoport and Orwant in a book of readings by Shubik (1964). Other articles in Shubik's book will give the reader a broader appreciation of normative issues that we neglect here. An elementary account of classical economic theory and a series of experimental tests are reported in Siegel and Fouraker (1960). Brief mention of the latter will be made in Sec. 7.4.

important role in the behavioral sciences, but in a certain sense they are not psychological theories. They are not concerned with the task of providing an analysis of how the organism receives stimuli from his environment and then uses this information to adjust his behavior accordingly. In short, they do not offer an account of the fundamental psychological processes that would lead an organism to exhibit one behavior pattern rather than another. We offer these comments to justify our almost complete exclusion of normative models from this chapter. Although normative applications of mathematics have made significant contributions in the behavioral sciences, in our view they are not central to the principal goals of learning theory.

Within the realm of descriptive theories, we further narrow the spectrum of this chapter to work in which learning is an important aspect of the social situation. Our restriction to social interactions where learning is exhibited implies a concern with the responses of individual subjects rather than with an index defined on a population of individuals (for example, rate of information spread) or on a small group (for example, group cohesiveness). Hence, we exclude social interactions in which the analysis of individual behaviors is not of interest.

The chief aim of this chapter, then, is to illustrate mathematical learning theory predictions of individual behavior in social situations. In an actual social interaction, learning might include processes such as becoming aware of what response alternatives are available, changes in utility or attractiveness of a goal, etc. However, for our immediate purposes learning is defined simply as the effect of reinforcement on response probability. The social aspect of the situation arises from the fact that the reinforcement schedule for a given subject depends jointly on his own actions and on the actions of the other subjects. We illustrate the application of learning models to social behavior via two examples, one representing a two-person interaction (Sec. 7.1), and the other a simulated economic market (Sec. 7.4).

Under the heading of social interaction we consider an experimental situation in which two individuals are pitted against each other in a game. On every play of the game each player is required to make either a "cooperative" response or a "noncooperative" response. If both players cooperate, then both have a small probability of winning; if both fail to cooperate, neither wins. But an important aspect of the game is that if one player cooperates and the other does not, then only the latter has a high probability of winning. Thus the game pits "collective rationality" on the one hand against "self-interest rationality" on the other. The model attempts to predict properties of each player's response sequences, as well as his overall response probabilities. As our example of a simulated economic situation, we consider a seller's duopoly market. Several firms produce the same fictitious commodity, and each sets a price at which it is willing to sell the commodity. However, the sale is awarded only to the low bidder, thus injecting the element of competition into the situation. The model attempts to describe how the policy-making members of a firm set prices and production quotas from one fiscal period to the next.

This preliminary description of the procedures suffices to indicate why we consider these two topics in the same chapter. Both involve inter-action in that the reinforcement schedule for any given subject is contingent on the responses of the other subjects. In both paradigms, the interaction is minimal, because there is no direct communication between the participants. Given these procedural similarities, it will not be surprising to discover that the two corresponding learning models share many features. In particular, both are Markov chain models of a type not treated earlier in this book, so in Sec. 7.2 some additional mathematical techniques will be developed.

7.1　TWO-PERSON INTERACTIONS:　EXPERIMENTAL PROCEDURE AND THEORY

In this section we describe a model for a two-person game. The model can be generalized to quite complex multiperson interactions but the two-person problem has particular advantages for expository purposes.

We consider a game between two players, each of whom has a finite number of strategies. Each play of the game constitutes a trial, and a player's choice of a strategy for a given trial corresponds to the selection of a response. Rules of the game require the two players to exhibit their choices simultaneously (as in a game of matching pennies) and the trial terminates with each player's being told whether he has won or lost. The probability that a player's response will lead to a win on a particular trial depends both on his response and on the response of his opponent. It is by virtue of this dependency that the game aspect of the experiment arises.

We designate the two players as A and B and let A_i ($i = 1, \ldots, m$) and B_j ($j = 1, \ldots, m'$) denote the responses available to the players on each trial. The set of payoff probabilities prescribed by the experimenter may be represented by a matrix $[a_{ij}, b_{ij}]$ analogous to the "payoff matrix" familiar in game theory. The number a_{ij} represents the probability that player A wins on any trial of the experiment, given the response pair A_iB_j; similarly, b_{ij} is the probability that player B wins given the response pair A_iB_j. For the game we consider each player has two responses

$(m = m' = 2)$, and the game is described by the payoff matrix

(7.1)

$$
\begin{array}{c}
\\
A_1 \\
A_2
\end{array}
\begin{array}{cc}
B_1 & B_2 \\
\left[\begin{array}{cc}
(0, 0) & (a, 1 - a) \\
(1 - a, a) & (\tfrac{1}{2}, \tfrac{1}{2})
\end{array}\right].
\end{array}
$$

Thus, if both players make response 1, they are both sure to lose; if both make response 2, then each player independently has probability $\tfrac{1}{2}$ of winning. When the players disagree in their responses (A_1B_2 and A_2B_1), then the player making response 1 wins with probability a, and independently the player making response 2 wins with probability $1 - a$.

If $a > \tfrac{1}{2}$, then the task resembles the famous class of games known as the prisoner's dilemma.* The essential feature of the prisoner's dilemma is the conflict posed between "collective rationality" on the one hand and "self-interest rationality" on the other. If both players select the co-operative strategy (that is, response 2), then they both win with probability $\tfrac{1}{2}$; if they both select the noncooperative strategy (that is, response 1), then they are both certain to lose. However, if they choose different strategies, then the player who selects the cooperative strategy has a high probability of losing, whereas the player who selects the noncooperative strategy has a high probability of winning.

The game we consider is not identical to the classical prisoner's dilemma, because in the latter the entries in the payoff matrix are magnitudes of gains and losses, rather than probabilities. Nevertheless the essential aspects of the dilemma still are present when $a > \tfrac{1}{2}$. If one player (say A) consistently cooperates (makes response A_2), then it is to his opponent's advantage to refuse to cooperate (make response B_1). But the danger of responding B_1 is that player A might retaliate by making response A_1, reducing to zero the probability of a win for either player. A more complete treatment of the prisoner's dilemma and related psychological research is available in articles by Rapoport and Orwant, and by Wilson and Bixenstine (Chapters 20 and 23 in Shubik, 1959).

---

* The term "prisoner's dilemma" is used because of its analogy to the following situation (Luce and Raiffa, 1957, p. 95). "Two suspects are taken into custody and separated. The district attorney is certain that they are guilty of a specific crime, but he does not have adequate evidence to convict them at a trial. He points out to each prisoner that each has two alternatives; to confess to the crime the police are sure they have done, or not to confess. If neither suspect confesses, then the district attorney states he will book them on some very minor trumped-up charge such as petty larceny and illegal possession of a weapon, and they will both receive minor punishment; if they both confess they will be prosecuted, but he will recommend less than the most severe sentence; but if one confesses and the other does not, then the confessor will receive lenient treatment for turning state's evidence whereas the latter will get 'the book' slapped at him."

Model

These are the rules of the game, and we now turn to the task of describing behavior in this situation. The model to be considered is extremely simple and yet is an excellent predictor of behavior in games of this type. The model will be formulated in terms of the following two axioms:

Axiom 1. If a subject makes a response that leads to a win, then with probability 1 he will repeat that response on the next trial.

Axiom 2. If a subject makes a response that leads to a loss, then with probability θ he will make the alternative response on the next trial.

Note that these axioms say that a player's response depends solely on whether he won or lost on the previous trial, but not on the fate of his opponent. These axioms would need to be revised for experiments where a subject knew the trial outcome for his adversary. This same point arises in the oligopoly, and is discussed in Sec. 7.4.

We now apply these axioms to the game described above. In making the application we, of course, assume that both players satisfy the axioms. Further, to simplify the analysis, we will not examine all possible response pairs that can occur on a trial (namely, A_1B_1, A_1B_2, A_2B_1, A_2B_2) but only the following categorization of responses:

State S_1 = neither player cooperates (A_1B_1)

State S_2 = both players cooperate (A_2B_2)

State S_3 = one player cooperates, but the other does not (either response pair A_1B_2 or A_2B_1).

Each trial will be characterized by the occurrence of one of these three states.

Now let us assume that state S_1 occurred on trial n of the experiment. Then, by the payoff matrix of Eq. 7.1, both players lose with probability 1. Hence, by Axiom 2, each player will switch to his other response on the next trial with probability θ. Given this payoff, the possible states on trial $n + 1$ are specified by the tree in Fig. 7.1. The derivation of the tree is straightforward:

(1) With probability θ^2 both players change responses ($A_1 \rightarrow A_2$ and $B_1 \rightarrow B_2$); hence on trial $n + 1$ state S_2 occurs.

(2) With probability $\theta(1 - \theta)$ player A switches ($A_1 \rightarrow A_2$) and B does not; hence state S_3.

(3) With probability $\theta(1 - \theta)$ player B switches ($B_1 \rightarrow B_2$) but A does not; hence state S_3.

(4) With probability $(1 - \theta)^2$ neither player changes responses.

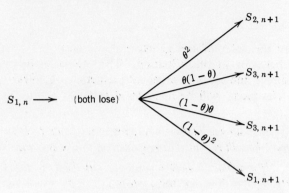

Figure 7.1.

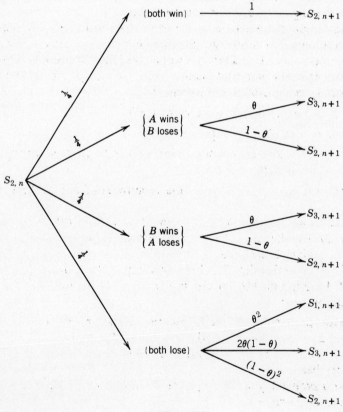

Figure 7.2.

Combining these results yields

$$Pr(S_{1,n+1} \mid S_{1,n}) = (1 - \theta)^2$$
(7.2) $$Pr(S_{2,n+1} \mid S_{1,n}) = \theta^2$$
$$Pr(S_{3,n+1} \mid S_{1,n}) = 2\theta(1 - \theta).$$

Suppose that state S_2 prevailed on trial n rather than S_1. Then each player has probability $\frac{1}{2}$ of winning. Hence the transition tree for state S_2 is the one given in Fig. 7.2. The derivation of this tree essentially is the same as the previous one:

(1) With probability $\frac{1}{4}$ both players win and state S_2 is repeated on the next trial.

(2) With probability $\frac{1}{4}$ player A wins and B loses. Hence A repeats A_2 on the next trial, but B switches to B_1 with probability θ. Hence, state S_3 occurs with probability θ and S_2 with probability $1 - \theta$.

(3) With probability $\frac{1}{4}$ player B wins and A loses. Hence B repeats B_2, but A switches to A_1 with probability θ. Hence, S_3 occurs with probability θ and S_2 with probability $1 - \theta$.

(4) On the last set of branches both players lose. With probability θ^2 both change their responses to yield state S_1 on the next trial; with probability $2\theta(1 - \theta)$ one changes responses and the other does not, thereby generating state S_3; and with probability $(1 - \theta)^2$ neither change.

Combining these results yields

$$Pr(S_{1,n+1} \mid S_{2,n}) = \tfrac{1}{4}\theta^2$$
(7.3) $$Pr(S_{2,n+1} \mid S_{2,n}) = \tfrac{1}{4} + \tfrac{1}{2}\theta(1 - \theta) + \tfrac{1}{4}(1 - \theta)^2 = 1 - \theta + \tfrac{1}{4}\theta^2$$
$$Pr(S_{3,n+1} \mid S_{2,n}) = \tfrac{1}{2}\theta + \tfrac{1}{2}\theta(1 - \theta) = \theta - \tfrac{1}{2}\theta^2.$$

The third possibility is that state S_3 prevails on trial n. Then the subject making response 1 is correct with probability a, and the subject making response 2 is correct with probability $1 - a$. The transition tree for S_3 is given in Fig. 7.3. The derivation is as follows:

(1) On the first branch both players win, and S_3 is repeated on the next trial.

(2) On the second set of branches the player making response 1 wins and repeats that response on the next trial. However, the player making response 2 loses and with probability θ changes to response 1. Hence state S_1 occurs on the next trial with probability θ, and state S_3 with probability $1 - \theta$.

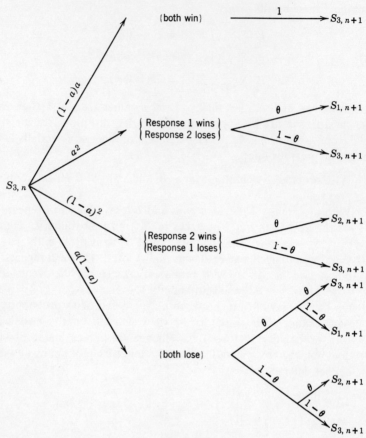

Figure 7.3.

(3) On the third set of branches the player making response 2 wins and perseverates on that response. But the player making response 1 loses, and with probability θ changes responses. Hence, state S_2 occurs on the next trial with probability θ, and state S_3 with probability $1 - \theta$.

(4) On the fourth set of branches both players lose. With probability θ^2 they both change responses, but this leads to a response pair on the next trial that is still classified as S_3. With probability $\theta(1 - \theta)$ the player making response 2 changes and the player making response 1 does not; consequently, S_1 occurs on the next trial. Similarly, with probability $\theta(1 - \theta)$ the player making response 1 changes and the player making response 2 does not, leading to state S_2. Finally, with probability $(1 - \theta)^2$ no change occurs.

Combining these results yields

$$Pr(S_{1,n+1} \mid S_{3,n}) = a\theta(1 - \theta + \theta a)$$

(7.4) $$Pr(S_{2,n+1} \mid S_{3,n}) = (1 - a)\theta(1 - a\theta)$$

$$Pr(S_{3,n+1} \mid S_{3,n}) = 1 - \theta + 2a(1 - a)\theta^2.$$

The results in Eqs. 7.2, 7.3, and 7.4 can be summarized in the form of a transition matrix as follows:

(7.5)

$$\mathbf{P} = \begin{array}{c} \\ S_{1,n} \\ S_{2,n} \\ S_{3,n} \end{array} \begin{array}{ccc} S_{1,n+1} & S_{2,n+1} & S_{3,n+1} \\ \left[\begin{array}{ccc} (1 - \theta)^2 & \theta^2 & 2\theta(1 - \theta) \\ \frac{1}{4}\theta^2 & 1 - \theta + \frac{1}{4}\theta^2 & \theta - \frac{1}{2}\theta^2 \\ a\theta(1 - \theta + \theta a) & (1 - a)\theta(1 - a\theta) & 1 - \theta + 2a(1 - a)\theta^2 \end{array} \right]. \end{array}$$

A natural way to test the model is to see whether the matrix in Eq. 7.5 does in fact predict observed transition frequencies. We also want to see whether it can predict the asymptotic probabilities of two cooperative responses on the same trial, of one cooperative and one noncooperative response, and so forth. Before these theoretical calculations can be made, we must develop a few more mathematical results. The new machinery is required because we have not previously analyzed Markov chains that have no absorbing states.

7.2   ERGODIC MARKOV CHAINS

From our axioms and from the derivation of the matrix in Eq. 7.5, we can see that the occurrence of state S_i on trial $n + 1$ depends on the state on trial n but is independent of the states occupied on all previous trials. Stated otherwise

$$Pr(S_{j,n+1} \mid S_{i,n}S_{k,n-1}S_{l,n-2} \cdots S_{m,1}) = Pr(S_{j,n+1} \mid S_{i,n}).$$

That is, on any trial n the conditional probability of transition from the current state to any other does not depend on how one arrived in the current state. Therefore, the process represented by Eq. 7.5 is indeed a Markov chain. Further, the transition probabilities $Pr(S_{j,n+1} \mid S_{i,n})$ are independent of the trial number n; that is,

$$Pr(S_{j,n+1} \mid S_{i,n}) = p_{ij}$$

where p_{ij} is a constant. As indicated earlier, when this is the case, the chain is said to be *homogeneous*.

We have encountered many other examples of homogeneous Markov chains in this book. But in all of the earlier applications at least one of the states in the chain was absorbing—absorbing in the sense that once the process had entered a particular state, it was impossible to leave that state. By inspection of the matrix in Eq. 7.5, we can see that none of its states are absorbing. Further, we see that every state can be reached from every other state. Markov chains with the property that it is possible to go from every state to every other state (not necessarily in one trial), are called *ergodic*. Ergodic chains play an important role in psychology, and we now describe some of their properties.

We begin by deriving a few results for a two-state chain and then generalize these to r-states. Consider the transition matrix

$$\mathbf{P} = \begin{array}{c} \\ S_1 \\ S_2 \end{array} \begin{array}{c} S_1 \quad S_2 \\ \begin{bmatrix} p_{11} & p_{12} \\ p_{21} & p_{22} \end{bmatrix}. \end{array}$$

Assume now that we want to compute the likelihood of being in state S_i at the start of trial n; this probability will be denoted $u_{i,n}$. Then it follows that

(7.6)
$$u_{1,n+1} = u_{1,n}p_{11} + u_{2,n}p_{21}$$
$$u_{2,n+1} = u_{1,n}p_{12} + u_{2,n}p_{22}.$$

That is, the probability, $u_{1,n+1}$, of being in state S_1 on trial $n+1$ is simply the probability of being in state S_1 on trial n and staying there (with probability p_{11}), plus the probability of being in state S_2 on trial n and moving to state S_1 (with probability p_{21}); likewise for $u_{2,n+1}$. In order to anticipate the general r-state case, it is helpful to see how these two equations look in matrix form. Let $[u_{1,n}, u_{2,n}]$ be a row vector of state probabilities on trial n; then

(7.7)
$$[u_{1,n+1}, u_{2,n+1}] = [u_{1,n}, u_{2,n}] \begin{bmatrix} p_{11} & p_{12} \\ p_{21} & p_{22} \end{bmatrix}.$$

Restating Eq. 7.6 for the general case of a Markov chain with r states gives

(7.8)
$$u_{j,n+1} = u_{1,n}p_{1j} + u_{2,n}p_{2j} + \cdots + u_{r,n}p_{rj}$$
$$= \sum_{i=1}^{r} u_{i,n}p_{ij}.$$

Let us now define a row vector $\mathbf{u}_n$ with components $u_{i,n}$; that is,

$$\mathbf{u}_n = [u_{1,n}, u_{2,n}, \ldots, u_{r,n}].$$

The components of this vector sum to one and specify the probability distribution of states on trial n. Thus $\mathbf{u}_1$ represents the probability distribution of states at the start of trial 1. Given the vector representation of the distribution of states on trial n, the r-state result of Eq. 7.8 can be written in matrix form, just as was done in Eq. 7.7 for the special case $r = 2$; namely

(7.9) $$\mathbf{u}_{n+1} = \mathbf{u}_n \mathbf{P}.$$

Using this equation recursively

$$\mathbf{u}_2 = \mathbf{u}_1 \mathbf{P}$$
$$\mathbf{u}_3 = \mathbf{u}_2 \mathbf{P} = \mathbf{u}_1 \mathbf{P}^2$$
$$\mathbf{u}_4 = \mathbf{u}_3 \mathbf{P} = \mathbf{u}_1 \mathbf{P}^3$$

or, in general,

(7.10) $$\mathbf{u}_n = \mathbf{u}_1 \mathbf{P}^{n-1}.$$

The gist of this equation is that to find the probability of each of the states at the start of trial n, we need only postmultiply the initial row vector $\mathbf{u}_1$ by the $(n - 1)$st power of the transition matrix $\mathbf{P}$. This rule for finding $\mathbf{u}_n$ holds for any Markov chain and is not restricted to the ergodic case.

To illustrate how the result in Eq. 7.10 may be applied, let us consider a chain with two states S_1 and S_2 and transition matrix

(7.11) $$\mathbf{P} = \begin{array}{c} \\ S_1 \\ S_2 \end{array} \overset{\begin{array}{cc} S_1 & S_2 \end{array}}{\begin{bmatrix} \frac{3}{4} & \frac{1}{4} \\ \frac{1}{2} & \frac{1}{2} \end{bmatrix}}.$$

If we let $u_{1,1} = u_{2,1} = \frac{1}{2}$ (that is, $\mathbf{u}_1 = [\frac{1}{2}, \frac{1}{2}]$), then

$$\mathbf{u}_2 = \mathbf{u}_1 \mathbf{P} = \begin{bmatrix} \frac{1}{2} & \frac{1}{2} \end{bmatrix} \begin{bmatrix} \frac{3}{4} & \frac{1}{4} \\ \frac{1}{2} & \frac{1}{2} \end{bmatrix} = \begin{bmatrix} \frac{5}{8} & \frac{3}{8} \end{bmatrix}.$$

Similarly

$$\mathbf{u}_3 = \mathbf{u}_2 \mathbf{P} = \begin{bmatrix} \frac{5}{8} & \frac{3}{8} \end{bmatrix} \begin{bmatrix} \frac{3}{4} & \frac{1}{4} \\ \frac{1}{2} & \frac{1}{2} \end{bmatrix} = \begin{bmatrix} \frac{21}{32} & \frac{11}{32} \end{bmatrix}$$

and so forth. Note that

$$\mathbf{P}^2 = \begin{bmatrix} \frac{11}{16} & \frac{5}{16} \\ \frac{5}{8} & \frac{3}{8} \end{bmatrix}$$

and that $\mathbf{u}_3$ could have been obtained as

$$\mathbf{u}_3 = \mathbf{u}_1 \mathbf{P}^2 = \begin{bmatrix} \frac{1}{2} & \frac{1}{2} \end{bmatrix} \begin{bmatrix} \frac{11}{16} & \frac{5}{16} \\ \frac{5}{8} & \frac{3}{8} \end{bmatrix} = \begin{bmatrix} \frac{21}{32} & \frac{11}{32} \end{bmatrix}.$$

By continuing to compute successive powers of **P** and premultiplying by $\mathbf{u}_1$ we obtain the following results:

Trial	1	2	3	4	5	6	7	8
$u_{1,n}$	0.500	0.625	0.656	0.664	0.666	0.667	0.667	0.667
$u_{2,n}$	0.500	0.375	0.344	0.336	0.334	0.333	0.333	0.333

An inspection of these results shows that $u_{1,n}$ approaches $\frac{2}{3}$ (and consequently that $u_{2,n}$ approaches $\frac{1}{3}$) as n becomes large.

Let us carry out the same computations for our two-state process, but with different initial conditions. In particular, assume that the process starts out in state S_1; that is, $\mathbf{u}_1 = [1, 0]$. Under these conditions, the results for $u_{1,n}$ and $u_{2,n}$ are as follows:

Trial	1	2	3	4	5	6	7	8
$u_{1,n}$	1.0	0.750	0.688	0.672	0.668	0.667	0.667	0.667
$u_{2,n}$	0	0.250	0.312	0.328	0.332	0.333	0.333	0.333

Despite the difference in initial conditions, it appears that this process approaches the same limits as the other process; that is, for both cases $u_{1,n}$ and $u_{2,n}$ approach $\frac{2}{3}$ and $\frac{1}{3}$, respectively.

Earlier, we stated that a Markov chain is ergodic if it is possible to go from every state to every other state. Interestingly enough, it can be shown that ergodic chains have the property that the limiting distribution of states is independent of the initial distribution, as was the case in the preceding numerical examples. Thus, after a large number of trials, an ergodic chain achieves statistical equilibrium in the sense that the probabilities $u_{i,n}$ tend to limits that are the same no matter what state the process started in. Formulated more precisely, for every state S_i of an ergodic chain, there is a number $u_i > 0$ such that

$$\lim_{n \to \infty} u_{i,n} = u_i$$

independent of the initial probability vector $\mathbf{u}_1$. The limiting quantities u_i generally are called the *stationary probabilities* of the Markov chains; as indicated above, they are all greater than zero for an ergodic chain. The row vector

$$\mathbf{u} = [u_1, u_2, u_3, \ldots, u_r]$$

is referred to as the *stationary probability vector* of the chain.

The problem of specifying when a Markov chain is ergodic is an important question in the theory of Markov chains but beyond the scope of this book.* For our purposes it will suffice to state without proof a rule for determining when a chain is ergodic. The rule is as follows: if some power of matrix $\mathbf{P}$ has only positive elements, then the corresponding Markov chain is ergodic. In practice this rule is easily applied and usually only the first, second, or third power of the transition matrix need be examined to establish that the chain is ergodic.

Having established that a Markov chain is ergodic, the next problem is to obtain the stationary probability vector. From Eq. 7.9 it follows that the vector $\mathbf{u}$ must satisfy the equation

$$\mathbf{u} = \mathbf{uP}.$$

Hence to obtain the stationary probabilities u_i, we need simply solve the following system of linear equations:

$$u_1 = u_1 p_{11} + u_2 p_{21} + u_3 p_{31} + \cdots + u_r p_{r1}$$

$$u_2 = u_1 p_{12} + u_2 p_{22} + u_3 p_{32} + \cdots + u_r p_{r2}$$

(7.12)

$$u_r = u_1 p_{1r} + u_2 p_{2r} + u_3 p_{3r} + \cdots + u_r p_{rr}.$$

The intuitive basis of this system of equations seems clear. Consider a two-state process. As indicated in Eq. 7.6 the probability of being in state S_1 on trial $n + 1$ is just

$$u_{1,n+1} = u_{1,n} p_{11} + u_{2,n} p_{21}.$$

But at asymptote $u_{1,n+1} = u_{1,n} = u_1$ and $u_{2,n} = u_2$, whence

$$u_1 = u_1 p_{11} + u_2 p_{21}.$$

This is the first of the two equations obtainable by setting $r = 2$ in Eq. 7.12. For our numerical example presented earlier, the two equations given by Eq. 7.12 are

$$u_1 = \tfrac{3}{4} u_1 + \tfrac{1}{2} u_2,$$

$$u_2 = \tfrac{1}{4} u_1 + \tfrac{1}{2} u_2.$$

But $u_1 + u_2 = 1$ or $u_2 = 1 - u_1$. Substituting this result in the first equation yields

$$u_1 = \tfrac{3}{4} u_1 + \tfrac{1}{2}(1 - u_1)$$

$$= \tfrac{2}{3}.$$

---

* For a discussion of this topic see Kemeny and Snell (1959), Feller (1957) or Parzen (1960).

Hence, the pair of equations has the unique solution $u_1 = \frac{2}{3}$ and $u_2 = \frac{1}{3}$, which verifies the conjecture made from the computational results.

In the analysis of our two-person game, we shall require the solution of Eq. 7.12 for the case of a 3×3 transition matrix. This solution is easily obtained by application of Cramér's rule and is given here without proof:

$$(7.13) \qquad u_i = \frac{D_i}{D_1 + D_2 + D_3}$$

where

$$D_1 = p_{21}p_{32} + p_{31}(1 - p_{22})$$
$$D_2 = p_{31}p_{12} + p_{32}(1 - p_{11})$$
$$D_3 = (1 - p_{11})(1 - p_{22}) - p_{21}p_{12}.$$

Likewise, the solution of Eq. 7.12 for the case of a 4×4 transition matrix (which also will be needed later) is

$$u_i = \frac{D_i}{D_1 + D_2 + D_3 + D_4},$$

where

$$
\begin{aligned}
D_1 &= [p_{21}p_{32}p_{43} + p_{31}p_{42}p_{23} + p_{41}(p_{22} - 1)(p_{33} - 1)] \\
&\quad - [p_{41}p_{32}p_{23} + p_{21}p_{42}(p_{33} - 1) + p_{31}(p_{22} - 1)p_{43}], \\
D_2 &= [p_{41}p_{32}p_{13} + (p_{11} - 1)p_{42}(p_{33} - 1) + p_{31}p_{12}p_{43}] \\
&\quad - [(p_{11} - 1)p_{32}p_{43} + p_{31}p_{42}p_{13} + p_{41}p_{12}(p_{33} - 1)], \\
D_3 &= [(p_{11} - 1)(p_{22} - 1)p_{43} + p_{21}p_{42}p_{13} + p_{41}p_{12}p_{23}] \\
&\quad - [p_{41}(p_{22} - 1)p_{13} + (p_{11} - 1)p_{42}p_{23} + p_{21}p_{12}p_{43}], \\
D_4 &= [p_{31}(p_{22} - 1)p_{13} + (p_{11} - 1)p_{32}p_{23} + p_{21}p_{12}(p_{33} - 1)] \\
&\quad - [(p_{11} - 1)(p_{22} - 1)(p_{33} - 1) + p_{21}p_{32}p_{13} + p_{31}p_{12}p_{23}].
\end{aligned}
$$

(7.14)

7.3 RESULTS AND ANALYSIS OF AN INTERACTION EXPERIMENT

College students were run in pairs and were instructed to view the experimental situation as a game of a rather complicated character between two players. They were told that on each trial they would win or lose and that their gains and losses over trials would depend not only on what they did, but also on what the other player did. Further, the subjects were instructed to maximize the number of trials on which their response led to a win.* The experimental session lasted for 210 trials and once a

---

* The instructions and procedure were the same as the ones used by Atkinson and Suppes (1959).

session was under way the subjects were told only whether they won or lost on each trial; they were not told the response made by the other player nor were they shown the payoff matrix. An analysis of the situation where each player is permitted to see the response of the other and is shown the payoff matrix is too complicated to be considered here; however, the previously cited book by Suppes and Atkinson includes an analysis of experimental games involving this type of extension.

In the present study, two experimental groups were run; there were 25 pairs of subjects in each group. The groups were distinguished by the value of the payoff parameter a used in the matrix of Eq. 7.1:

$$\text{Group I:} \quad a = 0.8$$
$$\text{Group II:} \quad a = 0.2.$$

Group I represents a situation resembling the prisoner's dilemma.

The response protocol for a pair of subjects was analyzed with regard to whether S_1, S_2, or S_3 occurred on each trial of the experiment. Figure 7.4 presents the average proportion of S_1 and S_3 outcomes in successive 30-trial blocks for the entire sequence of 210 trials; the S_2 proportions can be obtained by subtracting the sum of S_1 and S_3 from one. For both experimental groups the observed curves appear reasonably constant over the last four or five blocks of trials, and it will be assumed that a stable level of performance has been attained. The proportions computed over the last 100 trials will be used as estimates of asymptotic quantities; these asymptotic estimates are denoted as $Pr(S_i)$.

The predicted quantities that correspond to the observed proportions $Pr(S_i)$ are the components of the stationary probability vector $\mathbf{u} = [u_1, u_2, u_3]$. To obtain predictions for $Pr(S_i)$, we simply solve the system of linear equations generated by the transition matrix in Eq. 7.5. The general solution is given by Eq. 7.13; making the appropriate substitutions for the p_{ij} and simplifying yields

(7.15)
$$u_i(\theta) = \frac{D_i}{D_1 + D_2 + D_3}$$

where

$$D_1 = a(1 - \theta + \theta a)(4 - \theta) + \theta(1 - a)(1 - a\theta)$$

$$D_2 = 4a\theta(1 - \theta + \theta a) + 4(1 - a)(1 - a\theta)(2 - \theta)$$

$$D_3 = 8 - 6\theta.$$

The asymptotic probabilities are a function of θ, and hence the notation $u_i(\theta)$.

From these equations it follows that the probability of both subjects making response 2 (cooperating) decreases with increasing values of a.

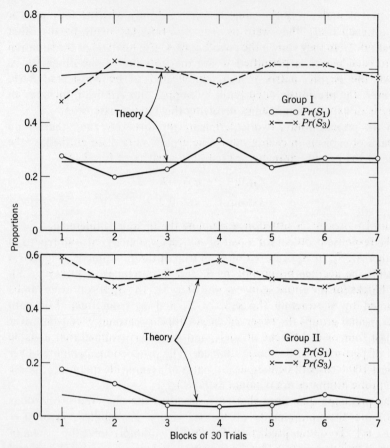

Fig. 7.4 Theoretical and observed proportions of S_1 and S_3 events in 30-trial blocks.

Moreover, the asymptotic probabilities depend on θ in a rather sharp way. For example, if $a = 1$ then

$$u_1(\theta) = \frac{4 - \theta}{12 - 3\theta} = \frac{1}{3}$$

$$u_2(\theta) = \frac{4\theta}{12 - 3\theta}$$

$$u_3(\theta) = \frac{8 - 6\theta}{12 - 3\theta}.$$

For this case, when $\theta = 1$, $u_1 = \frac{1}{3}$, $u_2 = \frac{4}{9}$, and $u_3 = \frac{2}{9}$. Whereas, if θ approaches zero $u_1 = \frac{1}{3}$, $u_2 = 0$, and $u_3 = \frac{2}{3}$. Thus, the likelihood of both players making response 1 is $\frac{1}{3}$ and is independent of the value of θ. However, as θ goes from zero to one, the probability of the two players making different responses (that is, state S_3) decreases. Stated differently, the likelihood of the cooperative outcome S_2 increases with θ, where θ may be regarded as a measure of the subject's ability to adaptively modify his behavior with successive payoffs.

In order to use $u_i(\theta)$ to predict $Pr(S_i)$ an estimate of θ is required.* The following equation is suitable for making this estimate:

$$(7.16) \quad \Delta(\theta) = \sum_{i=1}^{3} [u_i^{\mathrm{I}}(\theta) - Pr^{\mathrm{I}}(S_i)]^2 + \sum_{i=1}^{3} [u_i^{\mathrm{II}}(\theta) - Pr^{\mathrm{II}}(S_i)]^2,$$

where the superscripts I and II denote the two experimental groups. The equation above is simply the sum (over both experimental groups) of the squared deviations of the predicted values $u_i(\theta)$ from the observed values $Pr(S_i)$. Minimizing the function $\Delta(\theta)$ with respect to θ yields a least squares estimate of the parameter θ. More efficient methods of estimation can be used and are discussed in Sec. 9.2 and 9.4.

To minimize the function $\Delta(\theta)$ analytically leads to impossibly complex expressions. Hence we have simply calculated $\Delta(\theta)$ on a high-speed computer for a grid of values on θ ranging from 0.01 to 1.0 in increments of 0.01. Over this range of values, $\Delta(\theta)$ takes on its minimum when θ is 0.17; hence, we use this value as our estimate. Substituting this estimate in Eq. 7.15 along with the appropriate value of the payoff parameter a yields the following predictions:

Group I	Group II
$(a = 0.8)$	$(a = 0.2)$
$u_1 = 0.254$	$u_1 = 0.059$
$u_2 = 0.152$	$u_2 = 0.426$
$u_3 = 0.594$	$u_3 = 0.515.$

Note that the analog to the prisoner's dilemma game (Group I) yields less cooperation than Group II, for u_2 is larger in the latter group.

Figure 7.4 presents theoretical curves for the proportion of S_1 and S_3 events in successive blocks of 30 trials. These curves were obtained by

---

* We shall assume that θ is the same for all subjects. Undoubtedly, this is a poor assumption but it greatly simplifies the exposition. In a detailed analysis of these data, one would want to take account of inter-subject variability.

letting the probability vector at the start of trial 1 be

$$\mathbf{u}_1 = [0.25, 0.25, 0.50].$$

That is, we assume that responses 1 and 2 were equally likely for both subjects at the start of the experiment. The predicted curves were obtained by iteratively computing the vector $\mathbf{u}_n$ using Eq. 7.10 and then averaging the probabilities in successive blocks of 30 trials. Inspection of the figure indicates that the predicted and observed curves correspond reasonably well. Of course, the theoretical curves are virtually stable over all seven blocks of trials, as one might expect using a value of θ as large as 0.17. There is some indication in Fig. 7.5 that the observed changes in performance at the start of the experiment were slower than predicted by the value of θ estimated from the asymptotic data. This result is sometimes obtained for models of this type; that is, the change parameter (in this case θ) tends to be larger when estimated from the asymptotic data than when estimated from preasymptotic data. Such changes in θ could be incorporated into the model and subjected to formal testing, but this has not yet been done (for a discussion of this problem see Atkinson and Estes, 1963, p. 174).

Sequential Effects and Goodness-of-Fit Tests

So far we have offered a rather cursory analysis of the experiment. In a more detailed workup, we would look at the sequential properties of the data to determine whether they also are adequately described by the model. We will not carry out a complete analysis here, but will describe the basic procedures and a few results.

To begin with, for each pair of subjects, we can tabulate the number of transitions that occurred from state S_i to S_j over the course of the experiment. In particular, let us define the numbers

$n_{ij} =$ the number of transitions that occur from state S_i to S_j for a given pair of subjects,

$n_i =$ the number of times that state S_i occurs.

For the present experiment the number of first-order transitions for a given pair of subjects would be represented by the table

	S_1	S_2	S_3
S_1	n_{11}	n_{12}	n_{13}
S_2	n_{21}	n_{22}	n_{23}
S_3	n_{31}	n_{32}	$n_{33},$

where n_i would be the sum of row i. From this array an estimate of the transition probabilities p_{ij} can be obtained; namely,

$$(7.17) \qquad \hat{p}_{ij} = \frac{n_{ij}}{n_i}.$$

That is, the estimate of p_{ij} would be simply the number of times a transition occurred from state S_i to S_j divided by the total number of times state S_i occurred.* For example, given the sequence

$$S_1 S_2 S_1 S_3 S_2 S_1 S_1 S_3 S_3 S_2 S_2 S_1 S_2$$

running from left to right in time, the frequency table would be as follows:

	S_1	S_2	S_3
S_1	1	2	2
S_2	3	1	0
S_3	0	2	1·

Then $\hat{p}_{11} = \frac{1}{5}$, $\hat{p}_{21} = \frac{3}{4}$, $\hat{p}_{31} = 0$, $\hat{p}_{12} = \frac{2}{5}$, and so forth.

Given estimates of the transition probabilities, the next step would be to compare them with predicted values. Of course, theoretical expressions for p_{ij} depend on the parameter θ (see Eq. 7.5). However, once θ has been estimated, it is possible to make a χ^2 test of the goodness-of-fit between the predicted and the observed frequencies. We will let $p_{ij}(\hat{\theta})$ denote the theoretical transition probabilities based on the estimate $\hat{\theta}$; and, as before, $\hat{p}_{ij}$ will represent the observed transition probabilities. Then under the null hypothesis the quantity

$$(7.18) \qquad \sum_{i,j} n_i \frac{[\hat{p}_{ij} - p_{ij}(\hat{\theta})]^2}{p_{ij}(\hat{\theta})}$$

has the χ^2 limiting distribution with $r(r-1) - 1$ degrees of freedom, where r represents the number of states in the process. If q parameters are estimated for the model, then there are $r(r-1) - q$ degrees of freedom.** This statistic will be discussed in more detail in Sec. 9.4.

---

* It should be noted that Eq. 7.17 yields a maximum-likelihood estimate of the transition probabilities p_{ij} (Anderson and Goodman, 1957).

** There are certain problems involved in reducing the degrees of freedom by one for each estimated parameter when the parameter (or parameters) have not been estimated in an optimal fashion. To our knowledge the statistical problems at issue here are as yet unsolved. It is fairly certain, however, that by reducing the degrees of freedom by one for each estimated parameter we are adopting a policy that is likely to err only on the side of caution.

We have tabulated the n_{ij} transition frequencies for the two experimental groups and applied the goodness-of-fit test of Eq. 7.18. When the test is made on these data using $\theta = 0.17$, we obtain χ^2 values of 8.1 and 7.8 for Groups I and II, respectively. With five degrees of freedom, neither of these values are significant at the ten per cent level, indicating fairly good agreement between predicted and observed transition frequencies.

Despite the fact that the χ^2 test has the virtue of providing an overall measure of the adequacy of the Markov chain, it would be a mistake to construe the test as providing an index of the goodness-of-fit of the fundamental axioms to the data of the experiment. As we have seen, the fit of the Markov chain defined for states S_1, S_2, and S_3 is reasonably good; nevertheless, additional predictions from the theory may be clearly contradicted. For example, Axiom 1 requires that a response be repeated with probability one if it occurred and is followed by a win. This prediction provides a very sharp test, in fact, one that is sure to lead to rejection of the theory. On the other hand, this prediction cannot be derived from the Markov process represented by Eq. 7.5; that is, the Markov chain defined by this equation leads only to probabilistic predictions regarding transitions among the states S_1, S_2, and S_3 and makes no predictions concerning responses given specific reinforcement histories.

In terms of these remarks it is clear that the axioms do not yield realistic predictions for all aspects of the data. However, they do a surprisingly accurate job of predicting mean response probabilities and transition effects among the states S_1, S_2, and S_3. Of course, one can generalize the axioms so as to eliminate the deterministic predictions. In fact, the model presented here is a limiting case (one-element model) of the N-element pattern model of stimulus sampling theory to be discussed in Chapter 8. If we assume more than one element, the unrealistic prediction that a response must be repeated with probability one when it is followed by a win no longer holds. Unfortunately, for elaborate experimental procedures of the sort described in this section, the N-element case leads to complicated stochastic processes for which it is extremely difficult to carry out computations. Fortunately, for most of the cases that have been examined, the predicted mean response probabilities and certain gross sequential effects are usually independent of (or only slightly dependent on) the number of elements assumed. Therefore the one-element assumption may be viewed as a simple device for computing the grosser predictions of the general theory.

For exploratory work in complex situations, then, we recommend using the one-element model, because of the great difficulty in computing predictions for the N-element model. In advocating this approach, we are taking a methodological position with which some scientists do not agree. Our position is in contrast to one which asserts that a model should be discarded once it is clear that certain of its predictions are in error. But this position postulates a closer connection between models and the actual behavior of organisms than we are willing to grant. Naturally, it is always better to choose from the available models the one that best fits the data, but in the present state of psychological knowledge no single model is clearly superior to all others in every facet of analysis. The one-element model, despite some of its erroneous features, is in our judgment a valuable instrument for the initial exploration of a wide variety of complex experimental phenomena.

Other Social Interaction Models

Models and experiments for other multiperson experiments are treated in the previously cited book by Suppes and Atkinson and in a book edited by Criswell, Solomon, and Suppes (1962). The latter includes two articles which discuss the limitations of the type of work exemplified in this section: Moore and Anderson observe that in these experiments the amount of social interaction is minimal, whereas Bush cites the need to develop other types of experimental paradigms for the simulation of social interactions. In the same book, papers by Burke and by Hall present analyses of linear-operator models applied to multiperson interactions. Lieberman considers a three-person game and the possibility of coalition formation. Estes takes up the problem of monetary payoffs in an effort to bridge the gap with game theory, since for the latter it is the magnitude rather than the probability of reward that is determined by the response pair.

7.4 ECONOMIC OLIGOPOLY

In this section we examine a model of oligopoly that was proposed by Suppes and Atkinson (1960) and Suppes and Carlsmith (1962). The evidence for the model comes from an experimental simulation of a competitive market, and as such has severe limitations as a pragmatic theory of economic action. Nevertheless, insofar as the experimental situation bears a resemblance to a real economic situation, the approach is relevant to economic behavior. An important feature of the present theory is that it provides a dynamic mechanism for economic behavior, which is formulated in terms of basic psychological concepts. The classical economic theories of Cournot, Edgeworth, and more recently Chamberlain, Robinson, and others provide no such theory of behavior. Or rather, they offer a highly doubtful theory. Robinson (1933, p. 6) puts the matter as follows: "If individuals act in an erratic way only statistical methods will serve to discover the laws of economics, and if individuals act in a predictable way, but from a large number of complicated motives, the economist must resign his task to the psychologist. It is the assumption that any individual, in his economic life, will never undertake an action that adds more to his losses than to his gains, and will always undertake an action which adds more to his gains than to his losses, which makes the analysis of value possible."

This theory of rational economic behavior suffers from two major weaknesses. First, neither the formulation nor the method of application to situations involving uncertainty and risk is clear. Second, the theory is not dynamic; no provision is made for mechanisms of change or adjustment. The modern approaches to oligopoly via game theory, as exemplified by Shubik (1959), often yield specific dynamic models, but the basic postulates are normative rather than empirical in orientation. So far as we know, there have been no serious attempts to test their empirical adequacy. In fact, the experimental psychologist accustomed to fairly rigorous empirical tests of a proposed model might be surprised at the economist's apparent lack of concern. However, it is undoubtedly true that economists have a much more difficult task of data collection than do psychologists. In an experimental simulation of an oligopoly of the type conducted by Suppes and Carlsmith (1962), it is an easy task to run a 200-trial experiment with each trial corresponding to a quarterly decision on prices and production quotas. By contrast, it is very unlikely that economic data exist for an oligopoly of 50 years' duration. Even if such data do exist, perturbations like depressions and wars would seriously complicate their interpretation.

The difficulty of empirical confirmation suggests that it is not possible to join directly the issue between rationalistic and psychological theories of economic behavior. Without doubt, economists can offer evidence against the model to be considered here, but equally serious objections would hold vis-à-vis the economic theories of oligopoly. They also suffer from oversimplification and elimination of important variables.

Experimental Simulation of Economic Behavior

Before turning to an analysis of the model, it will be helpful to describe some of the experimental paradigms that have been used to simulate economic situations. Some of these paradigms were devised to ascertain the descriptive merits of normative theories; others are part of the endeavor to extend psychological analyses to economic situations.

Conflict is an integral part of the economic structure of our society, so it is not surprising that this element is prominent in most experimental designs. In common with the games described in the preceding section, a general characteristic of economic experiments is that the gain for each participant depends jointly on his own actions and on the actions of the other protagonists. Experiments are set up so that the economic goals of different individuals do not coincide, and furthermore so that promoting one's own goals may diminish another person's gains.

The simulation is either of a bargaining situation or of a competitive market (oligopoly). In essence, the bargaining case includes a buyer, a seller, and a commodity. The two persons bargain more or less by direct communication, tendering offers and counter-offers that may be either concessions or demands. The bargaining situation is partly cooperative in that it is in the subjects' mutual interests to continue until some kind of agreement has been reached, since otherwise neither is rewarded. An *oligopoly* is a market in which a small number of individuals (firms, etc.) seek to sell the same commodity or service. In a typical experiment, two subjects (that is, a duopoly) submit bids to an arbiter without knowledge of the other's bid, and the sale is awarded to the low bidder. Participants are then motivated to adjust their bids on the next transaction according to success in closing the previous sale. Thus, the bidding paradigm may be regarded as a two-person game of the type discussed in the preceding section.

In both situations, the relevant conflicts revolve around two matters; namely, price and quantity. Each player is motivated to achieve some goal (that is, optimal personal profits, or minimal profits to others); this goal is a function both of the price per unit and of the quantity (number of units) of the commodity exchanged. Depending on the particular experiment, a player is allowed to negotiate on price, quantity, or both. The specific price and quantity that one player seeks to set for the transaction depend on his own goal and differ from the price and quantity sought by his opponent. At least one action by each player must occur before the transaction is completed and the profits are allocated.

Classical economic theories have focused largely on final terms of the agreement rather than on learning from one transaction to the next. Let us amplify this point. Bargaining situations involve learning in the sense that buyers and sellers modify their own offers in response to counter-offers by the other party. Little has been done in formal economic theory to predict these trends. Instead, the objective is to state the price and quantity that will ultimately be agreed upon, assuming the participants adhere to one or another normative solution. Likewise, in market situations the main issue has been restricted to predicting how the pair will bid after the competitors have "felt each other out" during a preliminary sequence of transactions.

A series of studies by Siegel and Fouraker (Siegel and Fouraker, 1960; Fouraker and Siegel, 1963) simulated the typical bargaining situation. They pointed out that various classical economic theories differed in their normative solutions to bargaining and oligopoly conflicts. These differences stem from alternative assumptions regarding the possible goals adopted by the participants. For example, the quantity that an oligopoly member should set depends on whether he is trying to maximize individual profit, maximize aggregate profit for the group as a whole, or maximize the difference between his own and others' profits. Then they performed a series of bilateral monopoly (two-person bargaining), price-setting oligopoly, and quantity-setting oligopoly experiments. For each of the bargaining and oligopoly experiments, they calculated the price and quantity expected if the subjects had a particular goal, and similarly for the other possible goals. They were able to show, among other things, that in quantity-setting duopoly markets subjects appeared to be maximizing individual profits rather than either of the other above mentioned goals.

A Model for An Experimental Oligopoly

Before formally describing the model to be considered in this section, we want to indicate some of the general limitations of the analysis. The most severe one is the unrealistically small number of variables considered. No account is given of technological change, the introduction of competing products, the role of inventories, the cost of entry into the market, the effects of advertising, the liquidity of assets, secular changes in general business conditions, and the like. For this reason it is preferable to think of the model as one for experimental simulation of economic markets. In simulation studies, variables not included in the present theoretical framework can be controlled, as they cannot be in real economic environments. A second limitation is that in the model presented, the firms are restricted to offering their products at one of two prices, high (H) and low (L). This restriction is introduced to simplify the mathematics, and its relaxation does not introduce new conceptual problems.

We now turn to a consideration of the model. We shall begin by describing a one-commodity market with K consumers and N firms (or producers), and then consider the special case of a duopoly in some detail. From the theoretical standpoint there is nothing unique about $N = 2$. The same assumptions hold for $N > 2$, but the computations rapidly become more tedious.

The market is defined in probabilistic terms.* The price set by firm f is described by the variable

(7.19) $\kappa_f = \begin{cases} H_f, & \text{if firm } f \text{ sets the high price} \\ L_f, & \text{if firm } f \text{ sets the low price.} \end{cases}$

During any quarter the prices set by the N firms can be represented by the price vector $[\kappa_1 \kappa_2 \cdots \kappa_N]$. Furthermore, we shall assume a market such that each customer will purchase at most one unit of the commodity per quarter. The quantity

$$p_f(\kappa_1 \kappa_2 \cdots \kappa_N)$$

denotes the probability that an arbitrarily selected customer will make his purchase from firm f when the N firms have set prices $\kappa_1, \kappa_2, \ldots, \kappa_N$. The probability

$$p_0(\kappa_1 \kappa_2 \cdots \kappa_N)$$

is the likelihood that the consumer will make no purchase. Thus, for each price vector $[\kappa_1 \kappa_2 \cdots \kappa_N]$ we have

(7.20) $$\sum_{f=0}^{N} p_f(\kappa_1 \kappa_2 \cdots \kappa_N) = 1.$$

Various intuitive relations should hold among the probabilities p_f. We shall not enumerate them here; the important point is that the exact specification of these functions should vary from market to market. For firms setting the same price, inequalities in the probabilities p_f reflect the relative dominance of the firms in the market, and possibly differences in product quality.

As indicated earlier, the quarterly decisions about prices correspond to trials. Trial-to-trial changes will be accounted for by defining a conditioning function similar to the θ parameter of Sec. 7.1. Specifically,

$H_f(j) =$ probability that firm f will set price H on trial $n + 1$ given that it set price H on trial n and sold j commodities

$L_f(j) =$ probability that firm f will set price L on trial $n + 1$ given that it set price L on trial n and sold j commodities.

The two symbols defined above are the probabilities that firm f will perseverate on its previous price, given that it sold j commodities.

---

* An underlying demand function is not postulated, although the present assumptions come to essentially the same thing. The market assumptions made here are similar to those made by Shubik (1959, p. 81). If we had begun with individual demand schedules, we would have needed a concept similar to that of the contingent demand function that he uses. Actually, the present market description is objective and avoids any explicit mention of demand functions because the model does not require them.

We let the price vector $[\kappa_1 \kappa_2 \cdots \kappa_N]$ represent the *state* of the economic system on trial n; for our market κ_i can take on only the two values H and L, and therefore, there are 2^N possible states. From the assumptions of the model, it is clear that the sequence of states over trials has the Markov property. Further, the parameters $H_f(j)$ and $L_f(j)$ and the purchase probabilities $p_f(\kappa_1 \kappa_2 \cdots \kappa_N)$ are independent of the trial number; therefore, the states form a homogeneous chain. To derive the transition matrix for the chain, we could draw trees of the sort given in Figs. 7.1 to 7.3 for the two-person game. However, for this problem each tree has an enormous number of branches and is not very instructive. Actually with some thought it becomes clear that the transition probabilities are given in terms of the multinomial distribution defined by the market assumptions. For example, the probability that each firm will bid low, having bid low in the last quarter (or trial), is

$$(7.21) \quad Pr(L_1 L_2 \cdots L_N \mid L_1 L_2 \cdots L_N) =$$

$$\sum_{\substack{j_0 \cdots j_N \\ j_0 + j_1 + \cdots + j_N = K}} L_1(j_1) L_2(j_2) \cdots L_N(j_N) \frac{K!}{j_0! \, j_1! \, j_2! \cdots j_N!} \prod_{m=0}^{N} p_m(L_1 L_2 \cdots L_N)^{j_m}.$$

The number j_0 is the number of consumers who make no purchases; j_1 the number of consumers who purchase from firm 1, and so on. Of course, $\sum_{f=0}^{N} j_f = K$. The multinomial coefficient gives the number of possible ways that, of the K possible customers, j_0 do not make a purchase, j_1 purchase from firm 1, and so forth.

So far our treatment has been quite general in that we have been introducing notation, rather than making strong assumptions about the process. Without some such assumptions, it is difficult to proceed further. One possible continuation would be to impose constraints on the p_f function in Eq. 7.20. We might, for example, suppose that in each quarter the sales are divided equally among the low bidders, and no one buys from the high bidders. In the oligopolies simulated by Fouraker and Siegel, the person who bid lower than his opponent was awarded the sale with probability one.

Instead of adding assumptions about p_f, we shall proceed by introducing restrictions on the learning parameters $H_f(j)$ and $L_f(j)$. From here on we assume that for any given firm f these probabilities are monotonically increasing in j. This assumption means that the greater the reward, the more likely the firm is to perseverate on the price set in the last quarter. Perseveration is superficially plausible; it might be predicted by extrapolating the findings from simple learning experiments. However, it must be conceded that the monotonicity hypothesis appears dubious for the real market. A common phenomenon of our economy is the lowering of prices upon increase in sales volume. Conversely, sometimes when the price is "too low" an increase in sales encourages an increase in price.

For the present class of experimental conditions, however, experimental evidence by Suppes and Carlsmith (1962) suggests that $H_f(j)$ and $L_f(j)$ may not only be monotonic in j, but linear as well. The linearity assumption can be expressed as follows:

(7.22) $$H_f(j) = \alpha_f + \beta_f j, \qquad L_f(j) = a_f + b_f j.$$

Here $\alpha_f, a_f \geq 0$, $\beta_f, b_f \geq 0$. Further,

$$a_f + b_f K \leq 1,$$
$$\alpha_f + \beta_f K \leq 1,$$

to ensure that the functions are appropriately bounded between zero and one.

Duopoly Market

To avoid cumbersome notation we now limit discussion to the duopoly market ($N = 2$). For simplicity, let

$$p_f = p_f(L_1 L_2), \qquad q_f = p_f(L_1 H_2)$$
$$r_f = p_f(H_1 L_2), \qquad s_f = p_f(H_1 H_2)$$

for $f = 1, 2$. For example, r_1 is the probability that an arbitrarily selected customer will purchase from firm 1 if it sets the high price and its competition sets the low price. As the specialization of Eq. 7.21 we have

(7.23)
$$Pr(L_1 L_2 \mid L_1 L_2) = \sum_{\substack{j_0, j_1, j_2 \\ j_0 + j_1 + j_2 = K}} (a_1 + b_1 j_1)(a_2 + b_2 j_2) \frac{K!}{j_0! j_1! j_2!} p_0^{j_0} p_1^{j_1} p_2^{j_2}$$
$$= a_1 a_2 + a_1 b_2 E(j_2) + a_2 b_1 E(j_1) + b_1 b_2 E(j_1 j_2),$$

where the expectations are with respect to the given multinomial distribution. Now, for the multinomial distribution

$$E(j_1) = Kp_1, \quad E(j_2) = Kp_2, \quad E(j_1 j_2) = K(K-1)p_1 p_2.$$
Whence

(7.24) $$Pr(L_1 L_2 \mid L_1 L_2) = a_1 a_2 + a_1 b_2 K p_2 + a_2 b_1 K p_1 + b_1 b_2 K(K-1)p_1 p_2.$$

The remaining 15 transition probabilities can be derived likewise.

There are several observations to be made about the kind of economic behavior implied by such transition probabilities. In the first place, unlike the theories of Cournot and others, the model does not necessarily predict the eventual adoption of a pure strategy by either firm. Second, unlike the Edgeworth theory, which predicts cyclic behavior, the present model predicts random fluctuations in behavior for both firms; equilibrium exists, but in a statistical rather than deterministic sense. Third, the present model is more detailed than the classical economic theories of duopoly, for numerous predictions can be made about sequential behavior.

To gain insight into the model, let us consider some special cases; these will be stated as restrictions on p_f, q_f, r_f, and s_f. A necessary preliminary step is to specify more fully the linearity condition of Eq. 7.22. We assume the firms to be equally "attractive" in their noneconomic qualities, and thus that $a_1 = a_2$, $b_1 = b_2$, $\alpha_1 = \alpha_2$, and $\beta_1 = \beta_2$; hence we drop the subscripts 1 and 2 on these parameters. Next we assume that the conditioning functions in Eq. 7.22 are directly proportional to j, the number of sales by that firm in the preceding quarter, that is, $a = \alpha = 0$. It is natural to let $\beta = 1/K$, because this yields $H_f(j) = 1$, when $j = K$. We add the further tentative restriction that the maximum value of $L_f(j)$ will be $\frac{1}{2}$, representing in some sense a general reluctance to set a low price. By setting $j = K$, this last condition implies $b = 1/(2K)$.

Simple monopoly. Here we may assume that $p_2 = q_2 = r_2 = s_2 = 0$ in order to represent the fact that firm 2 has no portion of the market. Then by computing all transaction probabilities of the type given in Eq. 7.24 and making the four parameter restrictions, we obtain the transition matrix

$$(7.25) \quad \begin{array}{c} \\ L_1L_2 \\ L_1H_2 \\ H_1L_2 \\ H_1H_2 \end{array} \begin{array}{cccc} L_1L_2 & L_1H_2 & H_1L_2 & H_1H_2 \end{array} \\ \begin{bmatrix} 0 & \frac{1}{2}p_1 & 0 & 1 - \frac{1}{2}p_1 \\ \frac{1}{2}q_1 & 0 & 1 - \frac{1}{2}q_1 & 0 \\ 0 & 1 - r_1 & 0 & r_1 \\ 1 - s_1 & 0 & s_1 & 0 \end{bmatrix}.$$

Moreover, if the monopolist (firm 1) always sells to all K consumers regardless of the price set (that is, if $p_1 = q_1 = r_1 = s_1 = 1$), then the matrix is

$$\begin{bmatrix} 0 & \frac{1}{2} & 0 & \frac{1}{2} \\ \frac{1}{2} & 0 & \frac{1}{2} & 0 \\ 0 & 0 & 0 & 1 \\ 0 & 0 & 1 & 0 \end{bmatrix}$$

which has the proper set $\{H_1L_2, H_1H_2\}$ as an absorbing set. The appropriate result is then that the monopolist always sets the high price.

The other firm alternates between H and L. This latter result is not very realistic and stems from the simplifying assumptions made about $H_f(j)$ and $L_f(j)$.

On the other hand, suppose that the monopoly has the feature that no customers will make purchases when the high price is set ($r_1 = s_1 = 0$), but some will at the low price ($p_1, q_1 \neq 0$). Putting these assumptions into Eq. 7.25 and using Eq. 7.14 to solve for the stationary probabilities yields

(7.26)
$$u_{L_1 L_2} = \frac{q_1}{W}$$

$$u_{L_1 H_2} = \frac{p_1}{W}$$

$$u_{H_1 L_2} = \frac{p_1(1 - \frac{1}{2}q_1)}{W}$$

$$u_{H_1 H_2} = \frac{q_1(1 - \frac{1}{2}p_1)}{W}$$

where $W = 2(p_1 + q_1) - p_1 q_1$. Thus, the asymptotic probability of the monopolist (firm 1) setting the low price is

$$u_{L_1 L_2} + u_{L_1 H_2} = \frac{p_1 + q_1}{2(p_1 + q_1) - p_1 q_1} > \frac{1}{2}.$$

This inequality means that, owing to the absence of profit in quarters when the high price was in effect, the monopolist will in the long run tend to revert to the low price more often than not.

Symmetric duopoly. Here we consider the case where the firms are of equal strength. Also, for simplicity, we will assume that if at least one firm sets the low price, all K consumers will buy. Thus, $p_1 = p_2 = \frac{1}{2}$; and on the basis of symmetry $q_1 = r_2$ and $s_1 = s_2$. To eliminate the subscripts, let $q = q_1 = r_2$ and $s = s_1 = s_2$, where $0 \leq q \leq 1$ and $0 \leq s \leq \frac{1}{2}$. The transition matrix obtained from Eq. 7.24 may be simplified by taking $K \approx K - 1$ and combining the symmetric states $[H_1 L_2]$ and $[L_1 H_2]$ to obtain a 3×3 transition matrix, where state i ($i = 0, 1, 2$) corresponds to the number of firms setting the high price:

(7.27)

$$
\begin{array}{c c c c}
 & 0 & 1 & 2 \\
0 & \frac{1}{16} & \frac{6}{16} & \frac{9}{16} \\
1 & \frac{1}{2}q(1 - q) & 1 - \frac{3}{2}q + q^2 & q(1 - \frac{1}{2}q) \\
2 & (1 - s)^2 & 2s(1 - s) & s^2
\end{array}
$$

Using Eq. 7.13 one can derive expressions for u_0, u_1, and u_2, the stationary probabilities for this chain. Regarding the u_i, it turns out that whatever the values of q and s (given $0 \leq s \leq \frac{1}{2}$), the firms do not adopt the monopoly price of H or the competitive price of L with probability one. The probabilistic equilibrium has $0 < u_i < 1$ for all admissible q and s. The kind of predictions generated by Eq. 7.27 may be better understood by taking a numerical example. Let $q = 1$ and $s = 0.1$. This means that the firm setting the high price when the other firm sets the low price sells no products; and when both firms set the high price each sells to 0.1 of the consumers. In this case, $u_0 \approx 0.30$, $u_1 \approx 0.35$, and $u_2 \approx 0.35$; whence the probability of either firm setting a low price is $u_0 + \frac{1}{2}u_1 \approx 0.475$.

We shall examine an unpublished study by Suppes who attempted to test the present model in an experimental situation designed to simulate a symmetric duopoly. A more or less similar application has been reported in the previously cited article by Suppes and Carlsmith. Students in business administration acted as the decision makers for each firm. The general features of the market situation were described to the subjects, along with information regarding production costs and the two prices they were permitted to set on their product ($H = \$6$ and $L = \$3$). A given firm's sales in each quarter were randomly generated by the scheme described in the example above ($q = 1$ and $s = 0.1$), and at the end of a quarter each firm was given an accounting of its profits. The subjects were instructed to fix a price for their product at the start of each quarter and to use past sales and profit information so as to maximize their firm's gains over the course of the experimental simulation, which lasted for 200 trials (quarters).

In the present study, the observed asymptotic probability of either firm setting the lower price was 0.77. By an analysis of the transition data on price settings from one quarter to the next, we can estimate the parameters specifying the functions $H_f(j)$ and $L_f(j)$ of Eq. 7.22. The values were as follows: $a = 0.7$, $b = 0.2/K$, $\alpha = 0.4$, $\beta = 0.5/K$. Thus,

$$H(j) = 0.4 + \frac{0.5}{K} j,$$

$$L(j) = 0.7 + \frac{0.2}{K} j,$$

for both firms. Substituting these functions into the 16 equations like Eq. 7.24, and taking $q = 1$, $s = 0.1$, and $K \approx K - 1$, yields the following 3×3 transition matrix, where state i indicates the number of firms setting the high price:

$$
\begin{array}{c}
 \\
0 \\
1 \\
2
\end{array}
\begin{array}{ccc}
0 & 1 & 2 \\
\begin{bmatrix}
0.64 & 0.32 & 0.04 \\
0.54 & 0.42 & 0.04 \\
0.30 & 0.50 & 0.20
\end{bmatrix}
\end{array}.
$$

The stationary probabilities for this chain are $u_0 \approx 0.59$, $u_1 \approx 0.36$, and $u_2 \approx 0.05$. Hence, the probability of either firm's setting the low price is $u_0 + \frac{1}{2}u_1 \approx 0.77$, which agrees with the observed value. For further details on the experimental procedure and similar experimental results, the reader should consult the Suppes-Carlsmith article.

Economists have frequently discussed a duopoly model in which each duopolist acts as if the other firm's price were going to remain the same as it was in the previous period. Information about the other firm's price can be taken into account in this model by treating such information as discriminative stimuli. The price set by the competition during trial n can be identified as the salient stimulus for trial $n + 1$. In this case the stimuli controlling the decision-making process change from trial to trial and the situation may be analyzed as a discrimination problem, involving learning to make appropriate responses to different stimuli. Once the stimuli are identified as the prices set by the competitor, the derivation of the Markov process is a straightforward matter. Unfortunately, even in the case of a duopoly, the derivation is quite tedious because the process has 64 states. (The dynamics of discrimination learning models as applied to multiperson interactions are described in Suppes and Atkinson, 1960, Chapters 6 and 7.)

Unfortunately, it does not seem feasible to offer real economic data in support of the model presented in this section. It certainly is true that many more or less duopolistic markets do not seem to show the type of statistical fluctuations in prices that is predicted. Many factors can account for this discrepancy. We make no case for the economic realism of the model introduced in this section; it omits too many significant variables. However, the model does suggest an approach that, with further development, may prove more realistic than the classical economic and game-theory models of oligopoly. The central idea is to replace the concept of rational action with a specific psychological model of behavior.

7.5   OTHER DEVELOPMENTS

Social conformity is another area in which Markov models, resembling those discussed in this chapter, have been applied. The pioneer work in this field was done by Cohen (1958), who developed a model for behavior in the Asch-type (1953) conformity situation. In Asch's experiment, a naïve subject is required to make a series of psychophysical judgments in the face of unanimous and incorrect responses on the part of his peers. Unbeknown to the subject, the peers are confederates of the experimenter; and, as one might expect, the unanimity of the confederates in responding incorrectly tends to exert pressure on the subject to conform. The model formulated by Cohen gives a good account of behavior in this type of situation. It postulates four states with the property that the subject can absorb at either of two poles—always conform or never conform. More recently Cohen (1962) has generalized the model to the study of reference group phenomena; this extension and the related experimental work provides a basis for testing propositions that can be incorporated into a general theory of reference-group behavior. Suppes and Schlag-Rey (1962a) and Carterette and Wyman (1962) also have formulated models for conformity experiments. Both papers investigate the temporal factors involved in conformity behavior, and also attempt to separate social and perceptual factors. A general survey of models for social conformity and related topics is available in the previously cited book edited by Criswell, Solomon, and Suppes.

Related to this research is the development of a mathematical model by Binder, Wolin, and Terebinski (1965) to investigate the relationship between decision-making success and the likelihood of being voted "leader" (group decision maker) of a three-man group. Markov models, based on extensions of concepts used in mathematical learning theory, provide the theoretical framework. Each trial of the experiment begins with the selection of a leader by group vote, and ends after the designated leader makes a decision for the group. Binder, Wolin, and Terebinski find excellent agreement between obtained and theoretical results for vote shifting, asymptotic leadership, and learning trends in their experiments.

Recently, there has been a spurt of activity on yet another problem; one that is at the interface of learning theory and decision theory. The object is to apply normative techniques to a given learning model in order to specify the conditions that will lead to optimal performance. For example, if one has a model that gives a good account of paired-associate learning over a wide range of experimental situations, then it is natural to inquire about the implications of the model for determining optimal procedures of "instruction." If we know the stimulus presentation, response, and reinforcement histories through trial n, then we should be able to use the model to decide what item to present on trial $n + 1$ in order to maximize the amount of material that will be learned by the end of the experimental session. Stated otherwise, the logical structure of the behavioral model will specify how the stimuli should be selected from trial to trial in order to minimize or maximize some terminal goal that has been set for the student. Such developments have obvious implications for education; in principle, for any learning model we should be able to set up a related decision system that takes as input certain information from preceding trials and decides what instructional material should be presented next.

Some research on this topic has already been done, primarily for models of the sort considered in Chapter 3. Accounts of this work appear in Crothers (1965), Dear and Atkinson (1962), Matheson (1964), Smallwood (1962), and Suppes (1963). Much of this research employs iterative techniques resembling dynamic programming (Bellman, 1957; Howard, 1960) as its optimization method. This work, while rudimentary and oversimplified to date, has excited interest because of its implications for instructional procedures involving computer-controlled teaching programs (Coulson, 1962).

CHAPTER 8

STIMULUS
SAMPLING THEORY

In this chapter we depart from our previous *modus operandi*. We will not consider any specific experimental problems as in the former chapters, but rather will be concerned only with the exposition of a class of stochastic processes derived from stimulus sampling theory. This theory derives from the original papers by Estes (1950) and Estes and Burke (1953); an extensive axiomatic development of the theory has been treated in papers by Estes and Suppes (1959a, b), and these papers should be consulted for more complete coverage. The theoretical significance of empirical evidence collected before 1958 was reviewed by Estes (1959b), and Atkinson and Estes (1963) have surveyed a number of the more recent developments. It is appropriate that stimulus sampling theory be reviewed in this volume, since a major portion of present-day work in mathematical learning theory (and some work in psychophysics and social psychology) is formulated within this general framework. In fact, most of the models discussed in this book can be regarded as various special cases of the general theory. It will become apparent that this framework has considerable flexibility and generality. It is difficult to decide whether stimulus sampling theory is really a "theory" in the sense of implying definite consequences, or instead is a general conceptual approach to the analysis of behavioral situations. Viewed in the latter light, the theory provides a set of heuristic guides to the formulation of specific models.

8.1 THE GENERAL THEORY:
TERMINOLOGY AND BASIC ASSUMPTIONS

Roughly speaking, stimulus sampling theory views behavior as being elicited by antecedent stimulus events that are associated to responses.

343

The primitive terms of the theory are stimulus, response, association, and reinforcement. Excluding the response term, the other three concepts derive their meaning from the way they are used and interrelated in the axioms of the theory. The association term refers to a functional connection between a stimulus and a response; alternately, the relation may be described by saying, for example, that response A_i is conditioned to stimulus S_k. The phrase "functional connection" is used advisedly, since all that is being asserted is that the probability of response A_i is influenced by (is a function of) the presence or absence of stimulus S_k in the subject's representation of his current environment. No deeper meaning regarding connections of specific neural pathways or the like is intended.

The term "reinforcement" refers to a theoretical event that can produce changes in associations of stimuli present at the moment the reinforcing event occurs. Reinforcing events are classified according to the stimulus-response associations that are left unchanged by that event. Thus, if response classes A_1, A_2, ..., A_r have been identified then there will correspond r reinforcing events, labeled E_1, E_2, ..., E_r. If stimulus S_k is already associated to response A_i, then E_i is that reinforcing event that leaves the $S_k - A_i$ association unchanged; if stimulus S_k is associated to some other response A_j, then the occurrence of an E_i reinforcing event when S_k is present will tend to change the association of S_k so that it is now associated with A_i instead of the previous A_j. The change in association of a stimulus is assumed to be a discrete all-or-none switch: a previous association is erased (counterconditioned, unlearned, etc.) when a new response is associated to a stimulus. This notion is formalized in the theory by saying that at any point in time each stimulus is associated with exactly one response. The reinforcement postulates of the system are responsible, of course, for making it a dynamic, changing process. Learning is described as a change in the associations of the stimuli affecting the subject in a particular situation; repeated reinforcements of the "correct" response change "wrong" associations to "right" ones, where "wrong" and "right" depend upon the experimenter's designation of which response is correct for a particular stimulus. To complete the reinforcement postulates, a special null event E_0 is defined simply as that "reinforcing event" which leaves all associations unchanged—it preserves the status quo of all existing associations in the system.

The system is most often applied to discrete trial situations that can be characterized as follows: the trial starts with the presentation of one or more stimuli, the subject responds, and then the experimenter (or controlling agent in the environment) provides some outcome (such as a monetary payoff or reward, information about the correct response, an unconditioned stimulus eliciting some reflex reaction, etc.), and terminates the trial.

A large number of experiments in psychology can be described in these general terms. Within the theory it is assumed that the response set is so defined that (1) one and only one response from this set occurs on each trial, and (2) one and only one reinforcing event occurs on each trial. Letting $Pr(A_{i,n})$ and $Pr(E_{i,n})$ represent the probability of response A_i and reinforcing event E_i on trial n, respectively, the assumption is that

$$\sum_{i=1}^{r} Pr(A_{i,n}) = 1$$

and

$$\sum_{i=0}^{r} Pr(E_{i,n}) = 1.$$

Schedules and Outcome-reinforcement Relations

We wish to digress from the main theme for a brief discussion of two aspects of the above representation of reinforcing events. First, this representation allows us to state hypotheses concerning the classical parameters of reinforcement (magnitude, delay, etc.). It does so by permitting one to postulate probabilistic relations between observable experimental outcomes and the various hypothetical reinforcing events.

Let us consider a specific illustration of this procedure; namely, the case of differential amounts of food reward for a hungry rat learning a T-maze. The two response alternatives are left (A_1) and right (A_2) choices. The three possible reinforcing events are: E_1, reinforcement of a left turn; E_2, reinforcement of a right turn; and E_0, reinforcement of neither. The experiment is arranged so that a hungry rat receives a half gram of food when he makes A_1 and one-tenth gram when he makes A_2. This setup might be represented in the model by assuming that increasing the amount of reward given following response A_i increases the probability that the reinforcing event is E_i instead of E_0 on that trial. Thus, the average change in response probability would increase with the amount of reward.* Consider a similar case in human paired-associates learning. It is known that overall learning is faster when the subject is permitted more time to study the correct stimulus-response pairings on each trial. This fact might be represented in the theory by assuming that longer study times of the correct response A_i increase the probability of an E_i rather than an E_0 reinforcing event on that trial. Thus, we see that the parameters describing the observable trial outcomes can be represented in the theory in terms of their probabilistic connections to the hypothetical reinforcing events E_i. Of course, we could be satisfied with this type of solution to the problem, or we could develop more elemental

---

* See Clayton (1964) for results relevant to a model developed along these lines.

hypotheses that imply the probabilistic connections between outcomes and reinforcements.

A second feature we wish to discuss is the type of schedules of outcomes that can be devised from this representation of reinforcing events. By "schedule" we mean simply a scheme by which the experimenter decides which outcome to present on a particular trial. There is a large class of such schedules, and a considerable number have been investigated experimentally. At the general level of characterization, the probability that the experimenter decides to present a particular outcome on trial n can depend upon (1) the trial number, (2) the stimuli presented on some subset of preceding trials, (3) the responses given on a subset of earlier trials, (4) or any conjunction of these schemes. A few cases of each of these categories have been investigated experimentally. The most common case studied is that in which each outcome has a fixed probability of occurrence independent of the trial number and preceding events. This is called a "noncontingent" schedule by Estes (1957b); it is this simple case that we shall treat in this chapter.

Problems in Formally Representing the Stimulus

Returning to our main exposition, we have already discussed the general notions of response, association, and reinforcement. We now take up the concept of the stimulus. The reader will probably be distressed to find that although stimulus sampling theory has a very precise way of *representing* the stimulus situation, the theory is vague, in fact noncommital, concerning what is a stimulus. Paradoxically, the flexibility and scope of the theory arises in part because of this lack of commitment regarding how stimulus elements are to be defined.

The representation of the experimental situation is simple enough. A given experimental situation is conceived to involve an assemblage (population) of N distinct stimulus elements $S_1, S_2, \ldots, S_N$. A subset (that is, sample) of these will affect the subject on a particular trial, and his response will be determined by the associative connections of those elements in the sample. However, the basic notion of a stimulus element is left undefined. It is an example of a completely "open-ended" concept; essentially, the user of the theory can interpret the concept as required to describe the particular situation under study.

This lack of a general specification of the stimulus is characteristic of modern psychology and is not a limitation unique to stimulus sampling theory. In discussing the difficulty of defining the basic terms of stimulus-response psychology, Miller (1959, p. 242) writes ". . . stimulus-response psychologists may be said to know and care relatively little about either stimuli or responses; they are specialists on the hyphen between the S and R and could more aptly be called *hyphen psychologists*, or to use Thorndike's term, *connectionists*." The problem, of course, is not that we are unable to construct some specific interpretation of the stimulus; this is easily done but can be just as easily shown to be inadequate. Gibson (1960) has reviewed the astonishing variety of different concepts of the stimulus as employed in psychology, each use having some degree of legitimacy. Rather, the problem is that we are unable to construct an operational definition that covers all the diverse usages of the stimulus concept as it has been applied in practice. A few general examples will demonstrate the diversity of usages. In some cases, the stimulus is specified in terms of the pattern of neural activity produced at a peripheral receptor unit or aggregate of receptor units; or it may be specified by the physical characteristics of the energies striking the receptor surface; or by the entire spatial distribution and/or temporal sequence of activation of many different receptors. Sometimes, the stimulus is specified in terms of focal objects in the field (that is, a "dog" stimulus), which objects give rise to the physical energies striking the relevant receptors; such stimulus objects are further classified depending upon whether or not they are, in fact, stimulating the subject. Thus, the orientation of the person's receptors divides the field into "potential" versus "effective" stimuli. In other cases, the stimulus-as-reacted-to (or cue) is specified in terms of the output from some perceptual encoding mechanism or analyzing system; such encoding systems extract only the alleged "significant" features from the continuous sensory flux at the receptors. In still other instances, the effective stimuli are taken to correspond to feedback from implicit mediating responses (for example, verbal labels in human subjects) employed by the subject. Hull's concept of "the pure stimulus act," Miller and Dollard's "cue-producing responses," and Osgood's "mediational or representational process" are examples; Lawrence (1963) gives a useful review and critique of several different ideas along these lines.

The diversity of definitions of "the stimulus" makes one almost despair of giving any general characterization of the denotation of the term. In fact, it may be a point in its favor that stimulus sampling theory is noncommital on this issue. The user of the theory is free to consider any experimental identification of the stimulus elements that agrees with his formal or intuitive analysis of the situation confronting the subject.

It may be helpful to the reader if we go through a concrete illustration, spelling out several alternative interpretations of what we could mean by "the stimulus situation." Suppose that we place a college student in front of a projection screen, and tell him to "watch what appears on this screen." He then is given a series of trials on which either the trigram *POG* or the trigram *LIV* is projected onto the screen for two seconds. During this time he is to say "*A*" or "*B*," predicting whether the experimenter will follow the stimulus display with either an *A* or *B* outcome. Suppose the experimenter gives outcome *A* with probability π_1 on a *POG*-trial, and with probability π_2 on a *LIV*-trial (the rest of the time giving outcome *B*). Already in describing the experimental situation in natural language, we have made some implicit commitments to a view about how the subject perceives the stimuli. Nevertheless, let us list a few options for characterizing the stimulus situation.

(1) There are two stimulus elements—the pattern tagged "*POG*" and the pattern tagged "*LIV*."

(2) Our organism is conceived of as a grid-scanning pattern recognizer, which counts relations among straight lines and curved lines (contours) of patterns projected onto a sensory mosaic (that is, the retina). Each pattern is then characterized by the number of counts of these two features. If the machine scans the field at random and for a limited time, then these counts vary from one occasion to the next.

(3) The subject verbally encodes or labels each stimulus but may do so in a manner varying from one trial to the next. Sometimes the *POG* event is encoded as "*P*," sometimes as "*PG*," and so on. The encoding may be in terms of verbal associations, so that upon seeing *POG*, the subject sometimes stimulates himself by thinking "pollywog" or "dog" or "pig," and so forth.

(4) The effective stimuli are the entire constellation or pattern of internal and external energies striking the subject at the moment "*POG*" is presented. Components included in such patterns are feedback stimulation from his postural adjustments, from adjustment of his visual receptors, autonomic reactions, stray visual and auditory stimuli from the general background situation in which the experiment is being conducted, and the subject's current attention or inattention to minor specks on the projection screen. The combination of one value on each of these variables defines a stimulus pattern. Over the course of many "*POG*" trials, a number of such stimulus patterns will occur.

(5) The effective stimuli are sequential patterns consisting of (a) the current visual display, *POG*, (b) persisting after-effects of stimulus traces from the last several outcome events. There are, of course, a number of different patterns produced by the latter events. An example is the stimulus "*POG* preceded by the outcomes *ABA* on the last three trials." Such traces from the previous outcome (or response or stimulus) sequence might conceivably function as the stimulus elements controlling the subject's behavior. In what amounts to the same thing, we might suppose

the subject to be "testing out hypotheses" having to do with the stimulus and outcome sequence; such hypotheses can be characterized at another level in terms of which predictive response is associated with particular stimulus-outcome sequences when these latter are considered as the effective "stimulus elements" in the situation.

The foregoing listing, although by no means exhaustive, illustrates the range of possible identifications for a "stimulus element" in this particular situation. As stated earlier, stimulus sampling theory derives much of its flexibility from the fact that it is noncommittal about which identifications are appropriate or presumed to be correct. In principle at least, there are three approaches one may elect when using the theory. First, one may assume a particular task identification for stimulus elements, and then use the theory applied to this task to see how well it predicts behavior; if the predictions are accurate, both the theory and the stimulus identifications are supported. Second, one may not wish to hypothesize *a priori* about the stimulus elements in a particular task; rather, the theory is used along with the data to estimate the number of elements involved. Given this number, one may then search for stimulus identifications that lead to that number. Third, one may be interested mainly in testing how accurately the theory describes behavioral changes, without having any real concern for how many stimulus elements the theory says there are in the task nor how these are to be identified in the task being considered. It is this last approach that has characterized many applications of stimulus sampling theory. Indeed, in many cases of the general theory, one never estimates the number of stimulus elements, but rather bypasses the problem entirely by simply assuming that there are a "large number" of such elements in the task. Later we shall see how this approach works.

Stimulus Sampling Assumptions

As indicated earlier, a given stimulus situation is represented in terms of a set of stimulus elements; the size of the set will be denoted by N. These elements are considered to be completely distinct from one another. In particular, this means that the response associated to element S_i is left intact if the association to S_j is changed. Thus the elements are so defined that no transfer of conditioning relations occurs between them. Transfer or stimulus generalization effects between two tasks can be handled in the theory (see Estes, 1959b, and Atkinson and Estes, 1963) by assuming that the sets of stimulus elements for the two tasks have a number of common elements. However, we shall not trace that development of the theory here, since it diverts from our main purpose.

On any trial the N potential stimulus elements can be divided into a subset of those that are effective (that is, sampled on the trial), and a second subset consisting of the ineffective or unsampled elements. To determine which elements are in the sample requires the stipulation of a particular sampling scheme. Again the basic theory is noncommittal on what this sampling scheme should be; a number of different proposals have been investigated, but many more are conceivable. To characterize the situation in general, for element S_i we may define a sampling function $\sigma_i(h_n)$ giving the probability that S_i will be sampled on trial n given the particular history of samplings, responses, and outcomes up to and including trial $n - 1$. For example, the sampling function $\sigma_i(h_n)$ for the concept identification model in Chapter 2 is as follows: if the response to the single element (attribute) sampled on trial n was correct, the same element is sampled again on trial $n + 1$; if the response on trial n was incorrect the element sampled on the next trial is determined by random selection from the pool of N attributes. Consider another scheme investigated by Ginsberg (1964). The sampling routine is a Markov process with one-trial dependencies. Any element sampled on trial n has probability α of being sampled again on trial $n + 1$; elements not sampled on trial n have probability β of being sampled on trial $n + 1$. Ginsberg investigated the consequences of the assumption that α was higher and β lower the shorter the time intervals between trials. A final example, suggested by the work of Atkinson (1960a, 1961a) and Restle (1955a) is to suppose that $\sigma_i(h_n)$ depends on the history h_n in a manner so calculated as to make the sampling organism more adaptive or successful in some sense. Thus, via an auxiliary process such as observing responses, attention, or adaptation, the sampling probability of "relevant" stimulus elements increases over trials, while the sampling probability of irrelevant elements decreases.

The intent of these examples is to show how the flexibility of this scheme can be exploited. Once a particular sampling process [specific $\sigma_i(h_n)$ functions] has been postulated, the theory is then used to generate the consequences of such a scheme. Of course, in practice the main limitation upon the proposed sampling scheme is that it be simple enough to permit mathematical analysis of the resulting stochastic process. An additional constraint on investigations of a variety of sampling notions arises from the fact that relatively simple schemes yield models that display tolerable accuracy in describing data to which they have been applied. Thus, there has been insufficient motivation to investigate more elaborate schemes.

The primary reference papers on stimulus sampling theory (cf. Estes, 1950; Estes and Burke, 1953; Estes and Suppes, 1959a,b; Estes, 1959b; and Atkinson and Estes, 1963) have dealt principally with two sampling schemes. For both schemes, the sampling of stimulus elements is assumed to be stationary and independent of the past history. Additionally, it is required that the elements be sampled independently of one another. The two cases arise when it is further specified whether the number of elements sampled per trial is fixed or is a random variable. In the variable sample size case, the element S_i is assigned a probability θ_i of being sampled on each trial. The composition of the particular sample on trial n can be specified in terms of the products of N binomial probabilities. The average sample size will be $\sum_{i=1}^{N} \theta_i$ but it will fluctuate about this mean value, especially when N is small. Estes and Burke (1953) investigated the error involved in approximating the collection of θ_i values by assigning to each element the average sampling probability

$$\bar{\theta} = \frac{1}{N} \sum_{i=1}^{N} \theta_i \, .$$

They concluded that for N moderately large, the error of approximation was negligible and could be ignored. In the alternate case of fixed sample size (the sample size is labeled s), it has been assumed that the N elements all have equal probability of being sampled. Since the s elements are sampled without replacement from the pool of N elements, each element has probability s/N of appearing in the sample. The special case to be investigated in the remaining portion of this chapter arises when s is set equal to one. Because the one element sampled can be interpreted as the entire pattern of stimulation acting on that trial, the $s = 1$ case has been called the "pattern model" (Estes, 1959a).

Response Rules

We have discussed the representation of the experimental situation in terms of stimulus elements and have introduced the idea that the effective subset of elements on a trial is obtained by some sampling scheme. Recall that each stimulus element is assumed to be associated to one and only one of the available response alternatives, $A_1, A_2, \ldots, A_r$. In determining which response will be made, the model assumes first that only elements in the current sample influence the response on that trial; unsampled elements have no effect. Second, each element in the sample is given equal weight in determining the response. Stated differently, the probability that the subject makes response A_i is given by the number of elements in the sample that are associated with A_i divided by the size of the sample. For example, in a sample of size 10, if there were five elements associated to A_1, three elements associated to A_2, and two to A_3, then the probabilities of responses A_1, A_2, and A_3 would be 0.50, 0.30, and

0.20, respectively. Thus, the theory views performance as predictable by the simple process of averaging over the associative connections of the elements in the current sample. Of course, for the case of $s = 1$ the response rule is simply "make that response associated to the sampled element."

This simple averaging rule characterizes most of the models that have been derived from stimulus sampling theory. A further rationale for the rule would be to suppose that the subject scans his sample of elements and eventually picks one element at random and gives the associated response; such a procedure would lead to the averaging rule. An alternate response rule that has been explored is the "majority rule": that response is made to which a majority of the sampled elements are connected. Thus in our previous example, the A_1 elements predominated, so response A_1 would occur with probability one. A major obstacle in investigating the majority performance rule is the mathematical difficulties encountered, especially when the model is applied to schedules in which the reinforcing event depends upon the subject's response. However, the rule does seem to have several desirable features that deserve investigation (for example, for large s and N, this response rule will predict ultimately perfect performance in a discrimination task involving a number of common elements). Of course, for the pattern model ($s = 1$) the averaging rule and the majority rule reduce to the same result; namely, make that response to which the single sampled element is associated.

8.2   THE N-ELEMENT PATTERN MODEL

The preceding informal discussion of stimulus sampling theory was intended to familiarize the reader with the basic ideas involved, and to show the potential flexibility of the system. In this section, we take a particular set of assumptions and examine their consequences. This is done by analysis of the stochastic process specified from the theory. We begin by giving the axioms of the system. Models derived within the stimulus sampling framework generally have four separate groups of axioms. First, there are representation axioms, which specify how many stimulus elements, responses, and reinforcing events are to be considered and how they are to be labeled. Second, there are a set of conditioning axioms stating how reinforcing events modify stimulus-response connections. Third, there are a group of sampling axioms, specifying the sampling functions $\sigma_i(h_n)$ discussed earlier. Finally, there is a response axiom, stipulating how performance is related to the associations of the sampled elements. With these preliminaries aside, let us turn to a statement of the axioms for the N-element pattern model.

Representation Axioms

R1. *There are N stimulus elements, labeled $S_1, S_2, \ldots, S_N$.*
R2. *There are r responses, labeled $A_1, A_2, \ldots, A_r$. One of these responses occurs on each trial.*
R3. *There are $r + 1$ reinforcing events, labeled $E_0, E_1, \ldots, E_r$. One of these reinforcing events occurs on each trial.* (In the following, the phrase "response A_i is reinforced" should be interpreted "reinforcing event E_i occurs.")

Conditioning Axioms

C1. *At the start of a trial, each element is conditioned to exactly one response.*
C2. *If an element is sampled on a trial, it becomes conditioned with probability c to the response (if any) that is reinforced on that trial; with probability $1 - c$, it remains conditioned as before. If the sampled element is already conditioned to the reinforced response, it remains so.*
C3. *If event E_0 occurs on a trial, there is no change in conditioning of the sampled element.*
C4. *Stimulus elements that are not sampled on a trial do not change their state of conditioning on that trial.*
C5. *The probability, c, that a sampled element will become conditioned to the reinforced response is independent of the trial number and of events on preceding trials.*

Stimulus Sampling Axioms

S1. *Exactly one of the N elements is sampled on each trial.*
S2. *The probability of sampling any particular element may be a function of the trial number and the preceding events. If h_n denotes the sequence of stimuli, responses, and reinforcing events that occurred up to and including trial $n - 1$, then the probability of sampling element i on trial n is some function of h_n, denoted $\sigma_i(h_n)$.* (By Axiom S1

$$\sum_{i=1}^{N} \sigma_i(h_n) = 1$$

for every value of *n*.)

Response Axiom

On each trial that response is made to which the sampled element is conditioned.

These are the general axioms of the N-element pattern model. We will study the particular model derived by appending the following additional restrictions:

(1) The sampling function is $\sigma_i(h_n) = 1/N$, which is independent of i and h_n. In other words, each element has an equal probability, $1/N$, of being sampled on any trial.

(2) There are only two responses, A_1 and A_2, and only two reinforcing events, E_1 and E_2.

(3) The probability of event E_1 on any trial is a constant, π; the probability of event E_2 is $1 - \pi$.

These restrictions might be appropriate if the model were being applied to a simple learning situation, involving no discrimination from the experimenter's point of view. Restriction (3) obviously would be unsuitable in the numerous situations where the reinforcement is contingent on which of the responses occurred on that trial. Nevertheless, there are many cases for which the three restrictions appear plausible. One typical case is the two-response probability learning experiment, and the model has been used successfully in analyzing such experiments.* The typical arrangement is for the human subject to predict on each trial whether light 1 or light 2 will come on. After his prediction (A_1 or A_2), one of the lights comes on, informing him of the correct prediction on that trial (E_1 or E_2). With probability π, light 1 (E_1) comes on, and with probability $1 - \pi$ light 2 (E_2) comes on. The specific restrictions apply to other experiments besides the one outlined on probability learning; the probability learning experiment was mentioned so that the reader will have some concrete referent to enhance his understanding of the following analysis of the model.

8.3 CONDITIONING STATES AND RELATED PROBABILITIES

A subject run through the experiment will encounter a particular sequence of reinforcing events over trials. As he goes along, various stimulus elements will become conditioned to one response, then to another, and so on. We say that the stochastic process representing the subject is fully described at the start of any trial n by simply listing the N stimulus elements and the responses to which they are currently conditioned; once we know this listing, we have most of the information necessary to make a prediction of the response on trial n (what is not known is the stimulus element to be sampled on the trial). Since each

---

* See Chapter 5 (especially Secs. 5.6 and 5.7) for a discussion of probability learning.

stimulus element is sampled with equal likelihood, we do not really need to know *which* elements are conditioned to A_1, which to A_2, and so forth. All that is necessary is that we know *how many* of the elements are conditioned to each of the responses. If there are r responses, we could characterize the state of conditioning on any trial by a vector of $r - 1$ components. The first component would specify the number of elements conditioned to response A_1, the second component the number conditioned to A_2, and so on. Only $r - 1$ components need be specified since the rth component (representing the number of elements conditioned to response A_r) can be obtained by subtracting the other components from N. Because the ith component specifies the number of elements conditioned to A_i, it can take on any of the integer values 0, 1, 2, . . . , N.

With only two responses, the vector of $r - 1$ components reduces to a single number, namely, the number of elements conditioned to A_1. If i elements are conditioned to A_1, then $N - i$ elements must be conditioned to response A_2. Thus we find that the single number i gives us complete knowledge of the relative "strengths" of the two mutually exclusive responses. We introduce some notation for these states of conditioning. Specifically, the state of conditioning on trial n will be denoted $C_{i,n}$, where $i = 0, 1, 2, \ldots, N$. The subscript i indicates the number of elements conditioned to A_1, and $N - i$ indicates the number of elements conditioned to A_2.

We now wish to predict the subject's response on trial n. Not knowing which element will be sampled, the best we can do is to specify the probability that the response will be A_1. At this point knowledge of the subject's state of conditioning enters. We may know that i elements are conditioned to A_1. If so, then the probability that one of these i elements is sampled, and hence that A_1 occurs, will be i/N. Stated formally,

$$(8.1) \qquad Pr(A_{1,n} \mid C_{i,n}) = \frac{i}{N}.$$

That is, the probability of response A_1, conditional upon the subject being in state C_i at the beginning of trial n, is i/N. Note from Eq. 8.1 that the only admissible values of $Pr(A_{1,n})$ are $0/N, 1/N, 2/N, \ldots, (N - 1)/N,$ N/N which are all multiples of $1/N$. Hence $Pr(A_{1,n})$ can take on only a finite set of values, and therefore the learning is assumed to be a series of discrete "jumps" from one multiple of $1/N$ to another.

We will let $Pr(C_{i,n})$ denote the probability of being in state C_i at the start of trial n. Since the subject must be in one of the conditioning states on each trial, it follows that

$$\sum_{i=0}^{N} Pr(C_{i,n}) = 1.$$

Thus, the state of conditioning on trial n is a random variable, and $Pr(C_{i,n})$ is the associated probability measure.

Suppose that the probabilities $Pr(C_{i,n})$ are known. Then we can calculate the expected probability of response A_1 on trial n by summing over the possible states of conditioning as follows:

$$(8.2) \qquad Pr(A_{1,n}) = \sum_{i=0}^{N} Pr(A_{1,n} \,\&\, C_{i,n})$$

$$= \sum_{i=0}^{N} Pr(A_{1,n} \mid C_{i,n}) Pr(C_{i,n})$$

$$= \sum_{i=0}^{N} \frac{i}{N} Pr(C_{i,n}).$$

The first line involves expanding $Pr(A_{1,n})$ into a sum of probabilities of the joint events $A_{1,n}$ and $C_{i,n}$. The second line replaces the joint probability, $Pr(A \,\&\, C)$, by the conditionalized form $Pr(A \mid C) Pr(C)$. In the last line, we have substituted for $Pr(A_{1,n} \mid C_{i,n})$ in terms of the model expression, i/N, given in Eq. 8.1. Many of the derivations in the later parts of this chapter involve this standard sequence of operations: expand the expression into a sum of joint probabilities involving the states $C_{i,n}$, conditionalize upon the state, apply the model to simplify the expressions, and then collect terms and carry out the indicated summations.

The problem to be considered next is the calculation of the quantity $Pr(C_{i,n})$. Recall that the state of conditioning for any given subject is represented by an integer i $(0 \le i \le N)$ and this state can change from one trial to the next as the result of the reinforcement schedule. If we consider the trial-sequence of conditioning states, the model makes some strong assertions about this sequence. In brief, for noncontingent reinforcement the theory implies that the trial sequence of conditioning states is a Markov chain involving one-trial dependencies. This means that if we know the state of conditioning at the start of trial n, then we can calculate the probability of any other state of conditioning on trial $n + 1$. Let us show how the axioms of the model permit us to do this.

Suppose that the state of conditioning at the start of trial n is $C_{i,n}$; that is, i elements are conditioned to A_1 and $N - i$ to A_2. Recall that only one element is sampled per trial, so the state of conditioning can at most increase or decrease by one as the result of this trial. That is, from C_i, the process can move in one trial either to C_{i+1}, or to C_{i-1}, or stay in C_i. Under what circumstances will the state of conditioning move from C_i to C_{i+1}? Three events must be realized for this transition to occur: (1) one of the $N - i$ elements conditioned to A_2 must be sampled, this with

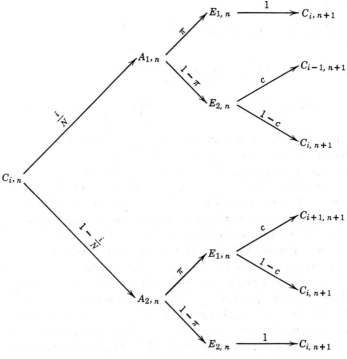

Figure 8.1.

probability $(N - i)/N$; (2) an E_1 reinforcing event must follow, this with probability π; and (3) the reinforcing event must be effective in altering the conditioning of the sampled element, this with probability c. Hence the probability of a transition from C_i to C_{i+1} on a single trial is the product of the probabilities of these three independent events, namely, $\dfrac{(N - i)}{N} \pi c$.

In similar fashion, the three events required to effect a transition from C_i to C_{i-1} are (1) one of the i elements conditioned to A_1 is sampled, this with probability i/N; (2) an E_2 reinforcing event occurs, this with probability $1 - \pi$; and (3) the reinforcing event is effective in altering the state of conditioning, this with probability c. Hence, the likelihood of a transition from C_i to C_{i-1} is $(i/N)(1 - \pi)c$. The scheme for generating these state-to-state transition probabilities is shown in the tree diagram of Fig. 8.1. Starting in state C_i at the beginning of trial n, we follow out a particular sequence of the three events—sampling, reinforcement, conditioning—to an end point, giving the state of conditioning at the start of trial $n + 1$. We may summarize the tree in Fig. 8.1 by the following set of conditional probabilities:

$$(8.3a) \quad Pr(C_{i+1,n+1} \mid C_{i,n}) = q_{i,i+1} = \left(1 - \frac{i}{N}\right)\pi c$$

$$(8.3b) \quad Pr(C_{i-1,n+1} \mid C_{i,n}) = q_{i,i-1} = \frac{i}{N}(1 - \pi)c$$

$$(8.3c) \quad Pr(C_{i,n+1} \mid C_{i,n}) = q_{i,i} = 1 - c\left[\left(1 - \frac{i}{N}\right)\pi + \frac{i}{N}(1 - \pi)\right].$$

Equation 8.3 is to be interpreted as the state-to-state transition probabilities of the Markov chain in the $C_{i,n}$'s. For the noncontingent case the transition probabilities depend only upon the state C_i and not upon the trial index n; hence we suppress the trial subscript and use the notation $q_{i,j}$ for the probability of a one-trial transition from state C_i on trial n to state C_j on trial $n + 1$. Recall that the state of conditioning index i can take on the values $0, 1, 2, \ldots, N$. In case $i = 0$, we see that Eq. 8.3b does not allow for any further downward transitions; likewise, when $i = N$, Eq. 8.3a allows no further upward transitions. It can be shown (see Atkinson and Estes, 1963) that if $c > 0$ and $0 < \pi < 1$, then the Markov chain specified by Eq. 8.3 is ergodic. We shall shortly calculate its limiting distribution. In case $\pi = 1$, it is seen that only upward movements can occur (since Eq. 8.3b is zero when $\pi = 1$); under these conditions the state where all elements are conditioned to A_1 (that is, state C_N) is an absorbing state. In the subsequent development, we shall suppose that π has a value intermediate between zero and one, and hence the resulting Markov process is ergodic. Given knowledge of what conditioning state the subject starts in on trial 1 and given the transition probabilities, we can calculate $Pr(C_{i,n})$ from trial to trial by the methods described in Sec. 7.2.

Asymptotic Distribution of Conditioning States

Next, we wish to find the limiting value of $Pr(C_{i,n})$ as n becomes large. To simplify the notation let u_i represent this limit; that is,

$$u_i = \lim_{n \to \infty} Pr(C_{i,n}).$$

As indicated in Sec. 7.2, for an ergodic chain, this limit exists and is independent of the state on trial 1.

The theorem to be proved is that all of the u_i can be expressed recursively in terms of u_0; since the u_i's must sum to unity, this recursion suffices to determine their entire distribution. First note that by Eq. 7.12,

$$u_0 = u_0 q_{0,0} + u_1 q_{1,0};$$

hence

$$\frac{u_0}{u_1} = \frac{q_{1,0}}{1 - q_{0,0}} = \frac{q_{1,0}}{q_{0,1}}.$$

We now prove by induction that a similar relation holds for any adjacent pair of states i and $i + 1$; namely, that

(8.4)
$$\frac{u_i}{u_{i+1}} = \frac{q_{i+1,i}}{q_{i,i+1}}.$$

First consider u_i, the probability of being in state i. Equation 7.12 yields the relation

$$u_i = u_{i-1}q_{i-1,i} + u_i q_{i,i} + u_{i+1}q_{i+1,i}.$$

That is, we may move into state C_i in one trial by either being in C_{i-1} and moving up, being in C_i and staying there, or being in C_{i+1} and moving down. Rearranging this equation yields

$$u_i(1 - q_{i,i}) = u_{i-1}q_{i-1,i} + u_{i+1}q_{i+1,i}.$$

At this point in the argument, let us replace u_{i-1} by its equivalent assuming that the inductive hypotheses given in Eq. 8.4 is true. Using Eq. 8.4, the equivalent of u_{i-1} would be $u_i q_{i,i-1}/q_{i-1,i}$. Substituting this expression for u_{i-1} in the line above gives

$$u_i(1 - q_{i,i}) = \frac{u_i q_{i,i-1}q_{i-1,i}}{q_{i-1,i}} + u_{i+1}q_{i+1,i}$$

$$= u_i q_{i,i-1} + u_{i+1}q_{i+1,i}.$$

Rearranging terms,

$$u_i(1 - q_{i,i} - q_{i,i-1}) = u_{i+1}q_{i+1,i}.$$

Now recall that from state C_i the only possible transitions are to C_{i-1}, C_i, or C_{i+1}. This means that

$$q_{i,i-1} + q_{i,i} + q_{i,i+1} = 1.$$

Hence, $q_{i,i+1}$ may be substituted for $1 - q_{i,i} - q_{i,i-1}$. After substitution, we obtain

$$u_i q_{i,i+1} = u_{i+1}q_{i+1,i},$$

and therefore

$$\frac{u_i}{u_{i+1}} = \frac{q_{i+1,i}}{q_{i,i+1}}.$$

Since this result verifies Eq. 8.4, the proof by induction is complete. To recapitulate, we showed that the relation hypothesized in Eq. 8.4 held for $i = 0$. Next we assumed the validity of Eq. 8.4 for arbitrary i. The burden of the proof involved showing that, given this assumption, Eq. 8.4 still holds when i is replaced by $i + 1$.

Having established Eq. 8.4, let us see how it is used to obtain u_i. The equation permits us to write

$$u_1 = \frac{q_{0,1}u_0}{q_{1,0}}, \qquad u_2 = \frac{q_{1,2}u_1}{q_{2,1}} = \frac{q_{0,1}q_{1,2}u_0}{q_{1,0}q_{2,1}},$$

and so forth. Since the u_i's must sum to unity, u_0 also is determined. Recall that the specific transition probabilities given in Eqs. 8.3a and 8.3b were

$$q_{i,i+1} = c\pi \frac{N - i}{N}$$

$$q_{i,i-1} = c(1 - \pi)\frac{i}{N}.$$

Taking ratios of the transition probabilities, we have

$$\frac{u_1}{u_0} = \frac{q_{0,1}}{q_{1,0}} = \frac{c\pi}{\dfrac{c}{N}(1 - \pi)} = \frac{N\pi}{(1 - \pi)}$$

$$\frac{u_2}{u_1} = \frac{q_{1,2}}{q_{2,1}} = \frac{c\pi\left(\dfrac{N - 1}{N}\right)}{c(1 - \pi)2/N} = \frac{(N - 1)\pi}{2(1 - \pi)},$$

and in general

$$(8.5) \qquad \frac{u_i}{u_{i-1}} = \frac{q_{i-1,i}}{q_{i,i-1}} = \frac{c\pi\left(\dfrac{N - i + 1}{N}\right)}{c(1 - \pi)\left(\dfrac{i}{N}\right)} = \frac{(N - i + 1)\pi}{i(1 - \pi)}.$$

This result on the ratio of u_i to u_{i-1} has two significant features. First, note that the ratios of asymptotic probabilities are independent of the conditioning parameter c. Second, the ratio of u_i to u_{i-1} is the same as that of neighboring terms of the binomial distribution. From this observation we conjecture that

$$(8.6) \qquad u_i = Pr(C_i) = \binom{N}{i}\pi^i(1 - \pi)^{N-i}.$$

It is easy to show that the u_i's defined by Eq. 8.6 do in fact satisfy the ratio in Eq. 8.5. That is,

$$\frac{u_i}{u_{i-1}} = \frac{\binom{N}{i}\pi^i(1-\pi)^{N-i}}{\binom{N}{i-1}\pi^{i-1}(1-\pi)^{N-i+1}}$$

$$= \left[\frac{\dfrac{N!}{i!\,(N-i)!}}{\dfrac{N!}{(i-1)!\,(N-i+1)!}}\right]\left[\frac{\pi}{(1-\pi)}\right].$$

Whence,

$$\frac{u_i}{u_{i-1}} = \frac{(N-i+1)\pi}{i(1-\pi)}$$

which is the result in Eq. 8.5.

The result of our lengthy derivations is quite simple. The limiting probabilities in this case are binomially distributed (Eq. 8.6). Thus, the asymptotic probability u_N that all N patterns are conditioned to A_1 is π^N; the probability that all but one of the N are conditioned to A_1 is $N\pi^{N-1}(1-\pi)$; and so forth. We should point out that there are two different but complementary ways to interpret the state probabilities of an ergodic Markov chain. One interpretation states that of a large group of subjects run to asymptote on this experiment, on any particular asymptotic trial we will find a proportion u_i of the subjects in conditioning state i. The alternate interpretation is that if a single subject were run for a large number of trials, then a proportion u_i of these trials would be spent in state C_i. Properties of ergodic chains assure us that given enough trials, a single sequence (subject) will faithfully trace out the complete asymptotic distribution.

8.4 THE MEAN LEARNING CURVE

We wish to find an expression for the probability of an A_1 response on trial n. Recall that by the developments in Eq. 8.2 we obtained the relation

(8.7) $$Pr(A_{1,n}) = \sum_{i=0}^{N}\frac{i}{N}\,Pr(C_{i,n}).$$

As stated earlier, to obtain explicit expressions for the quantities $Pr(C_{i,n})$ involves more complexity than we wish to deal with in this text. Fortunately, in computing $Pr(A_{1,n})$ we can circumvent the problem of calculating the $Pr(C_{i,n})$ values. The shortcut consists in deriving a difference equation relating $Pr(A_{1,n})$ to its prior value, $Pr(A_{1,n-1})$.

Let y_n denote the value of $Pr(A_{1,n})$ for an individual subject. Then the value of y_{n+1} must be either $y_n + 1/N$, $y_n - 1/N$, or y_n. The first possibility (that is, $y_{n+1} = y_n + 1/N$) arises if three conditions are met: (1) with probability $1 - y_n$ an element is sampled which is not conditioned to A_1; (2) with probability π reinforcement $E_{1,n}$ occurs, and (3) with probability c, the sampled element is conditioned to A_1. Multiplying together the probabilities of these events, we find that y_{n+1} takes on the value $y_n + 1/N$ with probability $(1 - y_n)\pi c$. The second possibility, that $y_{n+1} = y_n - 1/N$, occurs under conditions complementary to (1), (2), and (3). That is: ($1'$) on trial n the sampled element is connected to A_1; ($2'$) reinforcement $E_{2,n}$ occurs, and ($3'$) the element formerly connected to A_1 must become conditioned to A_2. Hence y_{n+1} takes on the value $y_n - 1/N$ with probability $y_n(1 - \pi)c$. The third possibility, that $y_{n+1} = y_n$, occurs with probability

$$Pr(y_{n+1} = y_n) = 1 - Pr\left(y_{n+1} = y_n + \frac{1}{N}\right) - Pr\left(y_{n+1} = y_n - \frac{1}{N}\right).$$

To summarize

$$y_{n+1} = \begin{cases} y_n + \dfrac{1}{N}, & \text{with probability } (1 - y_n)\pi c \\[2mm] y_n - \dfrac{1}{N}, & \text{with probability } y_n(1 - \pi)c \\[2mm] y_n, & \text{with probability } 1 - (1 - y_n)\pi c - y_n(1 - \pi)c. \end{cases}$$

Weighting these possible values of y_{n+1} by their probabilities of occurrence gives $E(y_{n+1})$ as a function of y_n

$$E(y_{n+1}) = \left(y_n + \frac{1}{N}\right)[(1 - y_n)\pi c] + \left(y_n - \frac{1}{N}\right)[y_n(1 - \pi)c]$$
$$+ y_n[1 - (1 - y_n)\pi c - y_n(1 - \pi)c].$$

Simplification yields

$$E(y_{n+1}) = \left(1 - \frac{c}{N}\right)y_n + \frac{c\pi}{N}.$$

The remaining step in finding the mean learning curve is to show that $E(y_{n+1})$ and y_n can be replaced in the equation above by $Pr(A_{1,n+1})$ and $Pr(A_{1,n})$, respectively. A proof would proceed in the fashion exemplified by Eq. 5.16; namely, taking all possible values of y_n, weighting each value by its probability of occurrence, and carrying out the appropriate summation. Since the relation in the equation above is linear, there is no need to illustrate this method of proof a second time; the reader can refer to Atkinson and Estes (1963, p. 183) for more details. Making the above mentioned substitutions completes the derivation of the recursion for the mean value of $Pr(A_{1,n})$:

$$Pr(A_{1,n+1}) = \left(1 - \frac{c}{N}\right) Pr(A_{1,n}) + \frac{c\pi}{N}.$$

This is a linear difference equation that can be solved by standard methods (see Eq. 5.19). The solution in this case is

$$(8.8) \qquad Pr(A_{1,n}) = \pi - [\pi - Pr(A_{1,1})]\left(1 - \frac{c}{N}\right)^{n-1}.$$

Thus, the theory predicts a negatively accelerated mean learning curve which starts at $Pr(A_{1,1})$ and approaches an asymptote of π as n becomes large; the rate of approach to the asymptote is determined by c/N.

Because of the variability typically displayed by single-trial estimates of $Pr(A_{1,n})$, experimenters frequently group trials into blocks and plot the average proportion of A_1 responses over successive blocks of trials. If we let K be the number of trials pooled in each block and let $P(m)$ be the average probability of an A_1 response during the mth block, then the formula derived from Eq. 8.8 is

$$P(m) = \pi - [\pi - P(1)]\left(1 - \frac{c}{N}\right)^{K(m-1)}.$$

The derivation of this result is similar to that given in Eq. 5.23, and we leave it as an exercise for the interested reader.

8.5 SEQUENTIAL PREDICTIONS

In this section certain sequential predictions are derived for the N-element pattern model. On each trial a response and reinforcing event occurs. One may consider the probability of response A_1 on the next trial given knowledge of either the prior response, the prior reinforcement, or both together. We consider the last case, since the former two are easily obtained from it. There are four events one trial back upon which we can conditionalize: A_1E_1, A_1E_2, A_2E_1, and A_2E_2. Similarly, going back two trials yields 16 events upon which to conditionalize.

Before undertaking a formal analysis of sequential effects, let us consider, in an intuitive way, the possible orderings of the probabilities of A_1, given the events A_1E_1, A_1E_2, A_2E_1 or A_2E_2 on the previous trial. First, it is reasonable to expect that the occurrence of an E_2 on trial n will reduce $Pr(A_{1,n+1})$; so holding constant the response emitted and varying the reinforcing event, we can expect the following orderings:

$$Pr(A_{1,n+1} \mid A_{1,n}E_{1,n}) \geq Pr(A_{1,n+1} \mid A_{1,n}E_{2,n})$$

and

$$Pr(A_{1,n+1} \mid A_{2,n}E_{1,n}) \geq Pr(A_{1,n+1} \mid A_{2,n}E_{2,n}).$$

Consider now the information given when we know the subject's response on trial n. It should be clear that the subject's response on trial n gives us some information about his conditioning state on that trial, and consequently tells us something about his state on trial $n + 1$. In particular, the fact that the subject made A_1 on trial n implies that his state of conditioning is probably more favorable to making another A_1 on trial $n + 1$ than would have been the case if he had made an A_2 on trial n. Thus, holding constant the reinforcing event, we would expect the following orderings of conditional probabilities:

$$Pr(A_{1,n+1} \mid A_{1,n}E_{1,n}) \geq Pr(A_{1,n+1} \mid A_{2,n}E_{1,n})$$

and

$$Pr(A_{1,n+1} \mid A_{1,n}E_{2,n}) \geq Pr(A_{1,n+1} \mid A_{2,n}E_{2,n}).$$

From these considerations, it is clear that $Pr(A_1 \mid A_1E_1)$ should have the highest value and $Pr(A_1 \mid A_2E_2)$ should have the lowest. The ordering of $Pr(A_1 \mid A_2E_1)$ and $Pr(A_1 \mid A_1E_2)$ is indeterminate since here the response and reinforcing effects are pitted against each other. We now undertake the derivation of these probabilities from the theory in order to establish the ordering and the magnitude of the differences to be expected. Let us consider first the mean probability of an A_1 response, given that it occurred and was reinforced on the preceding trial; this conditional probability may be written as

$$(8.9) \quad Pr(A_{1,n+1} \mid E_{1,n}A_{1,n}) = \frac{Pr(A_{1,n+1}E_{1,n}A_{1,n})}{Pr(E_{1,n}A_{1,n})} = \frac{Pr(A_{1,n+1}E_{1,n}A_{1,n})}{\pi Pr(A_{1,n})}.$$

The probability in the denominator can be written as $\pi Pr(A_{1,n})$ since the noncontingent reinforcement schedule makes the reinforcing events independent of the response. The term $Pr(A_{1,n})$ in the denominator was derived before in Eq. 8.8 so we know what that is. The only unknown is the joint probability in the numerator, which we shall derive next. We use the standard procedure mentioned previously, namely, expand the expression in terms of the possible conditioning states, conditionalize, then simplify and sum.

Since we are considering responses on trials n and $n + 1$, it is necessary to expand the joint probability in terms of the possible conditioning states on both trial n and $n + 1$. Let i index the former, and j index the latter.

The expanded version reads

$$(8.10) \qquad Pr(A_{1,n+1}E_{1,n}A_{1,n}) = \sum_{i=0}^{N} \sum_{j=0}^{N} Pr(A_{1,n+1}C_{j,n+1}E_{1,n}A_{1,n}C_{i,n}).$$

We now take this expanded probability (involving five variables) and repeatedly apply the rule for conditionalizing joint probabilities. An illustration of the repeated use of the rule is

$$
\begin{aligned}
Pr(ABCDE) &= Pr(A \mid BCDE)Pr(BCDE) \\
&= Pr(A \mid BCDE)Pr(B \mid CDE)Pr(CDE) \\
&= Pr(A \mid BCDE)Pr(B \mid CDE)Pr(C \mid DE)Pr(DE) \cdot \\
&= Pr(A \mid BCDE)Pr(B \mid CDE)Pr(C \mid DE)Pr(D \mid E)Pr(E),
\end{aligned}
$$

where A, B, C, D, and E are separate events. Applying this chain rule to our case yields

$$
\begin{aligned}
Pr(A_{1,n+1}&C_{j,n+1}E_{1,n}A_{1,n}C_{i,n}) \\
&= Pr(A_{1,n+1} \mid C_{j,n+1}E_{1,n}A_{1,n}C_{i,n})Pr(C_{j,n+1} \mid E_{1,n}A_{1,n}C_{i,n}) \\
&\times Pr(E_{1,n} \mid A_{1,n}C_{i,n})Pr(A_{1,n} \mid C_{i,n})Pr(C_{i,n}).
\end{aligned}
$$

Let us examine this last expression to see what simplifications can be effected. First, the term $Pr(E_{1,n} \mid A_{1,n}C_{i,n})$ can be rewritten as π because we are dealing with a noncontingent reinforcement schedule in which reinforcing events occur independently of the response made. Second, the term

$$Pr(A_{1,n+1} \mid C_{j,n+1}E_{1,n}A_{1,n}C_{i,n})$$

can be simplified to $Pr(A_{1,n+1} \mid C_{j,n+1})$. The model permits the deletion of the conditioning state, response, and reinforcement on the preceding trial because $Pr(A_{1,n+1})$ depends only upon the current conditioning state on trial $n + 1$.

Consider now the relation between the states $C_{i,n}$ and $C_{j,n+1}$. With no further knowledge, the model tells us that j can only be $i - 1$, i, or $i + 1$, which effects a simplification in the sum over j in Eq. 8.10. But the $C_{j,n+1}$ can be restricted even more because we know that an A_1 response and E_1 reinforcing event occurred on trial n. The fact that an A_1 response occurred on trial n means that one of the i elements conditioned to A_1 was sampled on trial n. Since the sampled element was already conditioned to the response reinforced by $E_{1,n}$, we know that no change in conditioning state is possible. In other words,

$$Pr(C_{j,n+1} \mid E_{1,n}A_{1,n}C_{i,n}) = \begin{cases} 1 & \text{if } j = i \\ 0 & \text{if } j \neq i. \end{cases}$$

We now collect this information together in carrying out the final summation:

$$\sum_{i=0}^{N} \sum_{j=0}^{N} Pr(A_{1,n+1} \mid C_{j,n+1}) Pr(C_{j,n+1} \mid E_{1,n} A_{1,n} C_{i,n}) Pr(E_{1,n})$$

$$\times\ Pr(A_{1,n} \mid C_{i,n}) Pr(C_{i,n})$$

$$= \sum_{i=0}^{N} Pr(A_{1,n+1} \mid C_{i,n+1}) \pi Pr(A_{1,n} \mid C_{i,n}) Pr(C_{i,n})$$

$$= \pi \sum_{i=0}^{N} \left(\frac{i}{N}\right)^2 Pr(C_{i,n}).$$

Let us define

$$\alpha_{2,n} = \sum_{i=0}^{N} \left(\frac{i}{N}\right)^2 Pr(C_{i,n}),$$

which is the second raw moment of the distribution. Inserting $\alpha_{2,n}$ into the above equation for $Pr(A_{1,n+1} E_{1,n} A_{1,n})$ yields

(8.11) $$Pr(A_{1,n+1} E_{1,n} A_{1,n}) = \pi \alpha_{2,n}.$$

We have thus reduced the joint probability in Eq. 8.10 to $\pi \alpha_{2,n}$. The conditional probability, according to Eq. 8.9, is

(8.12) $$Pr(A_{1,n+1} \mid E_{1,n} A_{1,n}) = \frac{\pi \alpha_{2,n}}{\pi Pr(A_{1,n})} = \frac{\alpha_{2,n}}{Pr(A_{1,n})}.$$

To obtain an explicit expression for this quantity requires an equation for $\alpha_{2,n}$. Although the latter can be derived without too much difficulty (see Estes and Suppes, 1959b), we bypass this problem and consider only the asymptotic case.

To write the asymptotic equation for $Pr(A_{1,n+1} \mid E_{1,n} A_{1,n})$ we need limiting expressions for both $Pr(A_{1,n})$ and $\alpha_{2,n}$. From Eq. 8.8 we have

$$\lim_{n \to \infty} Pr(A_{1,n}) = \pi.$$

The limit of $\alpha_{2,n}$ as n becomes large, denoted as α_2, can be obtained in terms of u_i. That is

$$\alpha_{2,n} = \sum_{i=0}^{N} \left(\frac{i}{N}\right)^2 Pr(C_{i,n}),$$

but in the limit $Pr(C_{i,n})$ can be replaced by u_i to yield

$$\alpha_2 = \sum_{i=0}^{N} \left(\frac{i}{N}\right)^2 u_i.$$

Recalling that the u_i are terms of the binomial distribution, we may write

$$\alpha_2 = \sum_i \frac{i^2}{N^2} \binom{N}{i} \pi^i (1 - \pi)^{N-i}$$

$$= \frac{1}{N^2} \sum_i i^2 \binom{N}{i} \pi^i (1 - \pi)^{N-i}.$$

The summation is the second raw moment of the binomial distribution with parameter π and sample size N. Therefore,

$$\alpha_2 = \frac{N\pi(1 - \pi) + N^2\pi^2}{N^2}$$

$$= \pi^2 + \frac{\pi(1 - \pi)}{N}.$$

Substituting these results into Eq. 8.12 yields:

(8.13) $$\lim_{n \to \infty} Pr(A_{1,n+1} \mid E_{1,n}A_{1,n}) = \pi + \frac{1 - \pi}{N}.$$

The asymptote of $Pr(A_{1,n})$ is π; therefore, Eq. 8.13 tells us that

$$\lim_{n \to \infty} Pr(A_{1,n+1} \mid E_{1,n}A_{1,n})$$

will be higher than the average asymptotic value of $Pr(A_{1,n})$. The magnitude of the sequential effect depends inversely upon N (the number of elements), but is independent of c.

To insure familiarity with the techniques involved, let us briefly go through the derivation of one other sequential probability; namely, $Pr(A_{1,n+1} \mid E_{1,n}A_{2,n})$. We expand the joint probability and then conditionalize successively to arrive at

(8.14) $Pr(A_{1,n+1}E_{1,n}A_{2,n})$

$$= \sum_{i=0}^{N} \sum_{j=0}^{N} Pr(A_{1,n+1} \mid C_{j,n+1})Pr(C_{j,n+1} \mid E_{1,n}A_{2,n}C_{i,n})$$

$$\times Pr(E_{1,n})Pr(A_{2,n} \mid C_{i,n})Pr(C_{i,n}).$$

Since an element conditioned to A_2 was sampled on trial n and an E_1 reinforcement occurred, the probabilities of the possible states of conditioning on trial $n + 1$ are

$$Pr(C_{j,n+1} \mid E_{1,n}A_{2,n}C_{i,n}) = \begin{cases} c & \text{for } j = i + 1 \\ 1 - c & \text{for } j = i \\ 0 & \text{otherwise.} \end{cases}$$

Using this restriction on j and substituting for the various terms, Eq. 8.14 can be reduced to

$$Pr(A_{1,n+1}E_{1,n}A_{2,n}) = \sum_{i=0}^{N}\left[c\frac{i+1}{N} + (1-c)\frac{i}{N}\right]\pi\left(1 - \frac{i}{N}\right)Pr(C_{i,n})$$

$$= \pi\left[\sum_{i=0}^{N}\frac{i}{N}\left(1 - \frac{i}{N}\right)Pr(C_{i,n}) + \frac{c}{N}\sum_{i=0}^{N}\left(1 - \frac{i}{N}\right)Pr(C_{i,n})\right]$$

$$= \pi\left\{Pr(A_{1,n}) - \alpha_{2,n} + \frac{c}{N}[1 - Pr(A_{1,n})]\right\}.$$

To convert this to the conditionalized form, we divide by $Pr(E_{1,n}A_{2,n}) = \pi[1 - Pr(A_{1,n})]$ to obtain

$$Pr(A_{1,n+1} \mid E_{1,n}A_{2,n}) = \frac{Pr(A_{1,n}) - \alpha_{2,n}}{1 - Pr(A_{1,n})} + \frac{c}{N}.$$

At asymptote

$$\lim_{n \to \infty} Pr(A_{1,n}) = \pi$$

and

$$\lim_{n \to \infty} \alpha_{2,n} = \pi^2 + \frac{\pi(1 - \pi)}{N}.$$

Hence

(8.15)
$$\lim_{n \to \infty} Pr(A_{1,n+1} \mid E_{1,n}A_{2,n}) = \pi + \frac{c - \pi}{N}.$$

Unless $c = 1$, this expression is less than the corresponding expression for $Pr(A_1 \mid E_1A_1)$, which agrees with the intuitive ordering given at the beginning of this section.

By use of identical techniques, we can derive the probability of A_1 conditional upon E_2A_1 or E_2A_2 on the prior trial. To summarize matters here, we list the asymptotic expressions for these four terms:

(8.16)
$$\lim_{n \to \infty} Pr(A_{1,n+1} \mid E_{1,n}A_{1,n}) = \pi\left(1 - \frac{1}{N}\right) + \frac{1}{N}$$

$$\lim_{n \to \infty} Pr(A_{1,n+1} \mid E_{1,n}A_{2,n}) = \pi\left(1 - \frac{1}{N}\right) + \frac{c}{N}$$

$$\lim_{n \to \infty} Pr(A_{1,n+1} \mid E_{2,n}A_{1,n}) = \pi\left(1 - \frac{1}{N}\right) + \frac{1-c}{N}$$

$$\lim_{n \to \infty} Pr(A_{1,n+1} \mid E_{2,n}A_{2,n}) = \pi\left(1 - \frac{1}{N}\right).$$

Note that these expressions satisfy the orderings conjectured at the beginning of this section. The intuitively indeterminate ordering of $Pr(A_1 \mid E_1A_2)$ and $Pr(A_1 \mid E_2A_1)$ is seen to depend upon the value of the conditioning parameter c. If $c > \frac{1}{2}$, the prior reinforcement dominates; if $c < \frac{1}{2}$, the prior response dominates.

An interesting relationship is revealed by the following differences between the terms in Eq. 8.16:

$$Pr(A_1 \mid E_1A_1) - Pr(A_1 \mid E_2A_1) = Pr(A_1 \mid E_1A_2) - Pr(A_1 \mid E_2A_2) = \frac{c}{N}.$$

The equivalence of these two differences can be interpreted as follows: when we take account of the information about the conditioning state provided by the prior response, the increment in $Pr(A_1)$ produced by an E_1 instead of an E_2 event is the same whether the subject is "rewarded" (makes A_1 and gets E_1) or "punished" (makes A_2 and gets E_1) by the event. We shall be especially interested in whether this prediction is borne out in the data to be considered.

The formulas in Eq. 8.16 give $Pr(A_{1,n+1})$ conditional upon the prior response and reinforcement. If we are interested in probabilities conditional upon only the prior response or the prior reinforcement, these expressions can be obtained from Eq. 8.16 by suitable use of the probability calculus. The general relation used is

$$Pr(A \mid B) = Pr(A \mid BC)Pr(C \mid B) + Pr(A \mid BD)Pr(D \mid B)$$

where B may be interpreted as the prior response and C and D as the prior reinforcements, or vice versa. The results are

$$\lim_{n \to \infty} Pr(A_{1,n+1} \mid A_{1,n}) = \pi + \frac{(1 - c)(1 - \pi)}{N}$$

$$\lim_{n \to \infty} Pr(A_{1,n+1} \mid A_{2,n}) = \pi - \frac{(1 - c)\pi}{N}$$

(8.17)

$$\lim_{n \to \infty} Pr(A_{1,n+1} \mid E_{1,n}) = \left(1 - \frac{c}{N}\right)\pi + \frac{c}{N}$$

$$\lim_{n \to \infty} Pr(A_{1,n+1} \mid E_{2,n}) = \left(1 - \frac{c}{N}\right)\pi.$$

Needless to say, these statistics are determined once $Pr(A_1 \mid E_iA_j)$ has been determined; hence, they do not constitute novel predictions to test the model.

A Specific Application

We shall illustrate use of these sequential expressions by examining data from a probability learning experiment reported by Suppes and Atkinson (1960, p. 196). In their experiment 30 college students were run, each for a series of 240 trials, in a two-response task. Each trial began with presentation of a ready signal; the subject's task was to respond to the signal by depressing one of a pair of response keys, A_1 or A_2, indicating his prediction as to which of two reinforcing lights would appear. The reinforcing lights were programmed by the experimenter to occur in a random sequence for each subject. The probability of an E_1 light was $\pi = 0.60$.

The transition data presented in Table 8.1 were obtained from the last 101 trials of the 240 trial series, during which time the mean response

Table 8.1   Transition Frequencies for
Suppes and Atkinson $\pi = 0.60$ Series

Events on Trial n	Response on Trial $n + 1$		Row Total
	A_1	A_2	
A_1E_1	748	298	1046
A_1E_2	394	342	736
A_2E_1	462	306	768
A_2E_2	186	264	450
Column Total	1790	1210	3000

probability was stable and judged to be asymptotic. The 100 trial-to-trial transition frequencies were tabulated for each subject, then summed over the 30 subjects, yielding 3000 observations. All statistics of immediate interest to us can be calculated from this table of transition frequencies.

First, we consider the model's prediction that the asymptotic $Pr(A_1)$ will be $\pi = 0.60$. Calculating the mean $Pr(A_1)$ from Table 8.1, it is found to be $1790/3000 = 0.596$, which is quite close to the predicted value. An estimate of the asymptotic probability of an A_1 response conditionalized upon the four combinations of events on the preceding trial may be obtained by dividing the first entry of each row by the row sum. This is done below, where we also repeat the relevant theoretical expressions:

$$Pr(A_1 \mid E_1A_1) = \pi\left(1 - \frac{1}{N}\right) + \frac{1}{N} = \frac{748}{1046} = 0.715$$

$$Pr(A_1 \mid E_2A_1) = \pi\left(1 - \frac{1}{N}\right) + \frac{1 - c}{N} = \frac{394}{739} = 0.535$$

$$Pr(A_1 \mid E_1A_2) = \pi\left(1 - \frac{1}{N}\right) + \frac{c}{N} = \frac{462}{768} = 0.601$$

$$Pr(A_1 \mid E_2A_2) = \pi\left(1 - \frac{1}{N}\right) = \frac{186}{450} = 0.413.$$

Table 8.2 Predicted and Observed Values
of Sequential Statistics for the Final 101
Trials of the $\pi = 0.6$ Series

Asymptotic Quantity	Predicted	Observed
$Pr(A_1 \mid E_1 A_1)$	0.715	0.715
$Pr(A_1 \mid E_2 A_1)$	0.541	0.535
$Pr(A_1 \mid E_1 A_2)$	0.601	0.601
$Pr(A_1 \mid E_2 A_2)$	0.428	0.413
$Pr(A_1 \mid A_1)$	0.645	0.641
$Pr(A_1 \mid A_2)$	0.532	0.532
$Pr(A_1 \mid E_1)$	0.669	0.667
$Pr(A_1 \mid E_2)$	0.496	0.489

These calculations reveal quite large sequential effects (from 0.413 to 0.715), so we judge that N is probably small and c is large.

We set the theoretical expression for $Pr(A_1 \mid E_1 A_1)$ equal to the observed value of 0.715, substitute $\pi = 0.60$, and solve for our estimate of N; that is

$$0.715 = 0.6\left(1 - \frac{1}{N}\right) + \frac{1}{N}$$

or $\hat{N} = 3.48$. To estimate c we choose $Pr(A_1 \mid E_1 A_2)$, since this is based on the second largest number of observations:

$$Pr(A_1 \mid E_1 A_2) = 0.601 = \pi\left(1 - \frac{1}{N}\right) + \frac{c}{N}.$$

Hence $\hat{c}/N = 0.174$. But $\hat{N} = 3.48$; therefore $\hat{c} = (3.48)(0.174) = 0.605$.

With these estimates of N and c, we can now see how well the theory predicts the other conditional probabilities. The entire set of predictions is given in Table 8.2. The reader is cautioned that there are only two independent entries in Table 8.2, namely, $Pr(A_1 \mid E_2 A_1)$ and $Pr(A_1 \mid E_2 A_2)$ since the others are constrained either by the fact that we have estimated two parameters, or by relations specified in the probability calculus.

Commenting briefly upon Table 8.2, we recall that the differences, $Pr(A_1 \mid E_1 A_1) - Pr(A_1 \mid E_2 A_1)$ and $Pr(A_1 \mid E_1 A_2) - Pr(A_1 \mid E_2 A_2)$, were expected to be equal. Calculation of these differences for the observed values indicate that the first one is 0.180 and the second is 0.188, which are tolerably close to one another. Recall also from our previous discussion that if $c > \frac{1}{2}$ (as it is in this case), then the prior reinforcement is more potent than the prior response. This is seen in the fact that $Pr(A_1 \mid E_1A_2) > Pr(A_1 \mid E_2A_1)$, and also in the fact that $Pr(A_1 \mid E_1) > Pr(A_1 \mid A_1)$ and $Pr(A_1 \mid E_2) < Pr(A_1 \mid A_2)$. Thus the model has given us a sensible interpretation of the sequential effects observed in this experiment.

8.6 CONCLUDING COMMENT

The purpose of this chapter has been to present a brief account of stimulus sampling theory and some of the mathematical techniques for analyzing a particular model derived from the theory. The general theoretical approach is quite viable, and in the past has led to a number of specific models which have enjoyed considerable success in various applications. For a sampling of these applications of the general theory, the interested reader is referred to reports by Estes (1959b, 1964), Atkinson and Estes (1963), and Suppes and Atkinson (1960). Because of the very general nature of the theory, the approach is incapable of "disproof" in the strong sense; we can show that specific models derived within the general framework are inaccurate or incomplete, but that could result from either incorrect assumptions or inappropriate correspondence rules at those points where the general theory is noncommittal. Much as with any general heuristic device, stimulus sampling theory should not be thought of as being provable or disprovable, right or wrong. Instead we judge the theory by how useful it is in suggesting specific models that may explain and bring some degree of orderliness into the data from particular experimental applications.

CHAPTER 9

PARAMETER
ESTIMATION

One of the most important features of mathematical models is that numerical predictions can be generated from the axioms. In turn, these predictions enable us to make a detailed evaluation of the fit of the model to data. In some cases, such predictions may be independent of specific parameter values, as illustrated in Chapter 4, where a number of predictions regarding choice behavior could be made without estimating any parameters. Nevertheless, for most models it is usually necessary to estimate one or several parameters before predictions can be made for a given set of data. For example, in Chapter 2 (see Eq. 2.27) the parameters p and c of the concept identification model were estimated by using the method of maximum likelihood. In Chapter 3 (see Eq. 3.7) the parameter c of the one-element paired-associate model was estimated by employing the method of moments.* In Chapter 5 (see Eq. 5.29) the sensitivity parameter σ of the signal detection model was estimated by the method of least squares. In fact, in every chapter some parameters had to be estimated; that is, it was necessary to sample a subset of the data to estimate a parameter (or parameters) before predictions could be made regarding the remainder of the data.

---

* Strictly speaking, the method of moments involves deriving equations for the first k moments of a given distribution function and equating them to the appropriate observed sample moments. The desired estimates are then obtained by solving the set of equations. A modification of this method has been used with regard to psychological models, which generally predict more than a single distribution function. Theoretical expressions and observed values of k statistics (which need not necessarily be the first k moments of the same distribution) are equated in order to estimate the parameters.

The problem of parameter estimation plays a central role in evaluating any quantitative theory. The reason that we have not treated the topic of estimation in any detail before now is that it involves advanced statistical techniques beyond the scope of this book. Also, problems of estimation may appear decidedly abstract until one has had the opportunity to appreciate the role of parameter estimates in individual applications of models to data. However, it is important for the reader to understand the basic statistical problems involved in parameter estimation. Consequently, we now turn to a brief discussion of the topic, and then conclude the chapter by considering several specific procedures. For expository purposes, it will be convenient to formulate the discussion in terms of a model that has a single parameter θ to be estimated from the data; however, our remarks can be readily generalized to the case of multiple-parameter estimation. A more complete discussion of parameter estimation in reference to psychological models is available (Bush, 1963).

9.1 PROPERTIES OF ESTIMATORS

Usually there are many ways of estimating the parameters of a model. Consequently, some rules need to be set forth to specify which estimators are desirable, which are not, and why. Intuitively, a good method of estimating some parameter θ is one that yields estimates close to the true value of the quantity being estimated. Let us try to make this concept of a good estimator more precise. Suppose that we have three different methods for estimating the parameter θ; we shall denote the estimates found by these three methods as $\hat{\theta}_1$, $\hat{\theta}_2$, and $\hat{\theta}_3$ (that is, $\hat{\theta}_1$ might be an estimate of θ using the method of moments, $\hat{\theta}_2$ might use the maximum likelihood method, and $\hat{\theta}_3$ a least squares procedure). Suppose also that we have a hypothetical subject with parameter value θ who behaves exactly as the theory requires. If our subject is run through an experiment, then at the end of the experiment we can take his data and apply our three methods of estimation to obtain $\hat{\theta}_1$, $\hat{\theta}_2$, and $\hat{\theta}_3$. Furthermore let us assume that the hypothetical subject can always be "reset" to his initial conditions at the conclusion of an experiment and then run through precisely the same experiment again. Since we are dealing with a probabilistic process, each repetition of the experiment will tend to generate a somewhat different set of data and hence different values for $\hat{\theta}_1$, $\hat{\theta}_2$, and $\hat{\theta}_3$. If our hypothetical subject is run through a large number of such identical experiments, then we would obtain a distribution of values for $\hat{\theta}_i$ for each of the estimation methods. We shall let $g(\hat{\theta}_i)$ be the density distribution of $\hat{\theta}_i$ in the case where an infinite number of such hypothetical experiments have been run.

Figure 9.1 illustrates possible density functions $g(\hat{\theta}_i)$ for the three methods of estimation. From this figure it is clear that $\hat{\theta}_1$ is the most desirable estimator. For any single experiment, the value of the estimate using $\hat{\theta}_2$, or even $\hat{\theta}_3$, may be closer to the true value of θ than the value of the estimate using $\hat{\theta}_1$; however, on the average the value of $\hat{\theta}_1$ will be nearer to the true value of θ than will be either $\hat{\theta}_2$ or $\hat{\theta}_3$. The criterion for

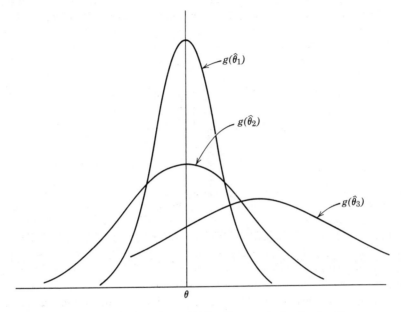

Fig. 9.1   Density functions $g(\theta_i)$ for three methods of estimation.

selecting $\hat{\theta}_1$ as the best estimator may be made more precise by defining the notion of *mean square error* with regard to the estimator $\hat{\theta}_i$. Let $E(\hat{\theta}_i - \theta)^2$ denote the mean square error, where

$$(9.1) \qquad E(\hat{\theta}_i - \theta)^2 = \int (\hat{\theta}_i - \theta)^2 g(\hat{\theta}_i) \, d\hat{\theta}_i$$

and the integral is over all possible values of $\hat{\theta}_i$. Thus, $E(\hat{\theta}_i - \theta)^2$ is a measure of the average variability of the estimate $\hat{\theta}_i$ about the true value θ. It is important to realize that the equation above is the second moment of the distribution about the true value θ, and not about the mean of the distribution.

Then, for example, in Fig. 9.1 the estimator $\hat{\theta}_1$ would be regarded as the most desirable, since $E(\hat{\theta}_1 - \theta)^2$ is smaller than either $E(\hat{\theta}_2 - \theta)^2$

or $E(\hat{\theta}_3 - \theta)^2$.* For the general case involving any number of possible methods of estimation, it is convenient to introduce the notion of the *best* estimator of the parameter θ. By definition, $\hat{\theta}_j$ is a best estimate of the parameter θ if $\hat{\theta}_j$ is such that

$$E(\hat{\theta}_j - \theta)^2 \leq E(\hat{\theta}_i - \theta)^2,$$

where $\hat{\theta}_i$ is any estimate of θ. That is, $\hat{\theta}_j$ is the best estimate if its mean square error is less than or equal to the mean square error of any other estimator.

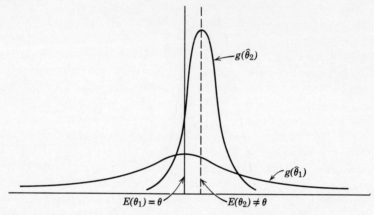

Fig. 9.2   Density functions for two estimators. Estimate $\hat{\theta}_2$ is biased, whereas estimate $\hat{\theta}_1$ is not.

For any estimator $\hat{\theta}_i$ we may also define its expected value; namely,

$$E(\hat{\theta}_i) = \int \hat{\theta}_i g(\hat{\theta}_i) \, d\hat{\theta}_i,$$

where, again, the integral is over all possible values of $\hat{\theta}_i$. If the estimator $\hat{\theta}_i$ has the property that $E(\hat{\theta}_i)$ equals the true parameter value θ, then $\hat{\theta}_i$ is an *unbiased* estimate of θ. In Fig. 9.1 it is clear that both θ_1 and θ_2 are unbiased estimators, but θ_3 is biased and tends to over estimate θ. Despite its desirability, the property of unbiasedness is of secondary importance. It is overruled by the demand for estimators that yield values

* A comparison between two estimators can be made quantitative by defining the notion of *relative efficiency*. Specifically, the efficiency of $\hat{\theta}_2$ relative to $\hat{\theta}_1$ is defined by the ratio

$$\frac{E(\hat{\theta}_1 - \theta)^2}{E(\hat{\theta}_2 - \theta)^2}.$$

If the ratio is less than one, then $\hat{\theta}_1$ is the more efficient estimator of θ; whereas, if the ratio is greater than one, $\hat{\theta}_2$ is the more efficient estimator.

in the neighborhood of the true value. For example, in Fig. 9.2 it is clear that the biased estimator θ_2 yields better estimates of θ than the unbiased estimator θ_1. The estimator θ_2 has a smaller mean square error than θ_1 and consequently will tend to yield estimates that are closer to θ than those generated by θ_1.

So far two properties of estimators have been discussed: the notion of an unbiased estimator and that of a best estimator. Two other properties of estimators are important in the present context. One is the property of *consistency*. We define a consistent estimate θ_i as one whose distribution $g(\theta_i)$ becomes more and more closely concentrated at the point θ as the sample size increases. Stated otherwise, an estimator is consistent if the probability that the estimate will be near the parameter value θ increases as the sample size increases. For most theoretical work, we are concerned with the problem of estimating parameters for individual subjects. Here, of course, sample size refers to the number of observations made on the subject. When data from different subjects are pooled, the sample size is determined by the total number of observations in the aggregate. Fortunately, almost any reasonable estimator will possess the property of being consistent.

Finally, let us define the notion of a *sufficient* estimator. Roughly speaking, an estimator θ_i is sufficient if it summarizes the whole of the relevant information supplied by the sample of data; that is, no additional information about the parameter θ can be supplied by any other statistic of the data. More precisely, an estimator θ_1 is said to be sufficient if, for any other estimator θ_2, the conditional distribution of θ_1 given θ_2 is independent of the parameter θ. Obviously, sufficient statistics are extremely desirable.

For many models considered in psychology it is very difficult, if not impossible, to obtain theoretical expressions for $g(\theta_i)$. Consequently, in most practical estimation problems, we are quite satisfied if we can compute the bias and variance of an estimator and from this information decide whether the estimator is adequate. If the computations are not feasible, then the prudent strategy is to be sure that we have a large number of observations for, as indicated earlier, most reasonable estimators possess the property of being consistent. Of course, sometimes for theoretical or practical reasons it is not possible to make a large number of observations. If this is the case and it also is impossible to compute some of the properties of $g(\theta_i)$, then one alternative is to resort to Monte Carlo methods.

Monte Carlo procedures involve generating pseudo-data by following precisely the rules specified by the model and consulting a random number generator whenever an event occurs in the process which is probabilistically determined. Thus the pseudo-data from a Monte Carlo run is an example of how real data would look if the model were correct and if the parameter θ had the value used in the Monte Carlo computations. Bush and Mosteller (1955) were among the first to use Monte Carlo methods in testing psychological models. They coined the term "stat-rat" to describe the hypothetical organism of a Monte Carlo run. Recall that in Chapter 6 Monte Carlos were run to simulate the two-operator linear model.*

Thus information can be obtained about $g(\hat{\theta}_i)$ by running a large number of Monte Carlos and applying the estimator $\hat{\theta}_i$ to the data of each run. Unfortunately, there are many difficulties associated with carrying out Monte Carlo runs and even with high speed computers the time involved may be prohibitive. Thus although the procedure sounds fine in theory, it sometimes becomes impossibly complex in practice. For an excellent discussion of the Monte Carlo method and some of the problems involved the reader should consult Bush and Mosteller (1955) and Bush (1963).

In the remaining sections of this chapter we shall outline the basic features of four estimators. The first example involves the application of maximum likelihood methods to Markov chains of the type considered in Chapter 7, and the second example applies this method to the one-element paired-associate learning model presented in Chapter 3. The third and fourth examples employ the method of minimum χ^2.

9.2   MAXIMUM LIKELIHOOD ESTIMATES
FOR MARKOV CHAINS

The principle of maximum likelihood provides an intuitively appealing method of estimation. As indicated earlier, we simply write out an expression $L(\theta)$, which expresses the likelihood of obtaining the particular set of observed data, and then select as the estimate of θ that value which maximizes the function. Aside from its intuitive attractiveness, the method of maximum likelihood has other desirable properties; these are set forth very lucidly by Cramér (1946). The most important of these properties will be summarized here. Under rather general conditions, maximum likelihood estimates are consistent; further, they often yield

---

* With the advent of high speed computers, a number of previously intractable problems in mathematical physics were solved using Monte Carlo methods. More recently Thorpe (1962) used Monte Carlo methods to devise a system for winning at the game of blackjack. Unfortunately, the system was so successful that many gambling casinos have changed the rules, making the game even more favorable to the house.

best estimates. Examples can be found where other methods are better, but for most applications the maximum likelihood method yields the best estimate or one that is very nearly so. Not all parameters have sufficient estimates; however, if a parameter does have sufficient estimators, then the maximum likelihood estimate will be a sufficient estimate. Another desirable property of maximum likelihood estimators is that for reasonably large samples, $g(\hat{\theta}_i)$ is approximately normally distributed with variance

$$\frac{1}{-E\left[\dfrac{\partial^2 \log L(\theta)}{\partial \theta^2}\right]}.$$

Thus normal curve methods can be used to determine the probability that the estimate will fall within a designated interval about θ. Despite these favorable properties, we should point out that maximum likelihood estimates may be biased; if we cannot compute $E(\hat{\theta}_i)$, then we cannot make appropriate adjustments for the bias.

Let us now apply the method of maximum likelihood to the case of an r-state Markov chain, where the states are directly observable, and the transition probabilities p_{ij} depend on a parameter θ. (For example, the three-state process described in Sec. 7.1.) Further, let a_n be a random variable that can take on any value from 1 to r on trial n; that is, the value of a_n will denote the state S_i that occurs on trial n of the experiment. Thus the sequence of values of the random variables $a_1, a_2, \ldots, a_n$ represents the outcome of an experiment from trial 1 through trial n. Further, let

$$Pr(a_1 a_2 \cdots a_n; \theta)$$

be the probability of observing the sequence of states $a_1, a_2, \ldots, a_n$ when the parameter is θ; this function is the likelihood function of the sample data. Then the maximum likelihood estimate of θ is the number $\hat{\theta}$ (if it exists) such that for all θ'

$$Pr(a_1 a_2 \cdots a_n; \hat{\theta}) \geqslant Pr(a_1 a_2 \cdots a_n; \theta').$$

By virtue of the Markov property of the process, we have

$$Pr(a_1 a_2 \cdots a_n; \theta)$$
$$= Pr(a_n \mid a_{n-1}; \theta)Pr(a_{n-1} \mid a_{n-2}; \theta) \cdots Pr(a_2 \mid a_1; \theta)Pr(a_1; \theta).$$

Therefore we want to find the value of θ that maximizes the expression

$$\prod_{m=2}^{n} Pr(a_m \mid a_{m-1}; \theta)Pr(a_1; \theta).$$

We shall let $p_{ij}(\theta)$ denote the function of θ which gives the probability of a transition from state i to state j. Also, let n_{ij} denote the observed number of transitions from state i to state j, summed over trials. (This notation was used in Sec. 7.3.) In terms of these quantities the above equation can be rewritten as

$$\prod_{i,j=1}^{r} p_{ij}^{n_{ij}}(\theta) Pr(a_1; \theta).$$

But it is often reasonable to assume that the probability of being in any state S_i at the outset of the experiment is independent of θ; that is, $Pr(a_1; \theta)$ will not depend on θ. Hence, it is sufficient to maximize the function

$$(9.2) \qquad L(\theta) = \prod_{i,j=1}^{r} p_{ij}^{n_{ij}}(\theta)$$

with respect to θ. To clarify this result suppose that our Markov chain generated the following sequence of states: $S_1 S_1 S_2 S_1 S_2 S_2 S_1 S_2$. Then $n_{11} = 1$, $n_{12} = 3$, $n_{21} = 2$, and $n_{22} = 1$. The use of the n_{ij}'s as exponents in Eq. 9.2 comes from the relation

$$L(\theta) = p_{11}p_{12}p_{21}p_{12}p_{22}p_{21}p_{12} = p_{11}p_{12}^{3}p_{21}^{2}p_{22}.$$

The value of θ that maximizes $L(\theta)$ also maximizes its logarithm, which in many cases is easier to work with. Consequently, we usually attempt to maximize the function

$$\log L(\theta) = \sum_{i,j} n_{ij} \log p_{ij}(\theta).$$

Ordinarily the function $\log L(\theta)$ will have a single maximum, and so θ is the appropriate solution to the equation

$$(9.3) \qquad \frac{\partial \log L(\theta)}{\partial \theta} = \sum_{i,j} n_{ij} \frac{p_{ij}'(\theta)}{p_{ij}(\theta)} = 0,$$

where $p_{ij}'(\theta)$ is the derivative of $p_{ij}(\theta)$ with respect to θ.

To illustrate this method consider a two-state Markov chain with the following transition matrix:

$$(9.4) \qquad \mathbf{P} = \begin{array}{c} \\ A_1 \\ A_2 \end{array} \begin{array}{c} A_1 \qquad\qquad A_2 \\ \begin{bmatrix} 1 - \theta + \pi\theta & (1 - \pi)\theta \\ \pi\theta & 1 - \pi\theta \end{bmatrix} \end{array}.$$

This matrix represents a special case of the pattern model of stimulus sampling theory applied to a probability learning experiment. (In fact the model developed in Chapter 8 reduces to this process when $N = 1$ and $c = \theta$.) The parameter π is set by the experimenter and determines the reinforcement schedule employed in the experiment; θ is a behavioral parameter that characterizes the subject's learning rate and must be estimated from the data. On each trial the subject makes either an A_1 or A_2 response, and the matrix $\mathbf{P}$ describes transitions between these two responses. From Eqs. 9.3 and 9.4 we obtain

$$\frac{\partial \log L(\theta)}{\partial \theta} = -\frac{n_{11}(1-\pi)}{1-\theta(1-\pi)} + \frac{n_{12}}{\theta} + \frac{n_{21}}{\theta} - \frac{n_{22}\pi}{1-\theta\pi}.$$

Setting this equation equal to zero and simplifying yields the quadratic equation

$$(9.5) \quad (n_{11} + n_{12} + n_{21} + n_{22})\pi(1-\pi)\theta^2$$
$$- [n_{11}(1-\pi) + n_{12} + n_{21} + n_{22} + n_{22}\pi]\theta + (n_{12} + n_{21}) = 0.$$

From Descartes' rule of signs, it follows that there are no negative roots. Further, it can be shown that the maximum likelihood estimate of θ is the smaller root of the equation. The proof that the smaller root is the appropriate one is straightforward and will not be given here.

Unfortunately, expressions for the maximum of the function $\log L(\theta)$ do not always simplify as neatly as our illustration might suggest. For example, if we apply Eq. 9.3 to the transition matrix derived in Sec. 7.1 (see Eq. 7.5), we obtain a complicated expression that cannot be readily solved for θ. When such complications arise, we may resort to numerical procedures and simply compute the function $\log L(\theta)$ for a grid of θ values. Plotting these results will give us some idea of what the function looks like and thus an approximation to its maximum value. In fact, the maximum can be approximated to any desired degree of accuracy simply by using a fine enough grid on θ when carrying out the computations. The complications involved in extending this numerical procedure to the case of multiple parameter estimates are discussed by Atkinson and Crothers (1964). When high-speed computers are available special iterative techniques known as *hill climbing* can be used to make multiple-parameter estimates; for a discussion of this topic see Green (1963).

The methods described in this section are applicable to Markov chains where the states of the process are directly observable. In many psychological models this is not the case; for example, in the models of Chapters 2, 3, and 8 the observed responses were probabilistically determined by the unobservable states of a Markov chain. When the states of a Markov chain are not directly observable, but can only be inferred probabilistically from the observable events, then the methods of parameter estimation discussed here need to be generalized. For a discussion of such generalizations, see Suppes and Atkinson (1960); in particular, see their discussion of pseudo-maximum likelihood estimates.

382 PARAMETER ESTIMATION CH. 9

9.3 MAXIMUM LIKELIHOOD ESTIMATE FOR THE ONE-ELEMENT PAIRED-ASSOCIATE MODEL

We now apply the method of maximum likelihood to the one-element paired-associate model of Chapter 3. Recall that for this model the acquisition of each stimulus-response pair is described by the transition matrix

$$\begin{array}{cc} & \begin{array}{cc} C & \bar{C} \end{array} \\ \begin{array}{c} C \\ \bar{C} \end{array} & \begin{bmatrix} 1 & 0 \\ c & 1-c \end{bmatrix}. \end{array}$$

In state C the probability of a correct response is 1, and in state $\bar{C}$ it is g. Also recall that in practice it is conventional to take $g = 1/r$, where r is the number of response alternatives and is fixed by the experimenter. Further, it was assumed in Chapter 3 that all items start out in state $\bar{C}$.

In order to apply the model to data an estimate of the parameter c is required. To simplify the discussion in Chapter 3, we chose to estimate c by the method of moments. First we obtained a theoretical expression for the expected number of errors per stimulus item (see Eq. 3.7); namely,

$$(9.6) \qquad\qquad E(T) = \frac{1-g}{c}.$$

Then c was estimated by substituting the observed average number of errors per subject-item in the above equation and solving for c. Using this estimate of c, predictions were generated for other quantities.

We now want to derive the maximum likelihood estimate of c for the one-element paired-associate model. Consider data for a single subject who has learned a list of M paired-associates; furthermore, assume that the M items are homogeneous in the sense that they all can be described by the same value of c. As in Chapter 3, define the random variable

$$x_n^{(i)} = \begin{cases} 0, & \text{if a correct response occurred to stimulus item } i \text{ on trial } n \\ 1, & \text{if an error occurred to stimulus item } i \text{ on trial } n. \end{cases}$$

Furthermore, let y_i denote the number of errors made on item i in the course of mastering the list; that is,

$$(9.7) \qquad\qquad y_i = \sum_{n=1}^{\infty} x_n^{(i)}.$$

Also, let l_i denote the trial number of the last error on item i; if no errors occur on item i then $l_i = 0$.* In terms of this notation, define

(9.8)
$$Y = \sum_{i=1}^{M} y_i$$

and

(9.9)
$$L = \sum_{i=1}^{M} l_i.$$

The quantity Y denotes the total number of errors made by the subject in mastering the M items, and L is the sum of the trial numbers of the last error. Finally, let s_0 be the number of items on which the subject made no errors.

To illustrate this notation consider the following hypothetical protocol for a subject learning a list of six items with $g = \frac{1}{2}$; the entries are the values of $x_n^{(i)}$.

Trial Number

	1	2	3	4	5	6	7	8	9	10
1	1	1	0	1	0	0	0	0	0	0
2	0	0	1	0	0	0	0	0	0	0
Stimulus 3	1	1	0	1	1	0	0	0	0	0
Item 4	0	0	0	0	0	0	0	0	0	0
(i) 5	1	0	0	1	0	1	0	0	0	0
6	1	0	0	0	0	0	0	0	0	0

If we assume that no additional errors occurred after trial 10, then

$$\begin{aligned} y_1 &= 3 & l_1 &= 4 \\ y_2 &= 1 & l_2 &= 3 \\ y_3 &= 4 & l_3 &= 5 \\ y_4 &= 0 & l_4 &= 0 \\ y_5 &= 3 & l_5 &= 6 \\ y_6 &= 1 & l_6 &= 1. \end{aligned}$$

Summing,

$$Y = 12,$$
$$L = 19.$$

Also $s_0 = 1$, because one item (item number 4) had no errors. The average number of errors per item is

$$\frac{Y}{M} = 2.0.$$

---

* In Chapter 3 the trial of last error was written as L.

Hence using Eq. 9.6 the moment estimate of c is simply

$$\hat{c} = \frac{1-g}{2} = 0.250.$$

Let us now consider the likelihood estimate of c. In Eqs. 3.10 and 3.15 we derived the following expressions for the probability that the last error occurred on trial number l_i for item i:

(9.10a) $Pr(l_i = 0) = bg$

(9.10b) $Pr(l_i = k) = b(1 - g)(1 - c)^{k-1}$ (for $k > 0$)

with $b = c/(1 - g + gc)$. Of course, because of the all-or-none nature of the process, if the last error occurred on trial l_i then

(9.11)
$$Pr(y_i = k \mid l_i > 0) = \binom{l_i - 1}{k - 1}(1 - g)^{k-1}g^{l_i-k}, \quad (\text{for } 1 \le k \le l_i)$$

$$Pr(y_i = 0 \mid l_i = 0) = 1.$$

That is, the probability of k errors, given that the last error occurred on trial l_i, is simply the binomial probability of $k - 1$ errors over the first $(l_i - 1)$ trials.

The likelihood of a particular response sequence for any item i follows directly from the considerations above

(9.12)
$$L(0, 0, \dots) = bg, \qquad\qquad (\text{for } l_i = 0)$$

$$L(x_1^{(i)}, x_2^{(i)}, \dots) = b(1 - g)^{y_i}g^{l_i-y_i}(1 - c)^{l_i-1}, \quad (\text{for } l_i > 0).$$

The first expression is the likelihood of a response sequence with no errors, which is the probability that $l_i = 0$ as given by Eq. 9.10a. The second expression is the likelihood of a response sequence, given that the last error occurs on trial $l_i > 0$. It is simply the probability that the last error occurred on trial l_i (see Eq. 9.10b) times the probability of a particular sequence of correct and incorrect responses on the first $(l_i - 1)$ trials; that is, the likelihood of the response sequence $(010010000\dots)$ is the probability that the last error occurred on trial 5 times $g^3(1 - g)$.

The likelihood of the set of M response sequences is then

(9.13) $$L(c) = (bg)^{s_0}\prod b(1 - g)^{y_i}g^{l_i-y_i}(1 - c)^{l_i-1}$$

where the product is taken over all response sequences with at least one error. Carrying out the product yields

(9.14) $$L(c) = b^M g^{L+s_0-Y}(1 - g)^Y(1 - c)^{L+s_0-M}$$

$$= \left(\frac{c}{1 - g + gc}\right)^M g^{L+s_0-Y}(1 - g)^Y(1 - c)^{L+s_0-M}.$$

But the value of c that maximizes $L(c)$ also maximizes its log. The latter (which takes us from products to more manageable sums) is

$$\log L(c) = M \log c - M \log (1 - g + gc) + (L + s_0 - Y) \log g$$
$$+ Y \log (1 - g) + (L + s_0 - M) \log (1 - c).$$

Then

(9.15)
$$\frac{\partial \log L(c)}{\partial c} = \frac{M(1 - g)}{c(1 - g + gc)} - \frac{L - M + s_0}{1 - c}.$$

Setting this derivative equal to zero yields a quadratic in the unknown parameter c:

(9.16) $g(L + s_0 - M)c^2 + (1 - g)(L + s_0)c - (1 - g)M = 0.$

It can be easily shown that the maximum likelihood estimate of c is the larger root; that is,

(9.17)
$$\hat{c} = \frac{\sqrt{(1 - g)^2(L + s_0)^2 + 4g(1 - g)M(L + s_0 - M)} - (1 - g)(L + s_0)}{2g(L + s_0 - M)},$$

where (from Eq. 9.16) $\hat{c} = 1$ if $L + s_0 = M$. Thus for our hypothetical set of data

$$\hat{c} = \frac{\sqrt{(\tfrac{1}{2})^2(19 + 1)^2 + 4(\tfrac{1}{2})(\tfrac{1}{2}) \, 6 \, (19 + 1 - 6)} - \tfrac{1}{2}(19 + 1)}{2(\tfrac{1}{2})(19 + 1 - 6)}$$
$$\approx 0.254.$$

In this example the maximum likelihood estimate of c turns out to be very close to the moments estimate, which was 0.250.

In concluding this discussion, we note that a good deal of research has been done by Kraemer (1964b) comparing the properties of the likelihood estimator and other estimators for this model (and also for related paired-associate models). Her article illustrates quite well the mathematical problems involved in investigating the properties of estimators for psychological models.

9.4   MINIMUM CHI-SQUARE ESTIMATES FOR MARKOV CHAINS

As in Sec. 9.2, we consider an r-state Markov chain whose states are directly observable, and let $p_{ij}(\theta)$ denote the theoretical transition probabilities, which are a function of θ. Furthermore n_{ij} will denote the observed number of transitions from state i to j; and n_i, the number of transitions from state i, is defined by the equation

$$n_i = n_{i1} + n_{i2} + \cdots + n_{ir}.$$

Then (as indicated in Sec. 7.3) the maximum likelihood estimate of p_{ij} is simply

(9.18)
$$\hat{p}_{ij} = \frac{n_{ij}}{n_i}.$$

In terms of these quantities we define the χ^2 function

(9.19)
$$\chi^2(\theta) = \sum_{i,j} \frac{n_i[\hat{p}_{ij} - p_{ij}(\theta)]^2}{p_{ij}(\theta)}.$$

This function nears its minimum as the predicted transition probabilities $p_{ij}(\theta)$ approach the observed values $\hat{p}_{ij}$; that is, the better the correspondence between predicted and observed values of p_{ij}, the smaller the χ^2. The method of minimum χ^2 requires that we select the estimate of θ so as to render $\chi^2(\theta)$ as small as possible.* Consequently, the estimate of θ is the solution of the equation

(9.20)
$$\frac{\partial \chi^2(\theta)}{\partial \theta} = \sum_{i,j} \left\{ \frac{n_i[\hat{p}_{ij}^2 - p_{ij}^2(\theta)]}{p_{ij}^2(\theta)} \frac{\partial p_{ij}(\theta)}{\partial \theta} \right\} = 0.$$

Even in simple cases this equation is often difficult to solve.** However, in many psychological applications it suffices to simply calculate the function $\chi^2(\theta)$ over a grid of possible values of θ and then use this information to approximate the minimum. This numerical method for computing the minimum can be generalized to the problem of estimating multiple parameters (Myers and Atkinson, 1964), and when high speed computers are available, the numerical approach is particularly useful.

As indicated in Sec. 7.3, under the null hypothesis the minimum χ^2 has a χ^2 limiting distribution with $[r(r - 1) - 1]$ degrees of freedom. More generally, if q parameters are estimated, then there remain $[r(r - 1) - q]$ degrees of freedom with which to evaluate the statistical significance of the computed χ^2. Thus the minimum χ^2 provides a measure of the adequacy of any single Markov model and, if the degrees of freedom are equal, a method for directly comparing the fits of several models.

---

* For a discussion of properties of the minimum χ^2 method, see Cramér (1946) and Anderson and Goodman (1957).
** Cramér (1946, p. 426) describes a modification of this method that greatly simplifies the minimization problem. It involves replacing the theoretical expression $p_{ij}(\theta)$ in the denominator of Eq. 9.19 by its observed value $\hat{p}_{ij}$.

If several models are being analyzed, each involving a different number of free parameters, then the probability levels of the minimum χ^2's can be compared. We return to this point later.

9.5 MINIMUM CHI-SQUARE ESTIMATES FOR SPECIFIC SEQUENCES

When the states of the model are unobservable (as is frequently the case with psychological models) a reasonable approach is to choose parameter estimates so as to maximize the model's fit to the observed frequencies of the possible response sequences. The fit can be measured by a minimum χ^2 criterion (Atkinson and Crothers, 1964). This routine, although originally developed for paired-associate learning models, is applicable whenever the requisite theoretical expressions for the response sequence probabilities can be derived. In fact, at the end of Sec. 6.2 we suggested that the minimum χ^2 method might improve the fit of the two-operator linear model to the response trigram (3-tuple) frequencies from the Solomon-Wynne avoidance conditioning experiment.

Linear model. In order to illustrate the advantages and limitations of this method, we select the single-operator linear model (see Sec. 3.4) and a set of paired-associate learning data reported by Calfee and Atkinson (1965).* Before presenting the data, however, we shall discuss the minimum χ^2 method in general terms and then derive the necessary equations.

Our immediate objective is to estimate the parameter α of the single-operator linear model. At this point a natural question is: why not simply estimate α by the maximum likelihood technique? The answer is that while the maximum likelihood procedure would be very satisfactory for the linear model, it would encounter serious analytical difficulties with many of the other models that we might want to apply to a particular set of data (for example, the long- and short-term retention model mentioned at the end of Sec. 3.5). Further, a comparison of models would be less satisfactory if we used one estimation method for one model and a different method for the next model. What we seek to provide with the minimum χ^2 is a single uniformly applicable technique that produces statistically satisfactory estimates.

The rationale for the present minimum χ^2 method becomes clearer when we recall that in paired-associates learning the basic datum is the response sequence of 1's and 0's for an individual subject-item; for many

---

* See their paper for a detailed account of the experimental procedure and results.

Table 9.1   Observed and Predicted Frequencies of Response Sequences for Trials 2 through 5

Notation	Sequence	Observed Frequency	Linear Model ($\hat{\alpha} = 0.85$)	One-Element Model ($\hat{c} = 0.15$)
s_1	0000	97	45.4	112.6
s_2	0001	11	24.2	6.8
s_3	0010	14	31.5	10.3
s_4	0011	12	16.8	13.5
s_5	0100	35	42.2	23.0
s_6	0101	14	22.5	13.5
s_7	0110	17	29.3	20.7
s_8	0111	20	15.6	27.1
s_9	1000	78	59.4	67.6
s_{10}	1001	15	31.7	13.5
s_{11}	1010	22	41.2	20.7
s_{12}	1011	30	22.0	27.1
s_{13}	1100	47	55.2	46.0
s_{14}	1101	16	29.5	27.1
s_{15}	1110	42	38.3	41.4
s_{16}	1111	55	20.4	54.1
χ^2			180.5	21.8

data analyses, the response sequences from different items and subjects are regarded as independent random samples from the same underlying stochastic process. Hence an "ideal" solution to the parameter estimation problem is straightforward: compute the sum over subjects and items of the observed frequencies of all possible sequences (for n trials there are 2^n possible sequences) and maximize the overall fit of predicted to observed frequencies. By thus basing the goodness-of-fit statistic on the raw sequential data, we ensure that the statistic uses all the information in the data.

Little reflection is needed to realize that this solution will usually not be feasible for two reasons. First, as n increases, 2^n rapidly becomes large, so there are too many sequences for which equations must be derived. Second, with increasing n, each individual expression rapidly becomes more complex. To circumvent these problems, we modify the method by examining only a subset of trials in the response sequence. If, say, we restrict attention to a sequence of four successive trials, then there are $2^4 = 16$ possible sequences of 1's and 0's and hence 16 expressions to be derived from the model.

Table 9.1 gives the observed frequency of each of the 16 possible sequences (tabulated over trials 2 to 5) for the data reported by Calfee and

Atkinson (1965) on a 21-item list. For brevity, the sequences have been labeled $s_1, s_2, \ldots, s_{16}$. Data from trial 1 were excluded, since results for this initial anticipation trial have no bearing on the empirical adequacy of the model's assumptions about learning.

The linear model example of the minimum χ^2 method is developed in two stages. First we derive the equation for the predicted probabilities of the various sequences. Then we write the χ^2 statistic as our measure of discrepancy between observed and predicted frequencies, and take up the question of how to find the value of α that minimizes the χ^2.

The derivation of the predicted probabilities, denoted as $Pr(s_i)$, is an elementary application of Eq. 3.22. Repeating that equation,

$$(9.21) \qquad\qquad q_n = \alpha^{n-1}q_1,$$

where q_n is the probability of an error on trial n. As in Sec. 3.4, the probability q_1 of a correct guess prior to the first reinforcement is assumed to be known *a priori*, leaving only α to be estimated from the data. Then for a particular sequence, say $s_{11} = \langle 1010 \rangle$, the predicted probability of occurrence over trials 2 to 5 is written in the usual response random variable notation:

$$Pr(s_{11}) = Pr(x_2 = 1 \ \& \ x_3 = 0 \ \& \ x_4 = 1 \ \& \ x_5 = 0)$$
$$= Pr(x_2 = 1)Pr(x_3 = 0)Pr(x_4 = 1)Pr(x_5 = 0).$$

As explained in Sec. 3.4, the second line is justified by the assumption made in the linear model that the x_n's are independent of one another. Replacing $Pr(x_n = 1)$ by q_n yields

$$Pr(s_{11}) = q_2(1 - q_3)q_4(1 - q_5)$$
$$= \alpha q_1(1 - \alpha^2 q_1)\alpha^3 q_1(1 - \alpha^4 q_1)$$
$$= \alpha^4 q_1^2(1 - \alpha^2 q_1)(1 - \alpha^4 q_1),$$

where the second line comes from Eq. 9.21. The corresponding equations for the other $Pr(s_i)$ are easily derived and need not be listed here. For example, $Pr(s_5) = Pr(0100) = (1 - \alpha q_1)\alpha^2 q_1(1 - \alpha^3 q_1)(1 - \alpha^4 q_1)$.

Suppose now that the total number of response sequences is T. The χ^2 statistic sets the grand total of predicted frequencies equal to T, so the predicted frequency corresponding to $Pr(s_i)$ is simply T times $Pr(s_i)$. If we denote the observed frequency as $N(s_i)$, then the χ^2 measure for the ith sequence is

$$\chi_i^2 = \frac{[TPr(s_i) - N(s_i)]^2}{TPr(s_i)}.$$

Assuming independent sequences, the sum of the χ_i^2 components over i also has a χ^2 distribution:

$$(9.22) \qquad \chi^2 = \sum_{i=1}^{16} \chi_i^2 = \sum_{i=1}^{16} \frac{[T Pr(s_i) - N(s_i)]^2}{T Pr(s_i)}.$$

Of course, in the general case of n-trial sequences, the sum would run from $i = 1$ to 2^n.

Now the goal is to find the value of α [using the known values of T, q_1, and the $N(s_i)$] that will minimize the right side of Eq. 9.22. An analytic solution would begin by deriving all the $Pr(s_i)$ equations in the fashion exemplified above for $Pr(s_5)$ and $Pr(s_{11})$. After inserting these 16 expressions in place of the $Pr(s_i)$ in Eq. 9.22, we would differentiate χ^2 with respect to α (the parameter being estimated), set this derivative equal to zero, and solve for α. However, this method often cannot be used because the algebraic operations involved in the differentiation become impossibly complex even for simple models.*

Instead, we resort to a numerical routine that has been developed as a program for a digital computer and that produces convenient, accurate estimates. The routine involves selecting a tentative numerical value of α, computing the associated $Pr(s_i)$'s and the χ^2, repeating the procedure with another value of α, and continuing thus until the range of possible values of α $(0 < \alpha \le 1)$ has been systematically explored. Next the program detects which one of the values of α yielded the lowest χ^2, and prints for this estimate of α each of the $Pr(s_i)$'s and the corresponding χ^2. When enough values of α are scanned, the method yields numerically close approximations to analytic solutions. Further details of the computer program need not concern us here.

For the Calfee and Atkinson study, we take $T = 525$ (25 subjects times 21 items) and $q_1 = \frac{2}{3}$, since three response alternatives were available. These values along with the observed $N(s_i)$ from Table 9.1 constitute the input to the minimization routine. The outcome of the calculation appears in the next-to-last column of Table 9.1. Our estimate is $\hat{\alpha} = 0.85$ and the associated minimum χ^2 equals 180.5. This χ^2 is evaluated with 14 degrees of freedom, because two constraints were imposed on the 16 cell entries of the table. One restriction is that the sum of the theoretical frequencies must equal the sum of the observed frequencies, and the second constraint arises from the fact that the parameter α is being estimated from the table. Entering a χ^2 table with 14 degrees of freedom,

---

* Even a modified minimum χ^2 method, whereby $N(s_i)$ replaces $T Pr(s_i)$ in the denominator of Eq. 9.22, generally does not permit sufficient simplification.

we see that a value of 180.5 falls well beyond the 0.001 level. Hence the linear model predictions deviate significantly from the observed $N(s_i)$'s.

From the output of the scanning routine we can plot a graph of χ^2 against α in order to see how sensitive the χ^2 value is to the exact magnitude of α. The curve is displayed in Fig. 9.3; it is concave upward with a single minimum, at $\alpha = 1 - 0.15 = 0.85$.

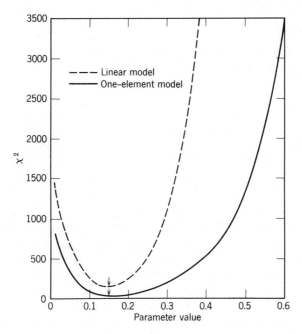

Fig. 9.3 χ^2 as a function of c for the one-element model, and as a function of $1 - \alpha$ for the linear model.

One-element model. To preface this final topic, we caution that the derivation of response sequence probabilities is easier with the linear model above than with alternative models suggested for paired-associate learning. In many models the response random variables x_n are not independent, so an expansion like that used in finding $Pr(s_{11})$ for the linear model is prohibited. Instead, we can find expressions by resorting to tree diagrams of the possible state transitions, perhaps aided by short cuts suggested by the structure of the model. The one-element model is a case in point here; let us indicate one way of deriving the 4-tuple probabilities (trials 2 to 5) for this model.

By referring to the trial-to-trial state transition matrix at the beginning of Sec. 9.3, we can sketch a tree diagram for any 4-tuple of interest. The sequence 0100 is depicted in Fig. 9.4. A point brought out by the figure is that this sequence has an error on trial 3, so the only possible state sequence on trials 2 and 3 is $\bar{C}_2 \to \bar{C}_3$. Summing the probabilities of the three branches in the figure yields our solution, which we leave in a heuristically meaningful form:

$$Pr(0100) = (1 - c)^2g(1 - g)\{c + (1 - c)gc + [(1 - c)g]^2\}.$$

Similarly, Fig. 9.5 shows that the sequence 1000 has probability

$$Pr(1000) = (1 - c)(1 - g)\{c + (1 - c)gc + [(1 - c)g]^2c + [(1 - c)g]^3\}$$

where the four terms inside the $\{\}$ come from the four branches, reading from top to bottom in the figure.

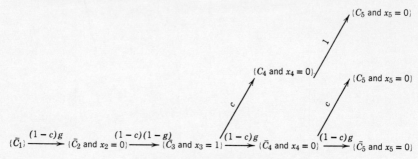

Fig. 9.4   Sequence 0100.

Most of the 14 remaining sequences include errors after trial 3, which renders the derivations quite simple. First, take the sequences beginning with a 0 (other than 0000). For example, the string 0010 has a 1 in the third position, so the first three responses in the sequence occurred in $\bar{C}$, which has probability $(1 - c)^3$. And the probability of two correct guesses and one error in $\bar{C}$ is $g^2(1 - g)$. Finally, the probability of being correct on trial 5, given state $\bar{C}$ on trial 4, is $c + (1 - c)g$. Combining these factors,

$$Pr(0010) = (1 - c)^3g^2(1 - g)[c + (1 - c)g].$$

The same reasoning shows that for trials 2 to 5

$$Pr(0001) = (1 - c)^4g^3(1 - g)$$
$$Pr(0010) = (1 - c)^3g^2(1 - g)[c + (1 - c)g]$$
$$Pr(0011) = (1 - c)^4g^2(1 - g)^2$$
$$Pr(0100) = (1 - c)^2g(1 - g)\{c + (1 - c)gc + [(1 - c)g^2]\}$$
$$Pr(0101) = (1 - c)^4g^2(1 - g)^2$$
$$Pr(0110) = (1 - c)^3g(1 - g)^2[c + (1 - c)g]$$
$$Pr(0111) = (1 - c)^4g(1 - g)^3.$$

Each sequence above has a 1 after trial 2, indicating that the subject was still in $\bar{C}$ on trial 2. Hence the equations for the sequences which begin with a 1 instead of a 0 are found simply by replacing a g with a $1 - g$ in the corresponding equations above. Thus from the result for $Pr(0001)$ we have

$$Pr(1001) = (1 - c)^4 g^2 (1 - g)^2.$$

Again, $Pr(1010) = Pr(0010)\,(1 - g)/g$, etc. After performing these calculations, we are left with only two unknown expressions, $Pr(0000)$ and $Pr(1000)$. The latter was found in Fig. 9.5, and $Pr(0000)$ is most easily

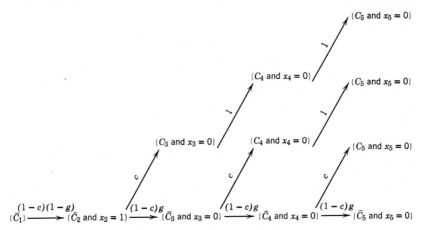

Fig. 9.5   Sequence 1000.

determined by summing the probabilities of the 15 other 4-tuples and subtracting this sum from unity. This calculation is legitimate, because the 16, 4-tuples are an exclusive and exhaustive partition, which means that their probabilities must sum to one.

Having derived the equations, we employ the minimization routine just as was done for the linear model. From the last column of Table 9.1, we see that $\hat{c} = 0.15$ and the associated χ^2 is 21.8, a figure well below the 180.5 obtained for the linear model. With 14 degrees of freedom, a χ^2 of 21.8 is significant at the 0.10 level. Figure 9.3 depicts the curve of χ^2 against c. The curve bears a similar shape to that for the linear model. At every possible parameter value, the χ^2 of the linear model exceeds that of the one-element model. In this instance the minimum occurs at the same point on the x-axis for c as for $1 - \alpha$; namely, at 0.15. (Usually the estimates for two models will differ.)

The foregoing method is readily elaborated for simultaneous estimation of two or three parameters in other models (see Atkinson and Crothers,

1964). Moreover, minimum χ^2 estimates are consistent in the sense of Sec. 9.1 and asymptotically efficient (as the sample size increases the variance of the estimate approaches the minimal variance attainable for any consistent estimate of the parameter, and the distribution of the estimate approaches a normal distribution).

The analysis above began with a general method for using n-tuple frequency data to estimate parameters; but, when the two models were applied to data, mathematical convenience dictated a reduction to the case of $n = 4$. This simplification means that data after trial 5 were ignored in estimating the parameter. Often, however, we would prefer an estimate that reflects data from all trials. Such an estimate would be especially worthwhile if numerous errors occur after trial 5. To this end, we outline a technique whereby the 4-tuple calculation can be extended to produce pseudo-χ^2's encompassing nonoverlapping blocks of four successive trials.

First of all, the method of deriving 4-tuples is easily generalized to any sequence of four consecutive trials; all that is needed is knowledge of the state vector at the start of the first trial in the 4-tuple. Given this information we can, for example, derive two sets of sequential equations from a model, one for trials 2 to 5 and another for trials 6 to 9. Then the quantity $\chi^2_{(2 \text{ to } 5)}$ can be defined for trials 2 to 5 precisely as was done in Eq. 9.22, and a similar quantity $\chi^2_{(6 \text{ to } 9)}$ for trials 6 to 9. Next define their sum

$$\chi^2_{(\text{sum})} = \chi^2_{(2 \text{ to } 5)} + \chi^2_{(6 \text{ to } 9)}.$$

Then the computer routine can be used to find the parameter value that minimizes $\chi^2_{(\text{sum})}$. Such a sum does not have a χ^2 distribution, because the trials 2 to 5 components are not independent of the corresponding trials 6 to 9 components. Hence we cannot ascertain the exact significance level associated with $\chi^2_{(\text{sum})}$. However, a few properties of the distribution of the sum are known (Holland, 1965). The expected value of $\chi^2_{(\text{sum})}$ equals the sum of the means of the two component χ^2's. For example, in our case each component χ^2 has 15 degrees of freedom; therefore, $\chi^2_{(\text{sum})}$ has a mean of $30 - 1 = 29$, the one being subtracted because of the estimated parameter. The variance of $\chi^2_{(\text{sum})}$ exceeds that of the sum of the two χ^2's, unless the events in one trial block are independent of those in the other. Also, it can be shown that when the χ^2 significance level is used as a rough guide to the significance level of $\chi^2_{(\text{sum})}$, we will err in the conservative direction of imputing too high a significance level to deviations of theory from data (that is, the bias will operate against the model). Applications of the pseudo-χ^2 routine to paired-associate models are reported in the previously cited paper by Calfee and Atkinson and also in an article by Calfee, Atkinson, and Shelton (1964).

Finally, we should like to comment on the question of how to decide whether the χ^2 fit is significantly better for one model than for another. We can form the ratio

$$\frac{\chi_1^2/f_1}{\chi_2^2/f_2},$$

where f stands for the number of degrees of freedom, and the subscript indexes the model. The value of this ratio determines whether one model is significantly more accurate than the other in fitting the response sequences. If the ratio is less than one, then Model 1 is better, whereas if the ratio is greater than one, Model 2 is better. When the chi-squares χ_1^2 and χ_2^2 are independent, then their ratio has an F distribution with f_1 and f_2 degrees of freedom, and a precise statistical evaluation can be made. For most applications of the type outlined in this section, the same set of data is used in computing both χ^2's, and hence they are not independent. When this is the case, we may still choose to interpret the ratio in terms of the F distribution keeping in mind possible sources of error. For a fuller discussion of this problem the reader should consult Holland (1965).

Bibliography

This bibliography includes most of the articles and books that are relevant to the material covered in the text. For the most part, technical reports and unpublished works are not included. Some of the articles listed here were not cited in the text; nevertheless, they represent pertinent supplementary readings. Articles in which the mathematical application to psychology is unrelated to the topics considered in this book are not included, since other texts would provide a more adequate reference source.

Adams, E. and S. Messick, 1958. An axiomatic formulation and generalization of successive intervals scaling. *Psychometrika*, **23,** 355–368.

Anderson, A. R., 1962. Logic, norms, and roles. In Joan Criswell, H. Solomon, and P. Suppes (Eds.), *Mathematical methods in small group processes.* Stanford: Stanford Univer. Press, pp. 11–22.

Anderson, N. H., 1959*a*. Temporal properties of response evocation. In R. R. Bush and W. K. Estes (Eds.), *Studies in mathematical learning theory.* Stanford: Stanford Univer. Press, pp. 125–134.

Anderson, N. H., 1959*b*. An analysis of sequential dependencies. In R. R. Bush and W. K. Estes (Eds.), *Studies in mathematical learning theory.* Stanford: Stanford Univer. Press, pp. 248–264.

Anderson, N. H., 1960. Effect of first-order conditional probability in a two-choice learning situation. *J. exp. Psychol.,* **59,** 73–93.

Anderson, N. H., 1961. Two learning models for responses measured on a continuous scale. *Psychometrika*, **26,** 391–403.

Anderson, N. H., 1964*a*. Note on weighted sum and linear operator models. *Psychon. Sci.,* **1,** 189–190.

Anderson, N. H., 1964*b*. Linear models for responses measured on a continuous scale. *J. math. Psychol.,* **1,** 121–142.

Anderson, N. H., 1964*c*. Test of a model for number-averaging behavior. *Psychon. Sci.,* **1,** 191–192.

Anderson, N. H. and D. A. Grant, 1957. A test of a statistical learning theory model for two-choice behavior with double stimulus events. *J. exp. Psychol.,* **54,** 305–317.

Anderson, N. H. and D. A. Grant, 1958. Correction and reanalysis. *J. exp. Psychol.,* **56,** 453–454.

Anderson, N. H. and C. I. Hovland, 1957. The representation of order effects in communication research. Append. in C. I. Hovland, *et al.* (Eds.), *The order of presentation in persuasion.* New Haven: Yale Univer. Press.

Anderson, N. H. and R. E. Whalen, 1960. Likelihood judgments and sequential effects in a two-choice probability learning situation. *J. exp. Psychol.,* **60,** 111–120.

Anderson, T. W., 1960. Some stochastic process models for intelligence test scores. In K. J. Arrow, S. Karlin, and P. Suppes (Eds.), *Mathematical methods in the social sciences.* Stanford: Stanford Univer. Press, pp. 205–220.

Anderson, T. W. and L. A. Goodman, 1957. Statistical inference about Markov chains. *Ann. math. Stat.*, **28**, 89–110.

Anger, D., 1956. The dependence of interresponse times upon the relative reinforcement of different interresponse times. *J. exp. Psychol.*, **52**, 145–161.

Arrow, K. J., S. Karlin, and P. Suppes (Eds.), 1960. *Mathematical methods in the social sciences.* Stanford: Stanford Univer. Press.

Asch, S. E., 1953. Effects of group pressure upon the modification and distortion of judgements. In D. Cartweight and A. Zander (Eds.), *Group dynamics.* London: Tavistock.

Asch, S. E., 1956. Studies of independence and conformity: I. A minority of one against a unanimous majority. *Psychol. Monogr.*, **70**, Whole No. 416.

Atkinson, R. C., 1956. An analysis of the effect of non-reinforced trials in terms of statistical learning theory. *J. exp. Psychol.*, **52**, 28–32.

Atkinson, R. C., 1957. A stochastic model for rote serial learning. *Psychometrika*, **22**, 87–96.

Atkinson, R. C., 1958. A Markov model for discrimination learning. *Psychometrika*, **23**, 309–322.

Atkinson, R. C., 1960*a*. A theory of stimulus discrimination learning. In K. J. Arrow, S. Karlin, and P. Suppes (Eds.), *Mathematical methods in the social sciences.* Stanford: Stanford Univer. Press, pp. 221–241.

Atkinson, R. C., 1960*b*. The use of models in experimental psychology. *Synthese*, **12**, 162–171.

Atkinson, R. C., 1961*a*. The observing response in discrimination learning. *J. exp. Psychol.*, **62**, 253–262.

Atkinson, R. C., 1961*b*. A generalization of stimulus sampling theory. *Psychometrika*, **26**, 281–290.

Atkinson, R. C., 1962. Choice behavior and monetary payoff: strong and weak conditioning. In Joan Criswell, H. Solomon, and P. Suppes (Eds.), *Mathematical methods in small group processes.* Stanford: Stanford Univer. Press, pp. 23–34.

Atkinson, R. C., 1963*a*. A variable sensitivity theory of signal detection. *Psychol. Rev.*, **70**, 91–106.

Atkinson, R. C., 1963*b*. Mathematical models in research on perception and learning. In M. Marx (Ed.), *Theories in contemporary psychology.* New York: Macmillan Co., pp. 551–564.

Atkinson, R. C. (Ed.), 1964. *Studies in mathematical psychology.* Stanford: Stanford Univer. Press.

Atkinson, R. C., W. H. Bogartz, and R. N. Turner, 1959. Supplementary report: discrimination learning with probabilistic reinforcement schedules. *J. exp. Psychol.*, **57**, 349–350.

Atkinson, R. C. and R. C. Calfee, 1964. The effects of forced-choice trials upon free-choice behavior. *Psychon. Sci.*, **1**, 55–56.

Atkinson, R. C. and R. C. Calfee, 1965. Mathematical learning theory. In B. B. Wolman (Ed.), *Scientific psychology.* New York: Basic Books, pp. 254–275.

Atkinson, R. C., R. C. Calfee, G. R. Sommer, and W. E. Jeffrey, 1964. A test of three models for stimulus compounding with children. *J. exp. Psychol.*, **67**, 52–58.

Atkinson, R. C., E. C. Carterette, and R. A. Kinchla, 1962. Sequential phenomena in psychophysical judgements: a theoretical analysis. *Inst. Radio Engineers Trans. on Information Theory*, IT-8, S155–162.

Atkinson, R. C., E. C. Carterette, and R. A. Kinchla, 1964. The effect of information feedback upon psychophysical judgements. *Psychon. Sci.*, **1**, 83–84.

Atkinson, R. C. and E. J. Crothers, 1964. A comparison of paired-associate learning models having different learning and retention axioms. *J. math. Psychol.*, **1**, 285–315.

Atkinson, R. C. and W. K. Estes, 1963. Stimulus sampling theory. In R. D. Luce, R. R. Bush, and E. Galanter (Eds.), *Handbook of mathematical psychology*, Vol. II. New York: Wiley, pp. 121–268.

Atkinson, R. C. and R. A. Kinchla, 1965. A learning model for forced-choice detection experiments. *Brit. J. math. statist. Psychol.*, **18**, in press.

Atkinson, R. C. and G. Sommer, 1960. Decision making by children as a function of amount of reinforcement. *Psychol. Rep.*, **6**, 299–306.

Atkinson, R. C. and P. Suppes, 1958. An analysis of two-person game situations in terms of statistical learning theory. *J. exp. Psychol.*, **55**, 369–378.

Atkinson, R. C. and P. Suppes, 1959. Applications of a Markov model to two-person non-cooperative games. In R. R. Bush and W. K. Estes (Eds.), *Studies in mathematical learning theory*. Stanford: Stanford Univer. Press, pp. 65–75.

Audley, R. J., 1957. A stochastic description of the learning behavior of an individual subject. *Quart. J. exp. Psychol.*, **9**, 12–20.

Audley, R. J., 1958. The inclusion of response times within a stochastic description of the learning behavior of individual subjects. *Psychometrika*, **23**, 25–31.

Audley, R. J., 1960. A stochastic model for individual choice behavior. *Psychol. Rev.*, **67**, 1–15.

Audley, R. J., 1962. A stochastic model for the act of choice. In E. Nagel, P. Suppes, and A. Tarski (Eds.), *Logic, methodology, and philosophy of science: Proceedings of the* 1960 *International Congress*. Stanford: Stanford Univer. Press, pp. 391–400.

Back, K. W., 1962. Can subjects be human and humans be subjects? In Joan Criswell, H. Solomon, and P. Suppes (Eds.), *Mathematical methods in small group processes*. Stanford: Stanford Univer. Press, pp. 35–48.

Bartlett, F., 1958. *Thinking*. New York: Basic Books.

Barucha-Reid, A. T., 1960. *Elements of the theory of Markov processes and their applications*. New York: McGraw-Hill.

Baum, M., 1954. Simple concept learning as a function of intra-list generalization. *J. exp. Psychol.*, **47**, 89–94.

Békésy, G. von, 1930. Über das Fechner'sche Gesetz und seine Bedeutung für die Theorie der aukustischen Beobachtungsfehler und die Theorie des Hörens. *Ann. Phys.* **7**, 329–359.

Békésy, G. von, 1962. *Experiments in hearing*. New York: McGraw-Hill.

Bellman, R., 1957. *Dynamic programming*. Princeton: Princeton Univer. Press.

Berger, J., B. Cohen, J. Snell, and M. Zelditch, Jr., 1961. *Types of formalization in small-group research*. Boston: Houghton Mifflin.

Berkson, J., 1957. Tables for the maximum-likelihood estimation of the logistic function. *Biometrics*, **13**, 28–34.

Billingsley, P., 1961. *Statistical inference for Markov processes*. Chicago: Univer. of Chicago Press.

Blackwell, H. R., 1953. Psychophysical thresholds: experimental studies of methods of measurement. *Bull. Engng. Res. Inst.*, No. 36, Ann Arbor, Michigan.

Binder, A. and S. E. Feldman, 1960. The effects of experimentally controlled experience upon recognition responses. *Psychol. Monogr.*, **74**, Whole No. 496.

Binder, A., B. R. Wolin, and S. J. Terebinski, 1965. Leadership in small groups: A mathematical approach. *J. exp. Psychol.*, **69**, 126–134.

Boring, E. G., 1950. *A history of experimental psychology.* New York: Appleton-Century-Crofts.

Bourne, L. E., 1957. Effects of delay of information feedback and task complexity in the identification of concepts. *J. exp. Psychol.,* **54,** 201–207.

Bourne, L. E. and C. U. Bunderson, 1965. Effects of delay of informative feedback and length of feedback interval on concept identification. *J. exp. Psychol.,* in press.

Bourne, L. E. and R. C. Haygood, 1959. The role of stimulus redundancy in concept identification. *J. exp. Psychol.,* **58,** 232–238.

Bourne, L. E. and R. C. Haygood, 1961. Supplementary report: effect of redundant relevant information upon the identification of concepts. *J. exp. Psychol.,* **61,** 259–260.

Bourne, L. E. and R. B. Pendleton, 1958. Concept identification as a function of completeness and probability of information feedback. *J. exp. Psychol.,* **56,** 413–419.

Bourne, L. E. and F. Restle, 1959. Mathematical theory of concept identification. *Psychol. Rev.,* **66,** 278–296.

Bousfield, W. A., 1961. The problem of meaning in verbal learning. In C. N. Cofer (Ed.), *Verbal learning and verbal behavior.* New York: McGraw-Hill.

Bower, G. H., 1959*a*. A theory of serial discrimination learning. In R. R. Bush and W. K. Estes (Eds.), *Studies in mathematical learning theory.* Stanford: Stanford Univer. Press, pp. 76–93.

Bower, G. H., 1959*b*. Choice-point behavior. In R. R. Bush and W. K. Estes (Eds.), *Studies in mathematical learning theory.* Stanford: Stanford Univer. Press, pp. 109–124.

Bower, G. H., 1960. Paired associates under two training conditions and different numbers of response alternatives. *Amer. Psychologist,* **15,** 451 (Abstract).

Bower, G. H., 1961*a*. Application of a model to paired-associate learning. *Psychometrika,* **26,** 255–280.

Bower, G. H., 1961*b*. Application of the all-or-none conditioning model to the learning of compound responses. Tech. Rep. No. 37, Institute for Mathematical Studies in the Social Sciences, Stanford University.

Bower, G. H., 1962*a*. A model for response and training variables in paired-associate learning. *Psychol. Rev.,* **69,** 34–53.

Bower, G. H., 1962*b*. Response strengths and choice probability: a consideration of two combination rules. In E. Nagel, P. Suppes, and A. Tarski (Eds.), *Logic, methodology and philosophy of science: Proceedings of the* 1960 *International Congress.* Stanford: Stanford Univer. Press, pp. 400–412.

Bower, G. H. and J. Theios, 1954. A learning model for discrete performance levels. In R. C. Atkinson (Ed.), *Studies in mathematical psychology.* Stanford: Stanford Univer. Press, pp. 1–31.

Bower, G. H. and T. R. Trabasso, 1964. Concept identification. In R. C. Atkinson (Ed.), *Studies in mathematical psychology.* Stanford: Stanford Univer. Press, pp. 32–94.

Bradley, R. A. and M. E. Terry, 1952. Rank analysis of incomplete block designs: I. The method of paired comparisons. *Biometrika,* **39,** 324–345.

Brehm, J. W. and A. R. Cohen, 1962. *Explorations in cognitive dissonance.* New York: Wiley.

Broadbent, D. E., 1958. *Perception and communication.* New York: Pergamon Press.

Brody, A. L., 1957. Statistical learning theory applied to an instrumental avoidance situation. *J. exp. Psychol.,* **54,** 240–245.

Brody, A. L., 1958. Independence in the learning of two consecutive responses per trial. *J. exp. Psychol.*, **56**, 16–20.

Bruner, J. S., J. J. Goodnow, and A. Austin, 1956. *A study of thinking*. New York: Wiley.

Brunswik, E., 1939. Probability as a determiner of rat behavior. *J. exp. Psychol.*, **25**, 175–197.

Bryant, S. J. and J. G. Marica, 1959. Strategies and learning models. *Psychometrika*, **24**, 253–256.

Burke, C. J., 1959. Applications of a linear model to two-person interactions. In R. R. Bush and W. K. Estes (Eds.), *Studies in mathematical learning theory*. Stanford: Stanford Univer. Press, pp. 180–203.

Burke, C. J., 1960. Some two-person interactions. In K. J. Arrow, S. Karlin, and P. Suppes (Eds.), *Mathematical methods in the social sciences*. Stanford: Stanford Univer. Press, pp. 242–253.

Burke, C. J., 1962. Two-person interactive learning: a progress report. In Joan Criswell, H. Solomon, and P. Suppes (Eds.), *Mathematical methods in small group processes*. Stanford: Stanford Univer. Press, pp. 49–68.

Burke, C. J. and W. K. Estes, 1957. A component model for stimulus variables in discrimination learning. *Psychometrika*, **22**, 133–145.

Burke, C. J., W. K. Estes, and S. Hellyer, 1954. Rate of verbal conditioning in relation to stimulus variability. *J. exp. Psychol.*, **48**, 153–161.

Bush, R. R., 1959. Sequential properties of linear models. In R. R. Bush and W. K. Estes (Eds.), *Studies in mathematical learning theory*. Stanford: Stanford Univer. Press, pp. 215–227.

Bush, R. R., 1960a. Some properties of Luce's beta model for learning. In K. J. Arrow, S. Karlin, and P. Suppes (Eds.), *Mathematical methods in the social sciences*. Stanford: Stanford Univer. Press, pp. 254–264.

Bush, R. R., 1960b. A survey of mathematical learning theory. In R. D. Luce (Ed.), *Developments in mathematical psychology*. Glencoe, Ill.: The Free Press, pp. 123–165.

Bush, R. R., 1962. The application of learning models to interactive behavior. In Joan Criswell, H. Solomon, and P. Suppes (Eds.), *Mathematical methods in small group processes*. Stanford: Stanford Univer. Press, pp. 69–73.

Bush, R. R., 1963. Estimation and evaluation. In R. D. Luce, R. R. Bush, and E. Galanter (Eds.), *Handbook of mathematical psychology*. Vol. I. New York: Wiley, pp. 429–469.

Bush, R. R. and W. K. Estes (Eds.), 1959. *Studies in mathematical learning theory*. Stanford: Stanford Univ. Press.

Bush, R. R., E. Galanter, and R. D. Luce, 1959. Tests of the beta model. In R. R. Bush and W. K. Estes (Eds.), *Studies in mathematical learning theory*. Stanford: Stanford Univer. Press, pp. 382–399.

Bush, R. R., E. Galanter, and R. D. Luce, 1963. Characterization and classification of choice experiments. In R. D. Luce, R. R. Bush, and E. Galanter (Eds.), *Handbook of mathematical psychology*. Vol. I. New York: Wiley, pp. 77–102.

Bush, R. R., R. D. Luce, and R. M. Rose, 1964. Learning models for psychophysics. In R. C. Atkinson (Ed.), *Studies in mathematical psychology*. Stanford: Stanford Univer. Press, pp. 201–217.

Bush, R. R. and F. Mosteller, 1951a. A mathematical model for simple learning. *Psychol. Rev.*, **58**, 313–323.

Bush, R. R. and F. Mosteller, 1951*b*. A model for stimulus generalization and discrimination. *Psychol. Rev.*, **58**, 413–423.

Bush, R. R. and F. Mosteller, 1953. A stochastic model in applications to learning. *Ann. math. Statist.*, **24**, 559–585.

Bush, R. R. and F. Mosteller, 1955. *Stochastic models for learning.* New York: Wiley.

Bush, R. R. and F. Mosteller, 1959. A comparison of eight models. In R. R. Bush and W. K. Estes (Eds.), *Studies in mathematical learning theory.* Stanford: Stanford Univer. Press, pp. 293–307.

Bush, R. R., F. Mosteller, and G. L. Thompson, 1954. A formal structure for multiple choice situations. In R. M. Thrall, C. H. Coombs, and R. L. Davis (Eds.), *Decision processes.* New York: Wiley, pp. 99–126.

Bush, R. R. and S. H. Sternberg, 1959. A single-operator model. In R. R. Bush and W. K. Estes (Eds.), *Studies in mathematical learning theory.* Stanford: Stanford Univer. Press, pp. 204–214.

Bush, R. R. and T. R. Wilson, 1956. Two choice behavior of paradise fish. *J. exp. Psychol.*, **51**, 315–322.

Calfee, R. C. and R. C. Atkinson, 1965. Paired-associate models and the effects of list length. *J. math. Psychol.*, **2**, 255–267.

Calfee, R. C., R. C. Atkinson, and T. Shelton, Jr., 1964. Mathematical models for verbal learning. Tech. Rep. No. 65, Institute for Mathematical Studies in the Social Sciences, Stanford University.

Carterette, E. C. and M. J. Wyman, 1962. Application of a Markov learning model to a simple detection situation involving social pressure. In Joan Criswell, H. Solomon, and P. Suppes (Eds.), *Mathematical methods in small group processes.* Stanford: Stanford Univer. Press, pp. 74–100.

Carterette, T. S., 1961. An application of stimulus sampling theory to summated generalization. *J. exp. Psychol.*, **62**, 448–455.

Cervin, V. B. and G. P. Henderson, 1961. Statistical theory of persuasion. *Psychol. Rev.*, **68**, 157–166.

Chomsky, N., 1963. Formal properties of grammars. In R. D. Luce, R. R. Bush, and E. Galanter (Eds.), *Handbook of mathematical psychology.* Vol. II. New York: Wiley, pp. 323–418.

Chomsky, N. and G. A. Miller, 1963. Introduction to the formal analysis of natural languages. In R. D. Luce, R. R. Bush, and E. Galanter (Eds.), *Handbook of mathematical psychology.* Vol. II. New York: Wiley.

Christie, L. S. and R. D. Luce, 1956. Decision structure and time relations in simple choice behavior. *Bull. math. Biophysics*, **18**, 89–112.

Clayton, K. N., 1964. *T*-maze choice learning as a joint function of the reward magnitudes for the alternatives. *J. comp. physiol. Psychol.*, **58**, 333–338.

Cofer, C. N., 1961. *Verbal learning and verbal behavior.* New York: McGraw-Hill.

Cofer, C. N. and B. S. Musgrave, 1963. *Verbal behavior and learning.* New York: McGraw-Hill.

Cohen, B. P., 1958. A probability model for conformity. *Sociometry*, **21**, 69–81.

Cohen, B. P., 1962. The process of choosing a reference group. In Joan Criswell, H. Solomon, and P. Suppes (Eds.), *Mathematical methods in small group processes.* Stanford: Stanford Univer. Press, pp. 101–118.

Cole, M., 1965. Search behavior: a correction procedure for three-choice probability learning. *J. math. Psychol.*, **2**, 145–170.

Coleman, J. S., 1960. The mathematical study of small groups. In H. Solomon (Ed.), *Mathematical thinking in the measurement of behavior*. Glencoe, Ill.: The Free Press, pp. 1–149.

Coleman, J. S., 1962. Reward structures and the allocation of effort. In Joan Criswell, H. Solomon, and P. Suppes (Eds.), *Mathematical methods in small group processes*. Stanford: Stanford Univer. Press, pp. 119–132.

Coombs, C. H., 1964. *A theory of data*. New York: Wiley.

Cotton, J. W., 1955. On making predictions from Hull's theory. *Psychol. Rev.*, **62**, 303–314.

Coulson, J. E. (Ed.), 1962. *Programmed learning and computer-based instruction*. New York: Wiley.

Cramér, H., 1946. *Mathematical methods of statistics*. Princeton: Princeton Univer. Press.

Criswell, Joan, H. Solomon, and P. Suppes (Eds.), 1962. *Mathematical methods in small group processes*. Stanford: Stanford Univer. Press.

Crothers, E. J., 1964. All-or-none learning with compound responses. In R. C. Atkinson (Ed.), *Studies in mathematical psychology*. Stanford: Stanford Univer. Press, pp. 95–115.

Crothers, E. J., 1965a. Learning model solution to a problem in constrained optimization. *J. math. Psychol.*, **2**, 19–25.

Crothers, E. J., 1965b. Optimal presentation orders for items from different categories. Tech. Rep. No. 71, Institute for Mathematical Studies in the Social Sciences, Stanford University.

Das, J. P., 1961. Mathematical solution in the acquisition of a verbal CR. *J. exp. Psychol.*, **61**, 376–378.

Davidson, D. and J. Marshak, 1959. Experimental tests of stochastic decision theories. In C. W. Churchman and P. H. Ratoosh (Eds.), *Measurement: definition and theories*. New York: Wiley, pp. 223–269.

Dear, R. E. and R. C. Atkinson, 1962. Optimal allocation of items in a single two-concept automated teaching model. In J. Coulson (Ed.), *Programmed learning and computer-based instruction*. New York: Wiley, pp. 25–45.

Debreu, G., 1958. Stochastic choice and cardinal utility. *Econometrica*, **25**, 440–444.

Deese, J., 1958. *The psychology of learning* (2nd ed.). New York: McGraw-Hill.

Detambel, M. H., 1955. A test of a model for multiple-choice behavior. *J. exp. Psychol.*, **49**, 97–104.

Deutsch, J. A., 1962. Theories of choice and the stimulus-response framework. In E. Nagel, P. Suppes, and A. Tarski (Eds.), *Logic, methodology and philosophy of science: Proceedings of the 1960 International Congress*. Stanford: Stanford Univer. Press, pp. 413–423.

Deutsch, M. and H. B. Berard, 1955. A study of normative and informational social influences upon individual judgment. *J. abnorm. soc. Psychol.*, **51**, 629–636.

DiVesta, F. J., 1959. Effects of confidence and motivation on susceptibility to informational social influence, *J. abnorm. soc. Psychol.*, **59**, 204–209.

Dodwell, P. C., 1964. A coupled system for coding and learning in shape discrimination. *Psychol. Rev.*, **71**, 148–159.

Ebbinghaus, H., 1885. *Über das Gedächtnis*. Leip-Duncker, trans. H. Rugere and C. E. Bussenius, New York: Columbia Teachers College, 1913.

Edwards, W., 1956. Reward probability, amount, and information as determiners of sequential two-alternative decisions. *J. exp. Psychol.*, **52**, 177–188.

Edwards, W., 1961a. Behavioral decision theory. *Annu. Rev. Psychol.*, **12**, 473–498.

Edwards, W., 1961b. Probability learning in 1000 trials. *J. exp. Psychol.*, **62**, 385–394.

Ehrenfreund, D., 1948. An experimental test of the continuity theory of discrimination with pattern vision. *J. comp. Psychol.*, **41**, 408–422.

Engler, Jean, 1958. Marginal and conditional stimulus and response probabilities in verbal conditioning. *J. exp. Psychol.*, **55**, 303–307.

Essman, W. B. and M. Jarvik, 1960. The retrograde effect of ether anesthesia on a conditioned avoidance response in mice. *Amer. Psychologist*, **15**, 498 (Abstract).

Estes, W. K., 1950. Toward a statistical theory of learning. *Psychol. Rev.*, **57**, 94–107.

Estes, W. K., 1954. Individual behavior in uncertain situations: an interpretation in terms of statistical association theory. In R. M. Thrall, C. H. Coombs, and R. L. Davis (Eds.), *Decision processes.* New York: Wiley, pp. 127–138.

Estes, W. K., 1955a. Statistical theory of spontaneous recovery and regression. *Psychol. Rev.*, **62**, 145–154.

Estes, W. K., 1955b. Statistical theory of distributional phenomena in learning. *Psychol. Rev.*, **62**, 369–377.

Estes, W. K., 1956. The problem of inference from curves based on group data. *Psychol. Bull.*, **53**, 134–140.

Estes, W. K., 1957a. Of models and men. *Amer. Psychologist*, **12**, 609–617.

Estes, W. K., 1957b. Theory of learning with constant, variable, or contingent probabilities of reinforcement. *Psychometrika*, **22**, 113–132.

Estes, W. K., 1958. Stimulus-response theory of drive. In M. R. Jones (Ed.), *Nebraska Symposium on Motivation.* Vol. VI., Lincoln, Nebraska: University of Nebraska Press, pp. 35–69.

Estes, W. K., 1959a. Component and pattern models with Markovian interpretations. In R. R. Bush and W. K. Estes (Eds.), *Studies in mathematical learning theory.* Stanford: Stanford Univer. Press, pp. 9–52.

Estes, W. K., 1959b. The statistical approach to learning theory. In S. Koch (Ed.), *Psychology: a study of a science.* Vol. II. New York: McGraw-Hill, pp. 380–491.

Estes, W. K., 1960a. Learning theory and the new mental chemistry. *Psychol. Rev.*, **67**, 207–223.

Estes, W. K., 1960b. A random walk model for choice behavior. In K. J. Arrow, S. Karlin, and P. Suppes (Eds.), *Mathematical methods in the social sciences.* Stanford: Stanford Univer. Press, pp. 265–276.

Estes, W. K., 1961a. Growth and function of mathematical models for learning. In *Current trends in psychological theory.* Pittsburgh: Univer. of Pittsburgh Press, pp. 134–151.

Estes, W. K., 1961b. New developments in statistical behavior theory: differential tests of axioms for associative learning. *Psychometrika*, **26**, 73–84.

Estes, W. K., 1962a. A descriptive approach to the dynamics of choice behavior. In E. Nagel, P. Suppes, and A. Tarski (Eds.), *Logic, methodology and philosophy of science: Proceedings of the 1960 International Congress.* Stanford: Stanford Univer. Press, pp. 424–433.

Estes, W. K., 1962b. Learning theory. *Annu. Rev. Psychol.*, **12**, 107–144.

Estes, W. K., 1962c. Theoretical treatments of differential reward in multiple-choice learning and two-person interactions. In Joan Criswell, H. Solomon, and P. Suppes (Eds.), *Mathematical methods in small group processes.* Stanford: Stanford Univer. Press, pp. 133–149.

Estes, W. K., 1964. Probability learning. In A. W. Melton (Ed.), *Categories of human learning.* New York: Academic Press.

Estes, W. K. and C. J. Burke, 1953. A theory of stimulus variability in learning. *Psychol. Rev.*, **60**, 276–286.

Estes, W. K. and C. J. Burke, 1955. Application of a statistical model to simple discrimination learning in human subjects. *J. exp. Psychol.*, **50**, 81–88.

Estes, W. K., C. J. Burke, R. C. Atkinson, and J. P. Frankmann, 1957. Probabilistic discrimination learning. *J. exp. Psychol.*, **54**, 233–239.

Estes, W. K. and B. L. Hopkins, 1961. Acquisition and transfer in pattern-vs.-component discrimination learning. *J. exp. Psychol.*, **61**, 322–328.

Estes, W. K., B. L. Hopkins, and E. J. Crothers, 1960. All-or-none and conservation effects in the learning and retention of paired-associates. *J. exp. Psychol.*, **60**, 329–339.

Estes, W. K. and J. H. Straughan, 1954. Analysis of a verbal conditioning situation in terms of statistical learning theory. *J. exp. Psychol.*, **47**, 225–234.

Estes, W. K. and P. Suppes, 1959a. Foundations of linear models. In R. R. Bush and W. K. Estes (Eds.), *Studies in mathematical learning theory.* Stanford: Stanford Univer. Press, pp. 137–179.

Estes, W. K. and P. Suppes, 1959b. Foundations of statistical learning theory, II. The stimulus sampling model for simple learning. Tech. Rep. No. 26, Institute for Mathematical Studies in the Social Sciences, Stanford University.

Ettlinger, H. J., 1926. A curve of growth designed to represent the learning process. *J. exp. Psychol.*, **9**, 409–414.

Fechner, G. T., 1860. *Elemente der Psychophysik.* .Leipzig, Breitkoph and Härtel.

Feldman, J., 1959. On the negative recency hypothesis in the prediction of a series of binary symbols. *Amer. J. Psychol.*, **72**, 597–599.

Feldman, J. and A. Newell, 1961. A note on a class of probability matching models. *Psychometrika*, **26**, 333–337.

Feller, W., 1957. *An introduction to probability theory and its applications.* (2nd ed.) New York: Wiley.

Felsinger, J. M., A. I. Gladstone, H. G. Yamaguchi, and C. L. Hull, 1947. Reaction latency (t) as a function of the number of reinforcements (N). *J. exp. Psychol.*, **37**, 214–228.

Festinger, L., 1957. *A theory of cognitive dissonance.* Evanston, Ill.: Row, Peterson.

Fey, C. F., 1961. An investigation of some mathematical models for learning. *J. exp. Psychol.*, **61**, 455–461.

Flament, C., 1959a. Ambiguité du stimulus, incertitude de la réponse et processus d'influence sociale. *Année Psychol.*, **1**, 73–92.

Flament, C., 1959b. Modèle straté gique des processes d'influence sociale sur les jugements perceptifs. *Psychol. Francaise*, **2**, 91–101.

Flament, C., 1962. Le théorème de Bayes et les processus d'influence sociale. In Joan Criswell, H. Solomon, and P. Suppes (Eds.), *Mathematical methods in small group processes.* Stanford: Stanford Univer. Press, pp. 150–165.

Flood, M. M., 1954a. A stochastic model for social interaction. *Trans. N.Y. Acad. Sci.*, **16**, 202–205.

Flood, M. M., 1954b. Environmental non-stationarity in a sequential decision-making experiment. In R. M. Thrall, C. H. Coombs, and R. L. Davis (Eds.), *Decision processes.* New York: Wiley, pp. 139–158.

Flood, M. M., 1954c. Game learning theory and some decision-making experiments. In R. M. Thrall, C. H. Coombs, and R. L. Davis (Eds.), *Decision processes.* New York: Wiley, pp. 127–137.

Foa, U. G., 1962. The structure of interpersonal behavior in the dyad. In Joan Criswell, H. Solomon, and P. Suppes (Eds.), *Mathematical methods in small group processes.* Stanford: Stanford Univer. Press, pp. 166–192.

Fouraker, L. E. and S. Siegel, 1963. *Bargaining behavior.* New York: McGraw-Hill.

Frederiksen, N. and H. Gulliksen (Eds.), 1964. *Contributions to mathematical psychology.* New York: Holt, Rinehart, and Winston.

Frick, F. C. and G. A. Miller, 1951. A statistical description of operant conditioning. *Amer. J. Pyschol.*, **64**, 20–36.

Friedman, M. P., C. J. Burke, M. Cole, L. Keller, R. B. Millward, and W. K. Estes, 1964. Two-choice behavior under extended training with shifting probabilities of reinforcement. In R. C. Atkinson (Ed.), *Studies in mathematical psychology.* Stanford: Stanford Univer. Press, pp. 250–316.

Friedman, M. P. and E. C. Carterette, 1964. Detection of Markovian sequences of signals. *J. acoust. Soc. Amer.*, **36**, 2334–2339.

Friedman, M. P. and H. Gelfand, 1964. Transfer effects in discrimination learning. *J. math. Psychol.*, **1**, 204–214.

Galanter, E. and R. R. Bush, 1959. Some T-maze experiments. In R. R. Bush and W. K. Estes (Eds.), *Studies in mathematical learning theory.* Stanford: Stanford Univer. Press, pp. 265–289.

Galanter, E. and G. A. Miller, 1960. Some comments on stochastic models and psychological theories. In K. J. Arrow, S. Karlin, and P. Suppes (Eds.), *Mathematical methods in the social sciences.* Stanford: Stanford Univer. Press, pp. 277–297.

Galanter, E. and W. A. S. Smith, 1958. Some experiments on a simple thought-problem. *Amer. J. Psychol.*, **71**, 359–366.

Gardner, R. A., 1957. Probability-learning with two and three choices. *Amer. J. Psychol.*, **70**, 174–185.

Garner, W. R., 1962. *Uncertainty and structure as psychological concepts.* New York: Wiley.

Gibson, Eleanor, J., 1940. A systematic application of the concepts of generalization and differentiation to verbal learning. *Psychol. Rev.*, **47**, 196–229.

Gibson, J. J., 1960. The concept of the stimulus in psychology. *Amer. Psychologist*, **15**, 694–703.

Ginsberg, Rose, 1964. Stimulus overlap in a massed-trial situation. *J. exp. Psychol.*, **67**, 553–559.

Gladstone, A. I., H. G. Yamaguchi, C. L. Hull, and J. M. Felsinger, 1947. Some functional relationships of reaction potential ($s Er$) and related phenomena. *J. exp. Psychol.*, **37**, 510–526.

Goldberg, S., 1958. *Introduction to difference equations.* New York: Wiley.

Goodman, L. A., 1953. A further note on "Finite Markov processes in psychology." *Psychometrika*, **18**, 245–248.

Goodnow, J. J., 1955a. Determinants of choice distributions in two-choice probability situations. *Amer. J. Psychol.*, **68**, 106–116.

Goodnow, J. J., 1955b. Response sequences in a pair of two-choice probability situations. *Amer. J. Psychol.*, **68**, 624–630.

Goodnow, J. J. and T. F. Pettigrew, 1955. Effect of prior patterns of experience upon strategies and learning sets. *J. exp. Psychol.*, **49**, 381–389.

Goodnow, J. J. and T. F. Pettigrew, 1956. Some sources of difficulty in solving simple problems. *J. exp. Psychol.*, **51**, 385–392.

Goodnow, J. J. and L. Postman, 1955. Probability learning in a problem-solving situation. *J. exp. Psychol.*, **49**, 16–22.

Grant, D. A., 1954. The discrimination of sequences in stimulus events and the transmission of information. *Amer. Psychologist*, **9**, 62–68.

Grant, D. A., H. W. Hake, and J. P. Hornseth, 1951. Acquisition and extinction of a verbal conditioned response to differing percentages of reinforcement. *J. exp. Psychol.*, **42**, 1–5.

Green, B. F., 1963. *Digital computers in research: an introduction for behavioral and social scientists.* New York: McGraw-Hill.

Green, D. M., 1960. Psychoacoustics and detection theory. *J. acoust. Soc. Amer.*, **32**, 1189–1203.

Green, D. M., 1961. Some comments and a correction of "Psychoacoustics and detection theory." *J. acoust. Soc. Amer.*, **33**, 965.

Green, E. J., 1958. A simplified model for stimulus discrimination. *Psychol. Rev.*, **65**, 56–63.

Greeno, J. G., 1962. Effects of nonreinforced trials in two-choice learning with non-contingent reinforcement. *J. exp. Psychol.*, **64**, 373–379.

Guilford, J. P., 1964. *Psychometric methods.* New York: Wiley.

Gulliksen, H., 1934. A rational equation of the learning curve based on Thorndike's law of effect. *J. gen. Psychol.*, **11**, 395–434.

Gulliksen, H. and D. L. Wolfle, 1938. A theory of learning and transfer: I. *Psychometrika*, **3**, 127–149.

Guthrie, E. R., 1952. *The psychology of learning.* (Rev. ed.) New York: Harper.

Guttman, N. and H. I. Kalish, 1956. Discriminability and stimulus generalization. *J. exp. Psychol.*, **51**, 79–88.

Hake, H. W., 1955. The perception of frequency of occurrence and the development of "expectancy" in human experimental subjects. In H. Quastler (Ed.), *Information theory in psychology, problems, and methods.* Glencoe, Ill.: The Free Press, pp. 257–281.

Hake, H. W. and R. Hyman, 1953. Perception of the statistical structure of a random series of binary symbols. *J. exp. Psychol.*, **45**, 67–74.

Hall, R. L., 1962. Two-alternative learning in interdependent dyads. In Joan Criswell, H. Solomon, and P. Suppes (Eds.), *Mathematical methods in small group processes.* Stanford: Stanford Univer. Press, pp. 180–192.

Hanania, M. I., 1959. A generalization of the Bush-Mosteller model with some significance tests. *Psychometrika*, **24**, 53–68.

Hanania, M. I., 1960. Two alternative learning situations in partial reinforcement. *Psychometrika*, **25**, 77–90.

Hays, D. G. and R. R. Bush, 1954. A study of group action. *Amer. sociological Rev.* **19**, 693–701.

Hays, W. L., 1963. *Statistics for psychologists.* New York: Holt, Rinehart, and Winston.

Hilgard, E. R., 1938. A summary and evaluation of alternative procedures for the construction of Vincent curves. *Psychol. Bull.*, **35**, 282–297.

Hodges, J. L., Jr., 1958. Fitting the logistic by maximum likelihood. *Biometrics*, **14**, 453–461.

Hoel, P. G., 1954. A test for Markov chains. *Biometrika*, **41**, 430–433.

Holland, P. W., 1965. Minimum chi-square procedures. Unpublished doctoral dissertation, Stanford University.

Homme, L. E., 1956. Spontaneous recovery and statistical learning theory. *J. exp. Psychol.*, **51**, 205–212.

Householder, A. S. and H. D. Landahl, 1945. *Mathematical biophysics of the central nervous system.* Bloomington, Ind.: Principia Press.

Hovland, C. I., 1951. Human learning and retention. In S. S. Stevens (Ed.), *Handbook of experimental psychology.* New York: Wiley, pp. 613–689.

Howard, R. A., 1960. *Dynamic programming and Markov processes.* Cambridge, Mass., and New York: M.I.T. Press and Wiley.

Howarth, C. I. and M. G. Bulmer, 1956. Non-random sequences in visual threshold experiments. *Quart. J. exp. Psychol.*, **8**, 163–171.

Hull, C. L., 1920. Quantitative aspects of the evolution of concepts. *Psychol. Monogr.*, **28**, Whole No. 23.

Hull, C. L., 1930. Simple trial-and-error learning: a study in psychological theory. *Psychol. Rev.*, **37**, 241–256.

Hull, C. L., 1943. *Principles of behavior: An introduction to behavior theory.* New York: Appleton-Century-Crofts.

Hull, C. L., 1951. *Essentials of behavior.* New Haven: Yale Univer. Press.

Hull, C. L., 1952. *A behavior system.* New Haven: Yale Univer. Press.

Hull, C. L., J. M. Felsinger, A. I. Gladstone, and H. G. Yamaguchi, 1947. A proposed quantification of habit strength. *Psychol. Rev.*, **47**, 237–254.

Hull, C. L., C. I. Hovland, R. T. Ross, M. Hall, D. T. Perkins, and F. B. Ritch, 1940. *Mathematico-deductive theory of rote learning.* New Haven: Yale Univer. Press.

Humphreys, L. G., 1939. Acquisition and extinction of verbal expectations in a situation analogous to conditioning. *J. exp. Psychol.*, **25**, 294–301.

Hunt, E. B., 1962. *Concept learning.* New York: Wiley.

Janis, I. L., C. I. Hovland, and H. H. Kelley, 1953. *Communication and persuasion.* New Haven: Yale Univer. Press.

Jarvik, M. E., 1951. Probability learning and a negative recency effect in the serial anticipation of alternating symbols. *J. exp. Psychol.*, **41**, 291–297.

Jordan, C., 1950. *Calculus of finite differences.* New York: Chelsea.

Kanal, L., 1962a. The asymptotic distribution for the two absorbing barrier beta model. *Psychometrika*, **27**, 105–109.

Kanal, L., 1962b. A functional equation analysis of two-learning models. *Psychometrika*, **27**, 89–104.

Karlin, S., 1953. Some random walks arising in learning models. *Pacific J. Math.*, **3**, 725–756.

Karlsson, G., 1962. Some aspects of power in small groups. In Joan Criswell, H. Solomon, and P. Suppes (Eds.), *Mathematical methods in small group processes.* Stanford: Stanford Univer. Press, pp. 193–202.

Katz, L. and C. H. Proctor, 1959. The concept of configuration of interpersonal relations in a group as a time-dependent stochastic process. *Psychometrika*, **24**, 317–327.

Kemeny, J. G. and J. L. Snell, 1957. Markov processes in learning theory. *Psychometrika*, **22**, 221–230.

Kemeny, J. G. and J. L. Snell, 1959. *Finite Markov chains.* Princeton: D. Van Nostrand Company.

Kemeny, J. G., J. L. Snell, and G. L. Thompson, 1957. *Introduction to finite mathematics.* New York: Prentice Hall.

Kimble, G. A., 1961. *Hilgard and Marquis' Conditioning and Learning.* New York: Appleton-Century-Crofts.

Kinchla, R. A., 1964. A learning factor in visual discrimination. In R. C. Atkinson

(Ed.), *Studies in mathematical psychology*. Stanford: Stanford Univer. Press, pp. 233–249.

Kintsch, W., 1963. A response time model for choice behavior. *Psychometrika*, **28**, 27–32.

Koch, S., 1954. Clark L. Hull. In W. K. Estes, S. Koch, K. MacCorquodale, P. E. Meehl, C. G. Mueller, Jr., W. N. Schoenfeld, and W. S. Verplanck (Eds.), *Modern learning theory*. New York: Appleton-Century-Crofts, pp. 1–176.

Kohler, W., 1947. *Gestalt psychology*. (Rev. ed.) New York: Liveright.

Kraemer, Helen C., 1964a. Estimation in the three-state Markov learning model. *Psychometrika*, **29**, 131–142.

Kraemer, Helen C., 1964b. Point estimation in learning models. *J. math. Psychol.*, **1**, 28–53.

Krechevsky, I., 1932. "Hypotheses" in rats. *Psychol. Rev.*, **39**, 516–532.

LaBerge, D. L., 1959a. The effect of preliminary trials on rate of conditioning in a simple prediction situation. *J. exp. Psychol.*, **57**, 20–24.

LaBerge, D. L., 1959b. A model with neutral elements. In R. R. Bush and W. K. Estes (Eds.), *Studies in mathematical learning theory*. Stanford: Stanford Univer. Press, pp. 53–64.

LaBerge, D. L., 1962. A recruitment theory of simple behavior. *Psychometrika*, **27**, 375–396.

LaBerge, D. L. and A. Smith, 1951. Selective sampling in discrimination learning. *J. exp. Psychol.*, **54**, 423–430.

Lamperti, J. and P. Suppes, 1959. Chains of infinite order and their applications to learning theory. *Pacific J. Math.*, **9**, 739–754.

Lamperti, J. and P. Suppes, 1960. Some asymptotic properties of Luce's beta learning model. *Psychometrika*, **25**, 233–241.

Larkin, W. D. and D. A. Norman, 1964. An extension and experimental analysis of the neural quantum theory. In R. C. Atkinson (Ed.), *Studies in mathematical psychology*. Stanford: Stanford Univer. Press, pp. 188–200.

Lashley, K. S., 1929. *Brain mechanisms and intelligence*. Chicago: University of Chicago Press.

Lawrence, D. H., 1963. The nature of a stimulus: some relationships between learning and perception. In S. Koch (Ed.), *Psychology: a study of a science*. Vol. V. New York: McGraw-Hill, pp. 179–212.

Levine, M., 1963. Mediating processes in humans at the outset of discrimination learning. *Psychol. Rev.*, **70**, 254–276.

Lewis, D., 1960. *Quantitative methods in psychology*. New York: McGraw-Hill.

Licklider, J. C. R., 1959. Three auditory theories. In S. Koch (Ed.), *Psychology: a study of a science*. Vol. I. New York: McGraw-Hill, pp. 41–144.

Licklider, J. C. R., 1960. Quasi-linear operator models in the study of manual tracking. In R. D. Luce (Ed.), *Developments in mathematical psychology*. Glencoe, Ill.: The Free press, pp. 171–280.

Lieberman, B., 1962. Experimental studies of conflict in some two-person and three-person games. In Joan Criswell, H. Solomon, and P. Suppes (Eds.), *Mathematical methods in small group processes*. Stanford: Stanford Univer. Press, pp. 203–220.

Lindsley, D. B., 1958. The reticular system and perceptual discrimination. In H. Jasper, L. Proctor, R. Kinghton, W. Noshay, and R. Costello (Eds.), *Reticular formation of the brain*. Boston: Little, Brown, pp. 519–532.

Logan, F. A., 1959. The Hull-Spence approach. In S. Koch (Ed.), *Psychology: a study of a science*. Vol. II. New York: McGraw-Hill, pp. 293–358.

Logan, F. A., 1960. *Incentive: How the conditions of reinforcement affect the performance of rats.* New Haven: Yale Univer. Press.

Lorge, I. and H. Solomon, 1962. Group and individual behavior in free-recall verbal learning. In Joan Criswell, H. Solomon, and P. Suppes (Eds.), *Mathematical methods in small group processes.* Stanford: Stanford Univer. Press, pp. 221–231.

Luce, R. D., 1958. A probabilistic theory of utility. *Econometrica*, **26**, 193–224.

Luce, R. D., 1959a. *Individual choice behavior: a theoretical analysis.* New York: Wiley.

Luce, R. D., 1959b. On the possible psychophysical laws. *Psychol. Rev.*, **66**, 81–95.

Luce, R. D., 1960a. Response latencies and probabilities. In K. J. Arrow, S. Karlin, and P. Suppes (Eds.), *Mathematical methods in the social sciences.* Stanford: Stanford Univer. Press, pp. 298–311.

Luce, R. D. (Ed.), 1960b. *Developments in mathematical psychology.* Glencoe, Ill.: The Free Press.

Luce, R. D., 1960c. The theory of selective information and some of its behavioral implications. In R. D. Luce (Ed.), *Developments in mathematical psychology.* Glencoe, Ill.: The Free press, pp. 5–119.

Luce, R. D., 1963a. A threshold theory for simple detection experiments. *Psychol. Rev.*, **70**, 61–79.

Luce, R. D., 1963b. Detection and recognition. In R. D. Luce, R. R. Bush, and E. Galanter (Eds.), *Handbook of mathematical psychology.* Vol. I. New York: Wiley, pp. 103–190.

Luce, R. D., 1964a. Some one-parameter families of commutative learning operators. In R. C. Atkinson (Ed.), *Studies in mathematical psychology.* Stanford: Stanford Univer. Press, pp. 380–398.

Luce, R. D., 1964b. Learning and optimal judgments. In M. W. Shelly and G. L. Bryan (Eds.), *Human judgments and optimality.* New York: Wiley, pp. 101–115.

Luce, R. D., R. R. Bush, and E. Galanter (Eds.), 1963a. *Handbook of mathematical psychology.* Vols. I and II. New York: Wiley.

Luce, R. D., R. R. Bush, and E. Galanter (Eds.), 1963b. *Readings in mathematical psychology.* Vol. I. New York: Wiley.

Luce, R. D. and E. Galanter, 1963a. Discrimination. In R. D. Luce, R. R. Bush, and E. Galanter (Eds.), *Handbook of mathematical psychology.* Vol. I. New York: Wiley, pp. 191–244.

Luce, R. D. and E. Galanter, 1963b. Psychophysical scaling. In R. D. Luce, R. R. Bush, and E. Galanter (Eds.), *Handbook of mathematical psychology.* Vol. I. New York: Wiley, pp. 245–308.

Luce, R. D. and H. Raiffa, 1957. *Games and decisions.* New York: Wiley.

Luce, R. D. and P. Suppes, 1965. Preference, utility, and subjective probability. In R. D. Luce, R. R. Bush, and E. Galanter (Eds.), *Handbook of mathematical psychology.* Vol. III. New York: Wiley, pp. 249–410.

Luce, R. D. and J. W. Tukey, 1964. Simultaneous conjoint measurement: a new type of fundamental measurement. *J. math. Psychol.*, **1**, 1–27.

Maatsch, J. L., 1959. Learning and fixation after a single shock trial. *J. comp. physiol. Psychol.*, **52**, 408–410.

Madansky, A., 1959. Least squares estimation in finite Markov processes. *Psychometrika*, **24**, 137–144.

Madsen, M. C. and J. L. McGaugh, 1961. The effect of ECS on one-trial avoidance learning. *J. comp. physiol. Psychol.*, **54**, 522–523.

Marschak, J., 1960. Binary-choice constraints and random utility indicators. In K. J. Arrow, S. Karlin, and P. Suppes (Eds.), *Mathematical methods in the social sciences.* Stanford: Stanford Univer. Press, pp. 312–328.

Matheson, J., 1964. Optimum teaching procedures derived from mathematical learning models. Report No. CCS-2. Institute in Engineering-Economic Systems, Stanford University.

McConnell, D., 1959. An augmented model for spontaneous regression and recovery. *Psychometrika,* **24,** 145–155.

McGeoch, J. A. and A. L. Irion, 1952. *The psychology of human learning.* (2nd ed.) New York: Longmans, Green.

McGill, W. J., 1954. Multivariate information transmission. *Psychometrika,* **19,** 97–116.

McGill, W. J., 1962. Random fluctuations of response rate. *Psychometrika,* **27,** 3–17.

McGill, W. J., 1963. Stochastic latency mechanisms. In R. D. Luce, R. R. Bush, and E. Galanter (Eds.), *Handbook of mathematical psychology.* Vol. I. New York: Wiley, pp. 309–360.

McGill, W. J., 1965. *Introduction to counter theory in psychophysics,* in preparation.

Melton, A. W. (Ed.), 1964. *Categories of human learning.* New York: Academic Press.

Messick, S. J. and A. H. Brayfield (Eds.), 1964. *Decision and choice: Contributions of Sidney Siegel.* New York: McGraw-Hill.

Messick, S. J. and C. M. Solley, 1957. Probability learning in children: some exploratory studies. *J. genet. Psychol.,* **90,** 23–32.

Millenson, J. R. and H. M. B. Hurwitz, 1961. Some temporal and sequential properties of behavior during conditioning and extinction. *J. exp. anal. Behav.* **4,** 97–106.

Miller, G. A., 1947. Sensitivity to changes in the intensity of white noise and its relation to masking and loudness. *J. acoust. Soc. Amer.,* **19,** 609–619.

Miller, G. A., 1951. *Language and communication.* New York: McGraw-Hill.

Miller, G. A., 1952. Finite Markov processes in psychology. *Psychometrika,* **17,** 149–167.

Miller, G. A., 1956. The magical number seven, plus or minus two: some limits on our capacity for processing information. *Psychol. Rev.,* **63,** 81–97.

Miller, G. A., 1964. *Mathematics and psychology.* New York: Wiley.

Miller, G. A. and N. Chomsky, 1963. Finitary models of language users. In R. D. Luce, R. R. Bush, and E. Galanter (Eds.), *Handbook of mathematical psychology.* Vol. II. New York: Wiley, pp. 419–492.

Miller, G. A. and F. C. Frick, 1949. Statistical behavioristics and sequences of responses. *Psychol. Rev.,* **56,** 311–324.

Miller, G. A. and W. J. McGill, 1952. A statistical description of verbal learning. *Psychometrika,* **17,** 369–396.

Miller, N. E., 1948. Studies of fear as an acquirable drive: I. Fear as motivation and fear-reduction as reinforcement in the learning of new responses. *J. exp. Psychol.,* **38,** 89–101.

Miller, N. E., 1951. Learnable drives and rewards. In S. S. Stevens (Ed.), *Handbook of experimental psychology.* New York: Wiley, pp. 435–472.

Miller, N. E., 1959. Liberalizations of basic *S-R* concepts: extensions to conflict behavior, motivation, and social learning. In S. Koch (Ed.), *Psychology: a study of a science.* Vol. V. New York: McGraw-Hill, pp. 196–292.

Moore, O. K. and A. R. Anderson, 1962. Some puzzling aspects of social interaction. In Joan Criswell, H. Solomon, and P. Suppes (Eds.), *Mathematical methods in small group processes.* Stanford: Stanford Univer. Press, pp. 232–249.

Morse, E. B. and W. N. Runquist, 1960. Probability matching with an unscheduled random sequence. *Amer. J. Psychol.*, **73**, 603–607.

Mosteller, F., 1951. Remarks on the method of paired comparisons: I. The least squares solution assuming equal standard deviations and equal correlations. *Psychometrika*, **16**, 3–9.

Mosteller, F. and M. Tatsuoka, 1960. Ultimate choice between two attractive goals: predictions from a model. *Psychometrika*, **25**, 1–18.

Mowrer, O. H., 1939. A stimulus-response analysis of anxiety and its role as a reinforcing agent. *Psychol. Rev.*, **46**, 553–564.

Mowrer, O. H., 1960. *Learning theory and behavior*. New York: Wiley.

Mueller, C. G., 1950. Theoretical relationships among some measures of conditioning. *Proc. Natl. Acad. Sci.*, **36**, 123–130.

Mueller, C. G., 1954. A quantitative theory of visual excitation for the single photoreceptor. *Proc. Natl. Acad. Sci.*, **40**, 853–863.

Mueller, C. G. and W. J. McGill, 1963. Theories in sensory perception. In M. H. Marx (Ed.), *Theories in contemporary psychology*. New York: Macmillan, pp. 575–614.

Murdock, B. B., Jr., 1961. Short-term retention of single paired-associates. *Psychol. Rep.*, **8**, 280.

Murdock, B. B., Jr., 1963. Short-term memory and paired-associate learning. *J. verb. Learn. and verb. Behav.*, **2**, 320–328.

Myers, J. L. and R. C. Atkinson, 1964. Choice behavior and reward structure. *J. math. Psychol.*, **1**, 170–203.

Nagel, E., 1961. *The structure of science*. New York: Harcourt, Brace, and World.

Neimark, Edith D., 1956. Effects of type of non-reinforcement and number of alternative responses in two verbal conditioning situations. *J. exp. Psychol.*, **52**, 209–220.

Neimark, Edith D. and S. Rosenberg, 1959. The effect of "social" discriminative cues on probability learning. *J. exp. Psychol.*, **58**, 302–311.

Newell, A. and H. A. Simon, 1963. Computers in psychology. In R. D. Luce, R. R. Bush, and E. Galanter (Eds.), *Handbook of mathematical psychology*. Vol. I. New York: Wiley, pp. 361–420.

Newman, E. B., 1951. Computational methods useful in analyzing series of binary data. *Amer. J. Psychol.*, **54**, 252–262.

Nicks, D. C., 1959. Prediction of sequential two-choice decisions from event runs. *J. exp. Psychol.*, **57**, 105–114.

Norman, D. A., 1964. Sensory thresholds, response biases, and the neural quantum theory. *J. math. Psychol.*, **1**, 88–120.

Norman, M. F., 1964a. Incremental learning on random trials. *J. math. Psychol.*, **1**, 336–350.

Norman, M. F., 1964b. A two-phase model and an application to verbal discrimination learning. In R. C. Atkinson (Ed.), *Studies in mathematical psychology*. Stanford: Stanford Univer. Press, pp. 173–187.

Norman, M. F., 1964c. A probabilistic model for free-responding. Tech. Rep. No. 67, Institute for Mathematical Studies in the Social Sciences, Stanford University.

Oldfield, R. C., 1955. Apparent fluctuations of a sensory threshold. *Quart. J. exp. Psychol.*, **7**, 101–115.

Overall, J. E., 1960. A cognitive probability model for learning. *Psychometrika*, **25**, 159–172.

Parzen, E., 1960. *Modern probability theory and its applications*. New York: Wiley.

Pearson, K., 1932. *Tables of the incomplete beta-function*. London: Cambridge Univer. Press.

Peterson, L. R. and Margaret J. Peterson, 1962. Minimal paired-associate learning. *J. exp. Psychol.*, **63**, 521–527.

Peterson, L. R., Dorothy Saltzman, K. Hillner, and Vera Land, 1962. Recency and frequency in paired-associate learning. *J. exp. Psychol.*, **63**, 396–403.

Peterson, W. W., T. G. Birdsall, and W. C. Fox, 1954. The theory of sign detectability. *Trans. IRE Professional Group in Information Theory*, PGIT2-4, 171–212.

Pirenne, M. H. and F. H. C. Marriott, 1959. The quantum theory of light and the psycho-physiology of vision. In S. Koch (Ed.), *Psychology: a study of a science.* Vol. I. New York: McGraw-Hill, pp. 288–361.

Pitts, W., 1943. A general theory of learning and conditioning. *Psychometrika*, **8**, 1–18; 131–140.

Popper, Juliet, 1959. Mediated generalization. In R. R. Bush and W. K. Estes (Eds.), *Studies in mathematical learning theory.* Stanford: Stanford Univer. Press, pp. 94–108.

Popper, Juliet and R. C. Atkinson, 1958. Discrimination learning in a verbal conditioning situation. *J. exp. Psychol.*, **56**, 21–25.

Postman, L., 1963. One-trial learning. In C. N. Cofer and B. S. Musgrave (Eds.), *Verbal behavior and learning*. New York: McGraw-Hill, pp. 295–333.

Prokasy, W. F., Jr., 1961. Non-random stimulus sampling in statistical learning theory. *Psychol. Rev.*, **68**, 219–224.

Rapoport, A., 1963. Mathematical models of social interaction. In R. D. Luce, R. R. Bush, and E. Galanter (Eds.), *Handbook of mathematical psychology*. Vol. II. New York: Wiley, pp. 493–579.

Rashevsky, N., 1951. *Mathematical biology of social behavior.* Chicago: Univer. of Chicago Press.

Restle, F., 1955a. Axioms of a theory of discrimination learning. *Psychometrika*, **20**, 201–208.

Restle, F., 1955b. A theory of discrimination learning. *Psychol. Rev.*, **62**, 11–19.

Restle, F., 1957a. Discrimination of cues in mazes: a resolution of the "place-vs.-response" question. *Psychol. Rev.*, **64**, 217–228.

Restle, F., 1957b. Theory of selective learning with probable reinforcements. *Psychol. Rev.*, **64**, 182–191.

Restle, F., 1958. Toward a quantitative description of learning set data. *Psychol. Rev.*, **65**, 77–91.

Restle, F., 1959. A survey and classification of learning models. In R. R. Bush and W. K. Estes (Eds.), *Studies in mathematical learning theory.* Stanford: Stanford Univer. Press, pp. 415–428.

Restle, F., 1961a. *Psychology of judgment and choice.* New York: Wiley.

Restle, F., 1961b. Statistical methods for a theory of cue learning. *Psychometrika*, **26**, 291–306.

Restle, F., 1962. Speed and accuracy of cognitive achievement in small groups. In Joan Criswell, H. Solomon, and P. Suppes (Eds.), *Mathematical methods in small group processes.* Stanford: Stanford Univer. Press, pp. 250–262.

Restle, F., 1964a. Sources of difficulty in learning paired associates. In R. C. Atkinson (Ed.), *Studies in mathematical psychology.* Stanford: Stanford Univer. Press, pp. 116–172.

Restle, F., 1964b. The relevance of mathematical models for education. In E. R. Hilgard (Ed.), *Theories of learning and instruction: The sixty-third yearbook of the*

National Society for the Study of Education. Chicago: Univer. of Chicago Press, pp. 111–132.

Robinson, Joan, 1933. *The economics of imperfect competition.* London: Macmillan.

Roby, T. B., 1962. Subtask phasing in small groups. In Joan Criswell, H. Solomon, and P. Suppes (Eds.), *Mathematical methods in small group processes.* Stanford: Stanford Univer. Press, pp. 263–281.

Rock, I. and W. Heimer, 1959. Further evidence of one-trial associative learning. *Amer. J. Psychol.,* **72,** 1–16.

Rose, R. M., 1964. Simple-sequence analyses of learning models and their application to psychophysics. In R. C. Atkinson (Ed.), *Studies in mathematical psychology.* Stanford: Stanford Univer. Press, pp. 399–414.

Rosenberg, S., 1962. Two-person interactions in a continuous-response task. In Joan Criswell, H. Solomon, and P. Suppes (Eds.), *Mathematical methods in small group processes.* Stanford: Stanford Univer. Press, pp. 282–304.

Ross, B. M. and N. Levy, 1958. Patterned predictions of chance events by children and adults. *Psychol. Rep.,* **4,** 87–124.

Rubinstein, I., 1959. Some factors in probability matching. *J. exp. Psychol.,* **57,** 413–416.

Rubinstein, I., 1961. Supplementary report: The influence of one stimulus on the prediction of the alternative stimulus in two-choice problems. *J. exp. Psychol.,* **62,** 311–312.

Runquist, W. N., 1962. Stimulus generalization in paired-associate learning. Paper read at Western Psychol. Assn., San Francisco, April 1962.

Ryle, G., 1949. *The concept of mind.* London: Hutchinson's Univer. Library.

Savage, L. J., 1957. The theory of statistical decision. *J. Amer. statist. Assoc.,* **48,** 238–248.

Schoeffler, M. S., 1954. Probability of response to compounds of discriminated stimuli. *J. exp. Psychol.,* **48,** 323–329.

Scodel, A., J. S. Minas, P. Ratoosh, and M. Lipetz, 1959. Some descriptive aspects of two-person non-zero sum games. *J. conflict Resolution,* **3,** 114–119.

Scott, D. and P. Suppes, 1958. Foundational aspects of theories of measurement. *J. symbolic Logic,* **23,** 113–128.

Senders, V. L. and A. Sowards, 1952. Analysis of response sequences in the setting of a psycho-physical experiment. *Amer. J. Psychol.,* **65,** 358–374.

Sheffield, F. D., 1948. Avoidance training and the contiguity principle. *J. comp. physiol. Psychol.,* **41,** 165–177.

Shelly, M. W., 1958. The effects of response contingent probabilities which favor response change. *J. exp. Psychol.,* **56,** 239–245.

Shelly, M. W., 1962. A topological approach to the measurement of social phenomena. In Joan Criswell, H. Solomon, and P. Suppes (Eds.), *Mathematical methods in small group processes.* Stanford: Stanford Univer. Press, pp. 305–321.

Shelly, M. W. and G. L. Bryan, 1964. *Human judgments and optimality.* New York: Wiley.

Shepard, R. N., 1957. Stimulus and response generalization: a stochastic model relating generalization to distance in psychological space. *Psychometrika,* **22,** 325–345.

Shepard, R. N., 1961. Application of a trace model to the retention of information in a recognition task. *Psychometrika,* **26,** 185–203.

Shepard, R. N., 1964. Attention and the metric structure of the stimulus. *J. math. Psychol.,* **1,** 54–87.

Sherif, M., 1935. A study of some social factors in perception. *Arch. Psychol.*, No. 187.

Shipley, Elizabeth F. and R. D. Luce, 1964. Discrimination among two- and three-element sets of weights. In R. C. Atkinson (Ed.), *Studies in mathematical psychology*. Stanford: Stanford Univer. Press, pp. 218–232.

Shubik, M., 1959. *Strategy and market structure*. New York: Wiley.

Shubik, M., 1964. *Game theory and related approaches to social behavior*. New York: Wiley.

Shuford, E. H., Jr., 1964. Some Bayesian learning processes. In M. W. Shelly and G. L. Bryan (Eds.), *Human judgments and optimality*. New York: Wiley, pp. 127–152.

Sidowski, J. B., 1957. Reward and punishment in a minimal social situation. *J. exp. Psychol.*, **54**, 318–326.

Sidowski, J. B., L. B. Wyckoff, and L. Tabory, 1956. The influence of reinforcement and punishment in a minimal social situation. *J. abnor. and soc. Psychol.*, **52**, 115–119.

Siegel, S., 1956. *Nonparametric statistics for the behavioral sciences*. New York: McGraw-Hill.

Siegel, S., 1959. Theoretical models of choice and strategy behavior: stable state behavior in the two-choice uncertain outcome situation. *Psychometrika*, **24**, 306–316.

Siegel, S., 1961. Decision-making and learning under varying conditions of reinforcement. *Ann. N.Y. Acad. Sci.*, **89**, 766–782.

Siegel, S. and L. E. Fouraker, 1960. *Experiments in bilateral monopoly*. New York: McGraw-Hill.

Siegel, S. and D. A. Goldstein, 1959. Decision-making behavior in a two-choice uncertain outcome situation. *J. exp. Psychol.*, **57**, 37–42.

Simon, H. A., 1956. A comparison of game theory and learning theory. *Psychometrika*, **21**, 267–272.

Simon, H. A. and H. Guetzkow, 1955. A model of short and long run mechanisms involved in pressures toward unification in groups. *Psychol. Rev.*, **62**, 56–68.

Skinner, B. F., 1938. *The behavior of organisms*. New York: Appleton-Century-Crofts.

Skinner, B. F., 1945. The operational analysis of psychological terms. *Psychol. Rev.*, **52**, 270–277.

Skinner, B. F., 1950. Are theories of learning necessary? *Psychol. Rev.*, **57**, 193–216.

Smallwood, R. D., 1962. *A decision structure for teaching machines*. Cambridge, Mass.: M.I.T. Press.

Smoke, W. H. and R. B. Zajonc, 1962. On the reliability of group judgments and decisions. In Joan Criswell, H. Solomon, and P. Suppes (Eds.), *Mathematical methods in small group processes*. Stanford: Stanford Univer. Press, pp. 322–333.

Solley, C. M. and S. J. Messick, 1957. Probability learning, the statistical structure of concepts, and the measurement of meaning. *Amer. J. Psychol.*, **70**, 161–173.

Solomon, R. L. and L. C. Wynne, 1953. Traumatic avoidance learning: acquisition in normal dogs. *Psychol. Monogr.*, **67**, No. 4.

Solomon, R. L. and L. C. Wynne, 1954. Traumatic avoidance learning: the principles of anxiety conservation and partial irreversibility. *Psychol. Rev.*, **61**, 353–385.

Spence, K. W., 1936. The nature of discrimination learning in animals. *Psychol. Rev.*, **43**, 427–449.

Spence, K. W., 1951. Theoretical interpretations of learning. In S. S. Stevens (Ed.), *Handbook of experimental psychology*. New York: Wiley.

Spence, K. W., 1956. *Behavior theory and conditioning.* New Haven: Yale Univer. Press.

Spence, K. W., 1960. Conceptual models of spatial and non-spatial selective learning. In K. W. Spence (Ed.), *Behavior theory and learning.* Englewood Cliffs, N.J.: Prentice-Hall.

Sternberg, S. H., 1959a. Applications of four models to sequential dependence in human learning. In R. R. Bush and W. K. Estes (Eds.), *Studies in mathematical learning theory.* Stanford: Stanford Univer. Press, pp. 340–381.

Sternberg, S. H., 1959b. A path-dependent linear model. In R. R. Bush and W. K. Estes (Eds.), *Studies in mathematical learning theory.* Stanford: Stanford Univer. Press, pp. 308–339.

Sternberg, S. H., 1963. Stochastic learning theory. In R. D. Luce, R. R. Bush, and E. Galanter (Eds.), *Handbook of mathematical psychology.* Vol. II. New York: Wiley, pp. 1–120.

Stevens, S. S., 1957. On the psychophysical law. *Psychol. Rev.,* **64,** 153–181.

Stone, M., 1960. Models for choice-reaction time. *Psychometrika,* **25,** 251–260.

Suppes, P., 1957. *Introduction to logic.* Princeton: Van Nostrand.

Suppes, P., 1959. A linear model for a continuum of responses. In R. R. Bush and W. K. Estes (Eds.), *Studies in mathematical learning theory.* Stanford: Stanford Univer. Press., pp. 400–414.

Suppes, P., 1960a. Stimulus-sampling theory for a continuum of responses. In K. J. Arrow, S. Karlin, and P. Suppes (Eds.), *Mathematical methods in the social sciences.* Stanford: Stanford Univer. Press, pp. 348–365.

Suppes, P., 1960b. A comparison of the meaning and uses of models in mathematics and the empirical sciences. *Synthese,* **12,** 287–301.

Suppes, P., 1961. Behavioristic foundations of utility. *Econometrica,* **29,** 186–202.

Suppes, P., 1962. Models of data. In E. Nagel, P. Suppes, and A. Tarski (Eds.), *Logic, methodology, and philosophy of science: Proceedings of the 1960 International Congress.* Stanford: Stanford Univer. Press, pp. 252–261.

Suppes, P., 1963. Problems of optimization in learning a list of simple items. Tech. Rep. No. 57, Institute for Mathematical studies in the Social Sciences, Stanford University.

Suppes, P. and R. C. Atkinson, 1960. *Markov learning models for multiperson interactions.* Stanford: Stanford Univer. Press.

Suppes, P. and J. M. Carlsmith, 1962. Experimental analysis of a duopoly situation from the standpoint of mathematical learning theory. *Int. Econ. Rev.,* **3,** 1–19.

Suppes, P. and R. W. Frankmann, 1961. Test of stimulus sampling theory for a continuum of responses with unimodal noncontingent determinate reinforcement. *J. exp. Psychol.,* **61,** 122–132.

Suppes, P. and Rose Ginsberg, 1962a. Application of a stimulus sampling model to children's concept formation with and without an overt correction response. *J. exp. Psych.,* **63,** 330–336.

Suppes, P. and Rose Ginsberg, 1962b. Experimental studies of mathematical concept formation in young children. *Sci. Educ.,* **46,** 230–240.

Suppes, P. and Rose Ginsberg, 1963. A fundamental property of all-or-none models. *Psychol. Rev.,* **70,** 139–161.

Suppes, P. and F. Krasne, 1961. Application of stimulus sampling theory to situations involving social pressure. *Psychol. Rev.,* **68,** 46–55.

Suppes, P. and H. Rouanet, 1964. A simple discrimination experiment with a continuum of responses. In R. C. Atkinson (Ed.), *Studies in mathematical psychology.* Stanford: Stanford Univer. Press, pp. 317–357.

Suppes, P., H. Rouanet, M. Levine, and R. W. Frankmann, 1964. Empirical comparison of models for a continuum of responses with noncontingent bimodal reinforcement. In R. C. Atkinson (Ed.), *Studies in mathematical psychology.* Stanford: Stanford Univer. Press, pp. 358–379.

Suppes, P. and Madeleine Schlag-Rey, 1962a. Analysis of social conformity in terms of generalized conditioning models. In Joan Criswell, H. Solomon, and P. Suppes (Eds.), *Mathematical methods in small group processes.* Stanford: Stanford Univer. Press, pp. 334–361.

Suppes, P. and Madeleine Schlag-Rey, 1962b. Test of some learning models for double contingent reinforcement. *Psychol. Rep.,* **10,** 259–268.

Suppes, P. and J. L. Zinnes, 1960. Stochastic learning models for a response continuum in nondeterminate reinforcement. *Psychometrika,* **26,** 373–390.

Suppes, P. and J. L. Zinnes, 1963. Basic measurement theory. In R. D. Luce, R. R. Bush, and E. Galanter (Eds.), *Handbook of mathematical psychology.* Vol. I. New York: Wiley, pp. 1–76.

Sutherland, N. S., 1959. Stimulus analyzing mechanisms. In *Proceedings of a symposium of the mechanization of thought processes.* Vol. II. London: Her Majesty's Stationery Office, pp. 575–609.

Swets, J. A., 1961. Is there a sensory threshold? *Science,* **134,** 168–177.

Swets, J. A., 1964. *Signal detection and recognition by human observers.* New York: Wiley.

Swets, J. A., W. P. Tanner, Jr., and T. G. Birdsall, 1955. The evidence for a decision making theory of visual detection. Tech. Rep. No. 40, Electronic Defense Group, University of Michigan.

Swets, J. A., W. P. Tanner, Jr., and T. G. Birdsall, 1961. Decision processes in perception. *Psychol. Rev.,* **68,** 301–340.

Tanner, W. P., Jr. and J. A. Swets, 1954. A decision making theory of visual detection. *Psychol. Rev.,* **61,** 401–409.

Tanner, W. P., Jr., J. A. Swets, and D. M. Green, 1956. Some general properties of the hearing mechanism. Tech. Rep. No. 30, Electronic Defense Group, University of Michigan.

Tatsuoka, M. and F. Mosteller, 1959. A commuting operator model. In R. R. Bush and W. K. Estes (Eds.), *Studies in mathematical learning theory.* Stanford: Stanford Univer. Press, pp. 228–247.

Taub, H. A. and J. L. Myers, 1961. Differential monetary gains in a two-choice situation. *J. exp. Psychol.,* **61,** 157–162.

Theios, J., 1961. A three-state Markov model for learning. Tech. Rep. No. 40. Institute for Mathematical Studies in the Social Sciences, Stanford University.

Theios, J., 1963. Simple conditioning as two-state all-or-none learning. *Psychol. Rev.,* **70,** 403–417.

Thorndike, E. L., 1898. Animal intelligence: an experimental study of the associative processes in animals. *Psychol. Monogr.,* **2,** No. 8.

Thorpe, E. O., 1962. *Beat the dealer: a winning strategy for the game of twenty-one.* New York: Random House.

Thrall, R. M., C. H. Coombs, and R. L. Davis (Eds.), 1954. *Decision processes.* New York: Wiley.

Thurstone, L. L., 1919. The learning curve equation. *Psychol. Monogr.,* **26,** No. 3.

Thurstone, L. L., 1927. A law of comparative judgment. *Psychol. Rev.*, **34**, 273–286.

Toda, M., 1962. Brain-computer approach to the theory of choice. In E. Nagel, P. Suppes, and A. Tarski (Eds.), *Logic, methodology and philosophy of science: Proceedings of the 1960 International Congress.* Stanford: Stanford Univer. Press, pp. 434–441.

Tolman, E. C., 1939. Prediction of vicarious trial-and-error by means of the schematic sow-bug. *Psychol. Rev.*, **46**, 318–336.

Torgerson, W. S., 1958. *Theory and methods of scaling.* New York: Wiley.

Trabasso, T. R. and G. H. Bower, 1964a. Memory in concept identification. *Psychonomic Sci.*, **1**, 133–134.

Trabasso, T. R. and G. H. Bower, 1964b. Component learning in the four-category concept problem. *J. math. Psychol.*, **1**, 143–169.

Uhr, L., 1963. Pattern recognition computers as models for form perception. *Psychol. Bull.*, **60**, 40–73.

Underwood, B. J. and G. Keppel, 1962. One-trial learning? *J. verb. Learn. verb. Behav.*, **1**, 1–13.

Underwood, B. J., W. N. Runquist, and R. W. Schulz, 1959. Response learning in paired-associate lists as a function of intralist similarity. *J. exp. Psychol.*, **58**, 70–78.

Underwood, B. J. and R. W. Schulz, 1960. *Meaningfulness and verbal learning.* Chicago: Lippincott.

Verplanck, W. S., 1955. The control of the content of conversation: reinforcement of statements of opinion. *J. abnorm. soc. Psychol.*, **51**, 668–678.

Verplanck, W. S., 1956. The operant conditioning of human motor behavior. *Psychol. Bull.*, **53**, 70–83.

Verplanck, W. S., G. H. Collier, and J. W. Cotton, 1952. Nonindependence of successive responses in measurement of the visual threshold. *J. exp. Psychol.*, **44**, 273–282.

Vincent, Stella B., 1912. The function of the vibrissae in the behavior of the white rat. *Behav. Monogr.*, **1**, No. 5.

Von Neumann, T. and O. Morgenstern, 1944. *Theory of games and economic behavior.* Princeton: Princeton Univer. Press.

Waugh, Nancy C. and J. E. K. Smith, 1962. A stochastic model for free recall. *Psychometrika*, **27**, 141–154.

Weiss, B., P. D. Coleman, and R. F. Green, 1955. A stochastic model for time-ordered dependencies in continuous scale repetitive judgments. *J. exp. Psychol.*, **50**, 237–244.

Wertheimer, M., 1953. An investigation of the randomness of threshold measurements. *J. exp. Psychol.*, **45**, 294–303.

Wickens, D. D., 1954. Stimulus-response theory as applied to perception. In *Learning theory, personality theory and clinical research: The Kentucky Symposium.* New York: Wiley, pp. 22–35.

Witte, R. S., 1959. A stimulus-trace hypothesis for statistical learning theory. *J exp. Psychol.*, **57**, 273–283.

Woodworth, R. S. and H. Schlosberg, 1954. *Experimental psychology.* (Rev. ed.) New York: Holt, Rinehart, and Winston.

Wyckoff, L. B., Jr., 1952. The role of observing responses in discrimination learning. *Psychol. Rev.*, **59**, 431–442.

Young, P. T., 1947. Studies of food preference, appetite, and dietary habit: VII. Palatability in relation to learning and performance. *J. comp. physiol. Psychol.*, **40**, 37–72.

AUTHOR INDEX

419

SUBJECT INDEX